DISCARD

Oxford Academy and Central School
High School Library

# FAMILY TREE

FAMILY TREE

# FAMILY TREE

COMPILED

AND EDITED BY

## Johanna Johnston &

## Murry Karmiller

AN ANTHOLOGY

OF THE WORLD'S

MOST DISTINGUISHED

FICTION AND

NONFICTION

ABOUT FAMILY

RELATIONSHIPS WITH

SOURCES RANGING

FROM THE BIBLE TO

THE NEW YORKER

9953

## THE WORLD PUBLISHING COMPANY

CLEVELAND AND NEW YORK

Oxford Academy and Central School
High School Library

Published by The World Publishing Company
2231 West 110th Street, Cleveland, Ohio 44102
Published simultaneously in Canada by
Nelson, Foster & Scott Ltd.

FIRST PRINTING 1967

Copyright © 1967 by The World Publishing Company
All rights reserved. No part of this book may be reproduced in
any form without written permission from the publisher,
except for brief passages included in a review appearing in a
newspaper or magazine.

Library of Congress Catalog Card Number: 67–22912
Printed in the United States of America

Designed by Klaus Gemming

## ACKNOWLEDGMENTS

808.1

The compilers and The World Publishing Company thank
the following authors, publishers, and agents for permission
to reprint poems or selections from the titles listed below. All
possible care has been taken to trace the ownership of every
selection included and to make full acknowledgment for its
use. If any errors have accidentally occurred, they will be cor-
rected in subsequent editions, provided notification is sent to
the publishers.

BASIC BOOKS, INC. *Free Associations* by Ernest Jones. © Katharine Jones
1959. Reprinted by permission of Basic Books, Inc., Publishers, New
York, and The Hogarth Press Ltd. THREE NOVELS: *Summer in Williamsburg* by Daniel Fuchs. Copyright 1934, 1936, 1937 by Daniel
Fuchs, © 1961 by Basic Books, Inc., Publishers, New York. Reprinted
by permission of Basic Books, Inc.

LURTON BLASSINGAME. *Chicken Every Sunday* by Rosemary Taylor. Copyright © 1943 by the McGraw-Hill Book Company, Inc. Reprinted by
permission of the author's agent, Lurton Blassingame.

THE BOBBS-MERRILL COMPANY, INC. *The Private Life of Helen of Troy* by
John Erskine. Copyright 1925 by The Bobbs-Merrill Company, Inc.,

R. 1953 by Helen Worden Erskine. Reprinted by permission of The Bobbs-Merrill Company, Inc.

THE BODLEY HEAD. *The Unbearable Bassington* by Saki. Reprinted by permission of The Bodley Head.

BRANDT & BRANDT. *Growth* by Booth Tarkington. Copyright, 1927, by Booth Tarkington. Copyright renewed © 1955, by Susannah Tarkington. Reprinted by permission of Brandt & Brandt and Curtis Brown Ltd. *National Velvet* by Enid Bagnold. Copyright, 1935, by Enid Bagnold Jones. Copyright renewed © 1963 by Enid Bagnold Jones. Reprinted by permission of Brandt & Brandt.

CURTIS BROWN LTD. "The Children's Hour" from *On the Contrary* by Phyllis McGinley. Copyright © 1932 by Phyllis McGinley. Renewed 1960 by Phyllis McGinley. Reprinted by permission of Curtis Brown Ltd.

THOMAS Y. CROWELL COMPANY. *Cheaper by the Dozen* by Frank B. Gilbreth, Jr., and Ernestine Gilbreth Carey. Copyright © 1963, 1948 by the authors. Reprinted by permission of Thomas Y. Crowell Company, New York, publishers, and William Heinemann Ltd.

DODD, MEAD & COMPANY, INC. *The History of Mr. Polly* by H. G. Wells. Copyright 1909, 1937 by H. G. Wells. Reprinted by permission of Dodd, Mead & Company, Inc., and the Executors of H. G. Wells.

DOUBLEDAY & COMPANY, INC. *Of Human Bondage* by W. Somerset Maugham. Copyright 1915 by W. Somerset Maugham. Reprinted by permission of Doubleday & Company, Inc. and the Literary Executor of W. Somerset Maugham, and William Heinemann Ltd.

E. P. DUTTON & CO., INC. *The Life of Charles Dickens* (Vol. 2) by John Forster. Copyright © 1961 by J. M. Dent & Sons, Ltd. Everyman's Library Edition. Reprinted by permission of E. P. Dutton & Co., Inc. and J. M. Dent & Sons, Ltd.

EDITIONS GALLIMARD. *The Thibaults* by Roger Martin du Gard. © Editions Gallimard 1922, 1940. Translation by Stuart Gilbert, copyright 1939, © 1967 by The Viking Press, Inc. Reprinted by permission of Editions Gallimard, The Viking Press, Inc., and The Bodley Head.

FARRAR, STRAUS AND GIROUX, INC. *Life Among the Savages* by Shirley Jackson. Copyright 1949 by Shirley Jackson. Reprinted by permission of Farrar, Straus and Giroux, Inc., and Brandt & Brandt. *My Mother's House* by Colette. Copyright 1953 by Farrar, Straus & Young, Inc. Reprinted by permission of Farrar, Straus and Giroux, Inc., and Martin Secker & Warburg, Limited.

HARCOURT, BRACE & WORLD, INC. *Cress Delahanty* by Jessamyn West. Copyright, 1948, by The Curtis Publishing Company. Reprinted by permission of Harcourt, Brace & World, Inc., and Hodder and Stoughton Limited. *Mama's Bank Account* by Kathryn Forbes. Copyright, 1943, by Kathryn Forbes. Reprinted by permission of Harcourt, Brace & World, Inc. and Curtis Brown Ltd. *My Sister Eileen* by Ruth Mc-

Kenney. Copyright, 1938, 1966, by Ruth McKenney. First printed in *The New Yorker*. Reprinted by permission of Harcourt, Brace & World, Inc., and Rupert Hart-Davis Limited.

HARPER & ROW, PUBLISHERS, INCORPORATED. *The Autobiography of Eleanor Roosevelt* by Eleanor Roosevelt. Reprinted by permission of Harper & Row, Publishers, Incorporated. *Black Boy* by Richard Wright. Copyright 1945 by Richard Wright. Reprinted by permission of Harper & Row, Publishers, Incorporated, and Paul R. Reynolds, Inc., 599 Fifth Avenue, New York, New York. *The Grandmothers* by Glenway Wescott. Copyright 1927 by Harper & Row, Publishers, Incorporated; renewed 1955 by Glenway Wescott. Reprinted by permission of Harper & Row, Publishers, Incorporated. *Kennedy* by Theodore C. Sorensen. Copyright, 1965, by Theodore C. Sorensen. Reprinted by permission of Harper & Row, Publishers, Incorporated. *A Tree Grows in Brooklyn* by Betty Smith. Copyright 1943 by Betty Smith. Reprinted by permission of Harper & Row, Publishers, Incorporated.

HARVARD UNIVERSITY PRESS. *The Odyssey*, Book II, by Homer. Translated by A. T. Murray. The Loeb Classical Library. Reprinted by permission of Harvard University Press.

HILL AND WANG, INC. *The Best of Simple* by Langston Hughes. © 1961 by Langston Hughes. Reprinted by permission of Hill and Wang, Inc.

HOLT, RINEHART AND WINSTON, INC. *The Bent Twig* by Dorothy Canfield. Copyright 1915 by Holt, Rinehart and Winston, Inc. Copyright 1943 by Dorothy Canfield Fisher. Reprinted by permission of Holt, Rinehart and Winston, Inc.

HORIZON PRESS. *Letters of Fyodor Dostoevsky to His Family and Friends* by Fyodor Dostoevsky. Copyright © 1961 by Horizon Press. Reprinted by permission of the Horizon Press.

ALFRED A. KNOPF, INC. *The Best of Clarence Day* by Clarence Day. Copyright 1934 by Clarence Day and renewed 1962 by Katherine B. Day. Reprinted by permission of Alfred A. Knopf, Inc. *Kristin Lavransdatter* by Sigrid Undset, translated by Charles Archer and J. S. Scott. Copyright 1923, 1925, 1927 by Alfred A. Knopf, Inc. Reprinted by permission of Alfred A. Knopf, Inc., and Cassell and Company Ltd.

J. B. LIPPINCOTT COMPANY. *The Story of the Trapp Family Singers* by Maria Augusta Trapp. Copyright, 1949, by Maria Augusta Trapp. Published by J. B. Lippincott Company. Reprinted by permission of J. B. Lippincott Company.

LITTLE, BROWN AND COMPANY. *In the Absence of Angels* by Hortense Calisher. Copyright 1948 by Hortense Calisher; originally appeared in *The New Yorker*. Reprinted by permission of Little, Brown and Company and Brandt & Brandt. *Jalna* by Mazo de la Roche. Copyright 1927 by Little, Brown and Company. Copyright 1955 by Mazo de la Roche. Reprinted by permission of Atlantic–Little, Brown and

ACKNOWLEDGMENTS

Company, the Estate of Mazo de la Roche, and Macmillan & Co. Ltd. *John Adams and the American Revolution* by Catherine Drinker Bowen. Copyright 1949, 1950, by Catherine Drinker Bowen. Reprinted by permission of Atlantic–Little, Brown and Company, and Harold Ober Associates.

THE MACMILLAN COMPANY. *Manchild in the Promised Land* by Claude Brown. Copyright © Claude Brown 1965. Reprinted with permission of The Macmillan Company. "A Prayer for My Daughter" from *Later Poems* by William Butler Yeats. Copyright The Macmillan Company 1924, renewed 1952 by Bertha Georgie Yeats. Reprinted with permission of The Macmillan Company, Mr. M. B. Yeats, and Macmillan & Co., Ltd.

WILLIAM MAXWELL, *They Came Like Swallows*. © William Maxwell 1937, 1960. Reprinted by permission of the author.

HAROLD OBER ASSOCIATES INCORPORATED. *The Good Earth* by Pearl S. Buck. Copyright 1931, 1949 by Pearl S. Buck. Reprinted by permission of Harold Ober Associates Incorporated, Pearl S. Buck, and Methuen & Co. Ltd.

RAND MCNALLY & COMPANY. *Heidi* by Johanna Spyri. "Bye Baby Bunting," "Coffee and Tea," and "There Was an Old Woman" from *The Real Mother Goose*.

RANDOM HOUSE, INC. *Act One* by Moss Hart. © Copyright 1959 by Catherine Carlisle Hart and Joseph M. Hyman, Trustees. Reprinted by permission of Random House, Inc., and Martin Secker & Warburg, Limited. *Grandfather Stories* by Samuel Hopkins Adams. © Copyright 1955 by Samuel Hopkins Adams. Reprinted by permission of Random House, Inc. and Brandt & Brandt. *Swann's Way*, Volume 1 from REMEMBRANCE OF THINGS PAST by Marcel Proust, translated by C. K. Scott Moncrieff. Copyright 1928 and renewed 1956 by The Modern Library. Reprinted by permission of Random House, Inc., The Literary Estate of C. K. Scott Moncrieff, and Chatto & Windus Ltd. *War and Peace* by Leo Tolstoy, translated by Constance Garnett. Reprinted by permission of Random House, Inc.

PAUL R. REYNOLDS, INC. "The Apostate" from *No More Trumpets* by George Milburn. Copyright 1933 by George Milburn. First printed in *The New Yorker*. Reprinted by permission of Paul R. Reynolds, Inc., 599 Fifth Avenue, New York 17, New York.

WILLIAM SAROYAN, *Inhale and Exhale*. Reprinted by permission of the author. © Modern Library, Inc., 1936. Copyright renewed by William Saroyan 1963.

CHARLES SCRIBNER'S SONS. *The Letters of F. Scott Fitzgerald*, edited by Andrew Turnbull. Copyright © 1963 Frances Scott Fitzgerald Lanahan. Reprinted by permission of Charles Scribner's Sons and The Bodley Head Ltd. *To Let* (Book III of THE FORSYTE SAGA) by John

ACKNOWLEDGMENTS

Galsworthy. Copyright 1921 Charles Scribner's Sons; renewal copyright 1949 Ada Galsworthy. Reprinted by permission of Charles Scribner's Sons and William Heinemann Ltd. *The Yearling* by Marjorie Kinnan Rawlings. Copyright 1938, Marjorie Kinnan Rawlings; renewal copyright © 1966 Norton Baskin. Reprinted by permission of Charles Scribner's Sons, Marjorie Kinnan Rawlings, and William Heinemann Ltd.

SIMON AND SCHUSTER, INC. *Father of the Bride* by Edward Streeter and Gluyas Williams. Copyright 1948, 1949 by the authors. Reprinted by permission of Simon and Schuster, Inc. *Grandma Called It Carnal* by Bertha Damon. Copyright © 1938, 1965 by Bertha Damon. Reprinted by permission of Simon and Schuster, Inc. *Kings Row* by Henry Bellamann. Copyright © 1940 by Henry Bellamann. Reprinted by permission of Simon and Schuster, Inc., and A. Watkins, Inc.

VANGUARD PRESS, INC. *Auntie Mame* by Patrick Dennis. Copyright © 1955 by Patrick Dennis. Reprinted by permission of the publisher, The Vanguard Press, and McIntosh and Otis, Inc.

THE VIKING PRESS, INC. *Death of a Salesman* by Arthur Miller. Copyright 1949 by Arthur Miller. Reprinted by permission of The Viking Press, Inc., and Elaine Greene Ltd. *The Grapes of Wrath* by John Steinbeck. Copyright 1939, 1967 by John Steinbeck. Reprinted by permission of The Viking Press, Inc. *Sons and Lovers* by D. H. Lawrence. Copyright 1913 by Thomas B. Seltzer, Inc. All rights reserved. Reprinted by permission of The Viking Press, Inc., William Heinemann Limited, Laurence Pollinger Limited, and the Estate of Mrs. Frieda Lawrence. "Girl's-Eye View of Relatives": "First Lesson," "The Turn of the Screw," "Triolet Against Sisters," "In Praise of Aunts," and "The Adversary," from *Times Three* by Phyllis McGinley. Originally appeared in *The New Yorker*. Copyright © 1959 by Phyllis McGinley. Reprinted by permission of The Viking Press, Inc., and Martin Secker & Warburg Limited.

A. WATKINS, INC. *A Breath of French Air* by H. E. Bates. Copyright 1959 by Evansford Productions, Ltd. Reprinted by permission of A. Watkins, Inc., and Michael Joseph Ltd.

A. P. WATT & SON. *The Old Wives' Tale* by Arnold Bennett. Copyright 1908 Mrs. Dorothy Cheston Bennett. Reprinted by permission of A. P. Watt, Hodder and Stoughton, and Mrs. Dorothy Cheston Bennett.

HAROLD WITT, "Now in November." © 1965 by The New York Times Company. Reprinted by permission of The New York Times Company and Harold Witt.

# INTRODUCTION

※ ※

For *Family Tree* we have tried to select some of the more dramatic and illuminating scenes, comments or reflections on family relationships from a variety of sources across the centuries. Some of the authors are familiar, some not so well known. Some of the selections are universal favorites, others more obscure. Each one, however, focuses on some particular family situation to show a particular relationship in revealing detail. Each one, we hope, will offer to the reader either the pleasure of recognizing something paralleling his own experiences or a rewarding insight into some aspect of why families behave as they do.

As we grouped the selections into the various categories of family relationships, we found that a certain intriguing pattern emerged in each section. Fathers behave a great deal differently to their daughters than they do to their sons. So do mothers. Aunts and uncles appear over and over again as generous protectors and defenders of their nieces and nephews when trouble strikes, often acting *in loco parentis* but with a useful detachment that parents rarely show. Grandparents seem to have a way of widening the horizons of the grandchildren who are close to them, either by making the past more vivid, as the time of their own youth, or by their longer view of life.

The selections are grouped within each section in a roughly chronological order, and this gives a glimpse of how some attitudes have changed through the years (or perhaps it is more that the expression of them has changed), and of how other emotions and reactions have remained constant despite variations in time and place.

With every person so inevitably part of some family group, it is inescapable that a great deal of the world's writing is about family relationships. Barring scientific writing, it is difficult to think of any prose or poetry that is not somehow infused with a family theme. Which makes it impossible for us, as editors, to make the usual apologies for the material that had to be omitted

5

from this anthology. Nobody could collect everything that has
been written about husbands, wives, mothers, fathers, daughters,
sons, sisters, brothers, grandparents, aunts, uncles, cousins, nieces,
and nephews. The family tree is a giant, embracing the world. But
we hope that among the leaves and branches of this particular
*Family Tree* there will be fruit for everybody.

For their help in preparing this collection we wish to acknowl-
edge with much gratitude, Cathryn O. Miles, Librarian of the
McCullough Library, North Bennington, Vermont; Mary C.
Jenkins, who handled much of the correspondence; Barbara
Karmiller and Abigail J. Lefkowitz, who assisted not only with the
typing but with suggestions; and Ruth Shair, whose coordinating
editorial work helped greatly.

*Johanna Johnston* and *Murry Karmiller*

# CONTENTS

⚥ ⚥

## Mothers and Sons

## Mothers and Daughters

## Brothers and Sisters

## Aunts, Uncles,
## Nieces, Nephews, and Cousins

## Grandmothers and Grandfathers

## Parents and Children

## Family Gatherings

# Husbands and Wives

# HOMER

⚔ ⚔

*The classic story of a wife's fidelity to her absent husband is from* The Odyssey.

THEN THE SPIRIT of Amphimedon answered him, and said: "Most glorious son of Atreus, king of men, Agamemnon, I remember all these things, O thou fostered of Zeus, even as thou dost tell them; and on my part I will frankly tell thee all the truth, how for us an evil end of death was wrought. We wooed the wife of Odysseus, that had long been gone, and she neither refused the hateful marriage, nor would she ever make an end, devising for us death and black fate. Nay, she contrived in her heart this guileful thing also: she set up in her halls a great web, and fell to weaving—fine of thread was the web and very wide; and straightway she spoke among us:

"'Young men, my wooers, since goodly Odysseus is dead, be patient, though eager for my marriage, until I finish this robe—I would not that my spinning should come to naught—a shroud for the lord Laertes against the time when the fell fate of grievous death shall strike him down; lest any of the Achaean women in the land should be wroth at me, if he were to lie without a shroud, who had won great possessions.'

"So she spoke, and our proud hearts consented. Then day by day she would weave at the great web, but by night would unravel it, when she had let place torches by her. Thus for three years she by her craft kept the Achaeans from knowing, and beguiled them; but when the fourth year came, as the seasons rolled on, as the months waned and many days were brought in their course, even then one of her women who knew all, told us, and we caught her unravelling the splendid web. So she finished it against her will perforce.

"Now when she had shewn us the robe, after weaving the great web and washing it, and it shone like the sun and the moon, then it was that some cruel god brought Odysseus from somewhere to

the border of the land, where the swineherd dwelt. Thither too
came the dear son of divine Odysseus on his return from sandy
Pylos in his black ship, and these two, when they had planned an
evil death for the wooers, came to the famous city, Odysseus verily
later, but Telemachus led the way before him. Now the swineherd brought his master, clad in mean raiment, in the likeness of a
woeful and aged beggar, leaning on a staff, and miserable was the
raiment that he wore about his body; and not one of us could
know that it was he, when he appeared so suddenly, no, not even
those that were older men, but we assailed him with evil words
and with missiles. Howbeit he with steadfast heart endured for a
time to be pelted and taunted in his own halls; but when at last
the will of Zeus, who bears the aegis, roused him, with the help of
Telemachus he took all the beautiful arms and laid them away in
the store-room and made fast the bolts. Then in his great cunning
he bade his wife set before the wooers his bow and the grey iron to
be a contest for us ill-fated men and the beginning of death. And
no man of us was able to stretch the string of the mighty bow;
nay, we fell far short of that strength. But when the great bow
came to the hands of Odysseus, then we all cried out aloud not to
give him the bow, how much soever he might speak; but Telemachus alone urged him on, and bade him take it. Then he took
the bow in his hand, the much-enduring, goodly Odysseus, and
with ease did he string it and send an arrow through the iron.
Then he went and stood on the threshold, and poured out the
swift arrows, glaring about him terribly, and smote king Antinous.
And thereafter upon the others he with sure aim let fly his shafts,
fraught with groanings, and the men fell thick and fast. Then was
it known that some god was their helper; for straightway rushing
on through the halls in their fury they slew men left and right,
and therefrom rose hideous groaning, as heads were smitten, and
all the floor swam with blood. Thus we perished, Agamemnon,
and even now our bodies still lie uncared-for in the halls of
Odysseus; for our friends in each man's home know naught as
yet—our friends who might wash the black blood from our
wounds and lay our bodies out with wailing; for that is the due of
the dead."

Then, the spirit of the son of Atreus answered him: "Happy

son of Laertes, Odysseus of many devices, of a truth full of all excellence was the wife thou didst win, so good of understanding was peerless Penelope, daughter of Icarius, in that she was loyally mindful of Odysseus, her wedded husband. Therefore the fame of her virtue shall never perish, but the immortals shall make among men on earth a pleasant song in honour of constant Penelope."

# SIGRID UNDSET

*The trilogy,* Kristin Lavransdatter, *recreates four-teenth-century Norway as it traces the life of its hero-ine from childhood to death. On one occasion, Kristin has a memorable reunion with her husband, Erlend.*

A WHILE AFTER, Kristin thought she heard a horse somewhere without. She went to the outer room and peered forth.

Down from the wooded slope above the farm-stead came a tall black horse harnessed to a load of firewood. Erlend walked by its side, driving. One dog sat atop of the wood; some others ran about the sleigh.

Soten, the Castilian, strained at his collar and dragged the wood-sleigh forward over the courtyard sward. One of the dogs dashed down the slope barking—Erlend, who had begun to unharness, marked now the flurry among the dogs that something must be afoot. He took the wood-axe from the load and walked toward the dwelling-house—

Kristin fled in again, dropping the latch behind her. She shrank in to the wall of the fire-place, and stood trembling and waiting.

Erlend strode in, with the wood-axe in his hand and the dogs tumbling over the threshold before and after him. They found the stranger forthwith, and greeted her with a storm of barking—

The first she saw was the wave of young, red blood that rushed over his face—the fluttering quiver about his fine, weak mouth, the great eyes deep in the shadow of the brows—

The sight of him took away her breath. She saw, indeed, the old stubble upon his lower face, she saw that his unkempt hair was iron-grey—but the colour came and went in his cheeks in hasty pulses, as when they were young—he was so young and so comely, 'twas as though naught had availed to quell him—

He was miserably clad—his blue shirt dirty and ragged; over it he wore a leathern jerkin, scarred and rubbed and rent at the laceholes, but fitting closely and pliant to the body's strong and gracious motions. His tight leathern breeches had a rent over the one knee, and the seam behind the other leg was burst. Yet never, more than now, had he seemed the son of chiefs and nobles. So fairly and easily he bore his tall slim form, with the broad shoulders somewhat stooped, the long, fine limbs—he stood there, resting a little on one foot, one hand laid on the belt about his slender waist, the other, with the axe in it, hanging at his side.

He had called the dogs back to him—stood looking at her— went red and pale and said no word. For a good while they both stood dumb. At last the man spoke, in a voice that wavered a little:

"Are you come hither, Kristin?"

"I was fain to see how it fared with you," answered she.

"Ay, you have seen it, then." He cast a glance about the room. "You see things are passably well with me here — 'tis good you chanced on a day when my house is trim and in order—" He grew aware of the shadow of a smile upon her face. "—Or maybe 'tis you who set it in order," said he, laughing low.

Erlend laid aside the axe and sat him down on the outer bench, with his back against the board. Of a sudden he grew grave:

"You stand there so—is aught amiss at home—at Jörundgaard, I mean—with the lads?"

"No." Now was her time to bring out what she had to say: "Our sons are thriving and doing well. But they long so for you, Erlend. This was my errand—I came hither, husband, to beg you to come home to us. We miss you, all of us—" She cast down her eyes.

"You look well, none the less, Kristin—" Erlend looked at her with a little smile.

Red, as though he struck her, Kristin stood:

" 'Tis not for that—"

"Nay, I know 'tis not because you deem you too young and fresh to live as a widow woman," Erlend went on, when she stopped short. "I trow but little good would come of it should I come back home, Kristin," said he, more soberly. "In your hands all goes well on Jörundgaard, that know I—you have fortune with you in your doings. And I am well content with the life I live here."

" 'Tis not well for the boys—that we should be at odds," she answered in a low voice.

"Oh—" Erlend lingered on the word. "They are so young. I can scarce believe they take it so to heart that they will not forget it when they leave their childhood behind. I care not if I tell you," he said with a little smile, "I meet them now and again—"

She knew it—but she felt as though it humbled her, and felt as 'twere so he had meant it—he had deemed she knew it not. The sons had never known that she knew. But she answered gravely:

"Then you know also that much on Jörundgaard is not as it should be—"

"We never talk of such-like things," said he, smiling as before. "We go a-hunting together—but you must be hungry and thirsty" —he leapt up. "And you are standing too—nay, set you up in the high-seat, Kristin—ay, do so, sweetheart! You shall have it to yourself—"

He fetched in the milk and the cheese, and brought out bread, butter, and dried meat. Kristin was hungry and yet more thirsty; but she found it hard to swallow down the food. Erlend ate hastily and slovenly, as had always been his wont when he was not with strangers—but he was soon done.

He talked of himself the while. The folk down the hill here tilled his land and brought him milk and a little food—for the most part he lay out on the fells hunting game and fishing. Howsoever, he said on a sudden, he had thoughts now of faring from the land. Seeking service with some outland chieftain—

"Oh, no, Erlend!"

He looked at her quickly and searchingly. But she said no more. It began to grow dusk in the room—her face and head-linen shone palely against the dark wall. Erlend rose and made a fire in the fire-place. Then he sat down aslant on the outer bench, turned towards her; the red glare from the fire flickered over his form.

But that he could even think of such a thing! He was nigh as old as had been her father when he died. And yet 'twas believable enough that he would do it one day—run after some such whimsy, off to seek for new adventures—

"Deem you 'tis not enough," said the wife vehemently, " 'tis not enough that you have forsaken the parish and your sons and me—would you flee the land from us now?"

"Had I known your thoughts of me, Kristin," said Erlend gravely, "then had I gone forth from *your* manor long ago. But I understand now that you have had to bear *much* from me—"

"You know full well, Erlend—you say *my* manor, but you have a husband's right over all that is mine." She heard herself how faint of voice she grew.

"Ay," answered Erlend. "But I know myself I was an ill husband of my own good." He was silent a while. "Naakkve—I mind the time he was unborn—you spoke of him that you bore beneath your girdle, that was to mount into my high-seat after me. I see now, Kristin—'twas hard for you—best let things be as they are. And I thrive full well in this life—"

Kristin looked around her in the darkening room, shuddering— the shadows filled every corner now, and the fire-light danced,—

"I understand not," she said, nigh sinking with heaviness, "that you can abide this house. Naught have you to do, none to bear you company—at least you might get you a house-carl, I trow—"

"You mean that I should work the farm myself—?" Erlend laughed. "Oh no, Kristin. Sure you must know how little fit I am to play the farmer. I cannot sit quiet—"

"Quiet—Here surely you sit quiet enough—the long winter through—"

Erlend smiled to himself, his eyes far off and strange:

"Ay, when 'tis in that way—When I need not to think of aught but what runs in my head—can go and come as I like—And you know well—it has ever been so with me, that when there's naught to wake for, I can sleep—I sleep like a bear in its winter lair when 'tis not weather for the fells—"

"Are you never afraid to be alone here?" whispered Kristin.

At first he looked at her as though he understood not. Then he laughed:

"Because folks say 'tis haunted? Never have I marked aught. Sometimes I had been fain that my kinsman Björn *would* visit me. Mind you that he said once he deemed I would ill abide to feel the knife-edge at my throat. I could e'en have a mind to answer the knight now that I was not greatly feared when I had the rope about my neck—"

A long shudder passed through the woman's body. She sat there dumb.

Erlend rose.

"I trow 'tis time we went to rest now, Kristin."

Stiff and cold, she watched Erlend take the covering that lay over his armour, spread it on the bed, and turn it down over the dirty pillows. "'Tis the best I have," said he.

"Erlend." She clasped her hands beneath her breast. She sought for something she might say to gain a little time yet—she was so afraid. Then she remembered the errand she was to fulfil:

"Erlend—I was given a message to bear to you. Simon prayed me, when he lay dying, that I would greet you from him and say he had repented him each day of the words he said to you when last you parted. Unmanly he called them himself—and he begged that you would forgive him for them."

"Simon." Erlend stood holding the bedpost with one hand, gazing down at the floor. "He is the man I am least fain to be remembered of."

"I know not what has been between you," said Kristin. Strangely heartless these words of Erlend's seemed to her. "But 'twere strange and unlike Simon if it were as he said, that he had shown him little-minded in his dealings with you. If so it be—I trow the blame was not all his."

Erlend shook his head: "He stood by me like a brother when

my need was greatest," he said low. "And I took help and friend-ship at his hands, and I knew not that all the time he could scarce endure me—

"—Me thinks it must have been easier to live in the old world, when two such fellows as he and I met together hand to hand—met on a holm and put it to the trial of arms which should win the fair-haired maid—"

He took an old cloak from the bench and flung it over his arm:

"Maybe you would have the dogs beside you to-night?"

Kristin had risen:

"Whither go you, Erlend?"

"Out to the barn to lie there—"

"No—!" Erlend stopped—he stood there, straight and slender and young in the dim red light of the waning embers. "I dare not lie alone here in this house—I dare not—"

"Dare you lie in my arms then?" She half saw his smile through the dusk, and drooped beneath it. "Are you not afraid I should crush you to death, Kristin—?"

"Would that you might—!" She sank into his arms.

# WILLIAM SHAKESPEARE

*The efforts of a determined man to humble a domineer-ing wife make* The Taming of the Shrew *one of Shakespeare's lustiest comedies. Here is Kate's testa-ment of submission.*

## From Act V, Scene 2

PETRUCHIO: Katharine, I charge thee, tell these headstrong women
  What duty they do owe their lords and husbands.

WIDOW: Come, come, you're mocking: we will have no telling.

PETRUCHIO: Come on, I say; and first begin with her.

WIDOW: She shall not.

PETRUCHIO: I say she shall: and first begin with her.

KATHARINA: Fie, fie! unknit that threatening unkind brow;
And dart not scornful glances from those eyes,
To wound thy lord, thy king, thy governor:
It blots thy beauty as frosts do bite the meads,
Confounds thy fame as whirlwinds shake fair buds,
And in no sense is meet or amiable.
A woman moved is like a fountain troubled,
Muddy, ill-seeming, thick, bereft of beauty;
And while it is so, none so dry or thirsty
Will deign to sip or touch one drop of it.
Thy husband is thy lord, thy life, thy keeper,
Thy head, thy sovereign; one that cares for thee,
And for thy maintenance commits his body
To painful labour both by sea and land,
To watch the night in storms, the day in cold,
Whilst thou liest warm at home, secure and safe;
And craves no other tribute at thy hands
But love, fair looks, and true obedience;
Too little payment for so great a debt.
Such duty as the subject owes the prince
Even such a woman oweth to her husband;
And when she is froward, peevish, sullen, sour,
And not obedient to his honest will,
What is she but a foul contending rebel,
And graceless traitor to her loving lord?
I am ashamed that women are so simple
To offer war where they should kneel for peace;
Or seek for rule, supremacy, and sway,
When they are bound to serve, love, and obey.
Why are our bodies soft and weak and smooth,
Unapt to toil and trouble in the world,
But that our soft conditions and our hearts
Should well agree with our external parts?
Come, come, you froward and unable worms!
My mind hath been as big as one of yours,
My heart as great, my reason haply more,
To bandy word for word and frown for frown;

But now I see our lances are but straws,
Our strength as weak, our weakness past compare,
That seeming to be most which we indeed least are.
Then vail your stomachs, for it is no boot,
And place your hands below your husband's foot:
In token of which duty, if he please,
My hand is ready, may it do him ease.

PETRUCHIO: Why, there's a wench! Come on, and kiss me, Kate.

LUCENTIO: Well, go thy ways, old lad; for thou shalt ha't.

VINCENTIO: 'Tis a good hearing, when children are toward.

LUCENTIO: But a harsh hearing, when women are froward.

PETRUCHIO: Come, Kate, we'll to bed.
We three are married, but you two are sped.
'Twas I won the wager, though you hit the white;

(To Lucentio)

And, being a winner, God give you good night!

(Exeunt Petruchio and Katharina)

HORTENSIO: Now, go thy ways; thou hast tamed a curst shrew.

LUCENTIO: 'Tis a wonder, by your leave, she will be tamed so.

(Exeunt)

# ANONYMOUS

*An English ballad from the sixteenth century sings
of the timeless ways of marital compromise.*

THIS WINTER'S weather it waxeth cold,
    And frost it freezeth on every hill,
And Boreas blows his blast so bold
    That all our cattle are like to spill.
Bell, my wife, she loves no strife;
    She said unto me quietlye,
Rise up, and save cow Crumbock's life!
    Man, put thine old cloak about thee!

*He.* O Bell my wife, why dost thou flyte?
    Thou kens my cloak is very thin:
  It is so bare and over worn,
    A crickè thereon cannot renn.
  Then I'll no longer borrow nor lend;
    For once I'll new apparell'd be;
  Tomorrow I'll to town and spend;
    For I'll have a new cloak about me.

*She.* Cow Crumbock is a very good cow:
    She has been always true to the pail:
  She has helped us to butter and cheese, I trow,
    And other things she will not fail.
  I would be loth to see her pine.
    Good husband, counsel take of me:
  It is not for us to go so fine—
 Man, take thine old cloak about thee!

*He.* My cloak it was a very good cloak,
    It hath been always true to the wear;
  But now it is not worth a groat:
    I have had it four and forty year'.
  Sometime it was of cloth in grain:
    'Tis now but a sigh clout, as you may see:
  It will neither hold out wind nor rain;
    And I'll have a new cloak about me.

*She.* It is four and forty years ago
    Sine the one of us the other did ken;
  And we have had, betwixt us two,
    Of children either nine or ten:
  We have brought them up to women and men:
    In the fear of God I trow they be.
  And why wilt thou thyself misken?
    Man, take thine old cloak about thee!

*He.* O Bell my wife, why dost thou flyte?
    Now is now, and then was then:
  Seek now all the world throughout,
    Thou kens not clowns from gentlemen:

They are clad in black, green, yellow and blue,
　　So far above their own degree.
Once in my life I'll take a view;
　　For I'll have a new cloak about me.

*She.* King Stephen was a worthy peer;
　　His breeches cost him but a crown;
He held them sixpence all too dear,
　　Therefore he called the tailor 'lown.'
He was a king and wore the crown,
　　And thou'se but of a low degree:
It's pride that puts this country down:
　　Man, take thy old cloak about thee!

*He.* Bell my wife, she loves not strife,
　　Yet she will lead me, if she can;
And to maintain an easy life
　　I oft must yield, though I'm good-man.
It's not for a man with a woman to threap,
　　Unless he first give o'er the plea:
As we began, so will we keep,
　　And I'll take my old cloak about me.

# ANNE BRADSTREET

*Anne Bradstreet, who came to America in 1630 with her family and husband-to-be, became one of the first poets of the English language in the New World. In "To My Dear and Loving Husband," she celebrates her happy marriage.*

IF EVER two were one, then surely we.
If ever man were lov'd by wife, then thee.

If ever wife was happy in a man,
Compare with me, ye women, if you can.
I prize thy love more than whole Mines of gold,
Or all the riches that the East doth hold.
My love is such that Rivers cannot quench,
Nor ought but love from thee give recompence.
Thy love is such I can no way repay;
The heavens reward thee manifold I pray.
Then while we live, in love let's so persever,
That when we live no more, we may live forever.

# JANE AUSTEN

*The world of English country families at the start of the nineteenth century was immortalized by Jane Austen. From* Pride and Prejudice, *here are Mr. and Mrs. Bennet.*

IT IS A TRUTH universally acknowledged, that a single man in possession of a good fortune must be in want of a wife.

However little known the feelings or views of such a man may be on his first entering a neighbourhood, this truth is so well fixed in the minds of the surrounding families, that he is considered the rightful property of some one or other of their daughters.

"My dear Mr. Bennet," said his lady to him one day, "have you heard that Netherfield Park is let at last?"

Mr. Bennet replied that he had not.

"But it is," returned she; "for Mrs. Long has just been here, and she told me all about it."

Mr. Bennet made no answer.

"Do not you want to know who has taken it?" cried his wife impatiently.

"*You* want to tell me, and I have no objection to hearing it."

This was invitation enough.

"Why, my dear, you must know, Mrs. Long says that Netherfield is taken by a young man of large fortune from the north of England; that he came down on Monday in a chaise and four to see the place, and was so much delighted with it that he agreed with Mr. Morris immediately; that he is to take possession before Michaelmas, and some of his servants are to be in the house by the end of next week."

"What is his name?"

"Bingley."

"Is he married or single?"

"Oh! single, my dear, to be sure! A single man of large fortune; four or five thousand a-year. What a fine thing for our girls!"

"How so? how can it affect them?"

"My dear Mr. Bennet," replied his wife, "how can you be so tiresome! You must know that I am thinking of his marrying one of them."

"Is that his design in settling here?"

"Design! nonsense, how can you talk so! But it is very likely that he *may* fall in love with one of them, and therefore you must visit him as soon as he comes."

"I see no occasion for that. You and the girls may go, or you may send them by themselves, which perhaps will be still better, for as you are as handsome as any of them, Mr. Bingley might like you the best of the party."

"My dear, you flatter me. I certainly *have* had my share of beauty, but I do not pretend to be anything extraordinary now. When a woman has five grown up daughters, she ought to give over thinking of her own beauty."

"In such cases, a woman has not often much beauty to think of."

"But, my dear, you must indeed go and see Mr. Bingley when he comes into the neighbourhood."

"It is more than I engage for, I assure you."

"But consider your daughters. Only think what an establishment it would be for one of them. Sir William and Lady Lucas are determined to go, merely on that account, for in general you know they visit no new comers. Indeed you must go, for it will be impossible for *us* to visit him if you do not."

"You are over scrupulous, surely. I dare say Bingley will be very glad to see you; and I will send a few lines by you to assure him of my hearty consent to his marrying which ever he chooses of the girls; though I must throw in a good word for my little Lizzy."

"I desire you will do no such thing. Lizzy is not a bit better than the others; and I am sure she is not half so handsome as Jane, nor half so good humoured as Lydia. But you are always giving *her* the preference."

"They have none of them much to recommend them," replied he; "they are all silly and ignorant, like other girls; but Lizzy has something more of quickness than her sisters."

"Mr. Bennet, how can you abuse your own children in such a way? You take delight in vexing me. You have no compassion on my poor nerves."

"You mistake me, my dear. I have a high respect for your nerves. They are my old friends. I have heard you mention them with consideration these twenty years at least."

"Ah! you do not know what I suffer."

"But I hope you will get over it, and live to see many young men of four thousand a year come into the neighbourhood."

"It will be no use to us, if twenty such should come, since you will not visit them."

"Depend upon it my dear, that when there are twenty, I will visit them all."

Mr. Bennet was so odd a mixture of quick parts, sarcastic humour, reserve, and caprice, that the experience of three and twenty years had been insufficient to make his wife understand his character. *Her* mind was less difficult to develop. She was a woman of mean understanding, little information, and uncertain temper. When she was discontented, she fancied herself nervous. The business of her life was to get her daughters married; its solace was visiting and news.

# HARRIET BEECHER STOWE

※ ※

*Uncle Tom's Cabin, published in 1852, presented the
world with a gallery of characters still unforgotten—
pious Uncle Tom, saintly little Eva, cruel Simon Le-
gree. Less stereotyped in public memory are the husband and wife, George and Eliza Harris, an intelligent
and handsome Negro couple.*

MRS. SHELBY had gone on her visit, and Eliza stood in the
verandah, rather dejectedly looking after the retreating carriage,
when a hand was laid on her shoulder. She turned and a bright
smile lighted up her eyes.

"George, is it you? How you frightened me! Well, I am so glad
you's come! Missis is gone to spend the afternoon; so come into my
little room, and we'll have the time all to ourselves."

Saying this, she drew him into a neat little apartment, opening
on the verandah, where she generally sat at her sewing, within
call of her mistress.

"How glad I am?—why don't you smile?—and look at Harry
—how he grows." The boy stood shyly regarding his father
through his curls, holding close to the skirts of his mother's dress.
"Isn't he beautiful?" said Eliza, lifting his long curls and kissing
him.

"I wish he'd never been born!" said George, bitterly. "I wish I'd
never been born myself!"

Surprised and frightened, Eliza sat down, leaned her head on
her husband's shoulder, and burst into tears.

"There now, Eliza, it's too bad for me to make you feel so, poor
girl!" said he, fondly; "it's too bad. O, how I wish you never had
seen me—you might have been happy!"

"George! George! how can you talk so? What dreadful thing has happened, or is going to happen? I'm sure we've been very happy, till lately."

"So we have, dear," said George. Then drawing his child on his knee, he gazed intently on his glorious dark eyes, and passed his hand through his long curls.

"Just like you, Eliza; and you are the handsomest woman I ever saw, and the best one I ever wish to see; but, oh, I wish I'd never seen you, nor you me!"

"O George, how can you!"

"Yes, Eliza, it's all misery, misery, misery! My life is bitter as wormwood; the very life is burning out of me. I'm a poor, miserable forlorn drudge; I shall only drag you down with me, that's all. What's the use of our trying to do anything, trying to know anything, trying to be anything? What's the use of living? I wish I was dead!"

"O now, dear George, that is really wicked! I know how you feel about losing your place in the factory, and you have a hard master; but pray be patient, and perhaps something—"

"Patient!" said he, interrupting her; "haven't I been patient? Did I say a word when he came and took me away, for no earthly reason, from the place where everybody was kind to me? I'd paid him truly every cent of my earnings,—and they all say I worked well."

"Well, it *is* dreadful," said Eliza; "but, after all, he is your master, you know."

"My master! and who made him my master? That's what I think of—what right has he to me? I'm a man as much as he is. I'm a better man than he is. I know more about business than he does; I am a better manager than he is; I can read better than he can; I can write a better hand,—and I've learned it all myself, and no thanks to him,—I've learned it in spite of him; and now what right has he to make a dray-horse of me?—to take me from things I can do, and do better than he can, and put me to work that any horse can do? He tries to do it; he says he'll bring me down and humble me, and he puts me to just the hardest, meanest, and dirtiest work, on purpose!"

"O George! George! you frighten me! Why, I never heard you talk so; I'm afraid you'll do something dreadful. I don't wonder at your feelings, at all; but oh, do be careful—do, do—for my sake—for Harry's!"

"I have been careful, and I have been patient, but it's growing worse and worse; flesh and blood can't bear it any longer;—every chance he can get to insult and torment me, he takes. I thought I could do my work well, and keep on quiet, and have some time to read and learn out of work hours; but the more he sees I can do, the more he loads on. He says that though I don't say anything, he sees I've got the devil in me, and he means to bring it out; and one of these days it will come out in a way that he won't like, or I'm mistaken!"

"O dear! what shall we do?" said Eliza, mournfully.

"It was only yesterday," said George, "as I was busy loading stones into a cart that young Mas'r Tom stood there, slashing his whip so near the horse that the creature was frightened. I asked him to stop, as pleasant as I could,—he just kept right on. I begged him again, and then he turned on me, and began striking me. I held his hand, and then he screamed and kicked and ran to his father, and told him that I was fighting him. He came in a rage, and said he'd teach me who was my master; and he tied me to a tree, and cut switches for young master, and told him that he might whip me till he was tired;—and he did do it! If I don't make him remember it, some time!" And the brow of the young man grew dark, and his eyes burned with an expression that made his young wife tremble. "Who made this man my master? That's what I want to know!" he said.

"Well," said Eliza, mournfully, "I always thought that I must obey my master and mistress, or I couldn't be a Christian."

"There is some sense in it, in your case; they have brought you up like a child, fed you, clothed you, indulged you, and taught you, so that you have a good education; that is some reason why they should claim you. But I have been kicked and cuffed and sworn at, and at the best only let alone; and what do I owe? I've paid for all my keeping a hundred times over. I won't bear it. No, I won't!" he said, clenching his hand with a fierce frown.

Eliza trembled, and was silent. She had never seen her husband in this mood before; and her gentle system of ethics seemed to bend like a reed in the surges of such passions.

"You know poor little Carlo, that you gave me," added George; "the creature has been about all the comfort that I've had. He has slept with me nights, and followed me around days, and kind of looked at me as if he understood how I felt. Well, the other day I was just feeding him with a few old scraps I picked up by the kitchen door, and Mas'r came along, and said I was feeding him up at his expense, and that he couldn't afford to have every nigger keeping his dog, and ordered me to tie a stone to his neck and throw him in the pond."

"O George, you didn't do it!"

"Do it? not I!—but he did. Mas'r and Tom pelted the poor drowning creature with stones. Poor thing! he looked at me so mournful, as if he wondered why I didn't save him. I had to take a flogging because I wouldn't do it myself. I don't care. Mas'r will find out that I'm one that whipping won't tame. My day will come yet, if he don't look out."

"What are you going to do? O George, don't do anything wicked; if you only trust in God, and try to do right, he'll deliver you."

"I ain't a Christian like you, Eliza; my heart's full of bitterness; I can't trust in God. Why does he let things be so?"

"O George, we must have faith. Mistress says that when all things go wrong to us, we must believe that God is doing the very best."

"That's easy to say for people that are sitting on their sofas and riding their carriages; but let 'em be where I am, I guess it would come some harder. I wish I could be good; but my heart burns, and can't be reconciled, anyhow. You couldn't, in my place,—you can't now, if I tell you all I've got to say. You don't know the whole yet!"

"What can be coming now?"

"Well, lately Mas'r had been saying that he was a fool to let me marry off the place; that he hates Mr. Shelby and all his tribe, because they are proud, and hold their heads up above him, and that I've got proud notions from you; and he says he won't let me come here any more, and that I shall take a wife and settle down on his place. At first he only scolded and grumbled these things; but yesterday he told me that I should take Mina for a wife, and settle down in a cabin with her, or he would sell me down river."

"Why—but you were married to *me,* by the minister, as much as if you'd been a white man!" said Eliza, simply.

"Don't you know a slave can't be married? There is no law in this country for that; I can't hold you for my wife, if he chooses to part us. That's why I wish I'd never seen you,—why I wish I'd never been born; it would have been better for us both,—it would have been better for this poor child if he had never been born. All this may happen to him yet!"

"O, but master is so kind!"

"Yes, but who knows?—he may die—and then he may be sold to nobody knows who. What pleasure is it that he is handsome, and smart, and bright? I tell you, Eliza, that a sword will pierce through your soul for every good and pleasant thing your child is or has; it will make him worth too much for you to keep!"

The words smote heavily on Eliza's heart; the vision of the trader came before her eyes, and, as if some one had struck her a deadly blow, she turned pale and gasped for breath. She looked nervously out on the verandah, where the boy, tired of the grave conversation, had retired, and where he was riding triumphantly up and down on Mr. Shelby's walking-stick. She would have spoken to tell her husband her fears, but checked herself.

"No, no,—he has enough to bear, poor fellow!" she thought. "No, I won't tell him; besides it an't true; Missus never deceives us."

"So Eliza, my girl," said the husband, mournfully, "bear up, now; and good-bye, for I'm going."

"Going, George! Going where?"

"To Canada," said he, straightening himself up, "and when I'm there, I'll buy you; that's all the hope that's left us. You have a kind master, that won't refuse to sell you. I'll buy you and the boy.—God helping me, I will!"

"O dreadful! if you should be taken?"

"I won't be taken, Eliza; I'll *die* first! I'll be free, or I'll die!"

"You won't kill yourself!"

"No need of that. They will kill me, fast enough; they never will get me down the river alive!"

"O George, for my sake, do be careful! Don't do anything wicked; don't lay hands on yourself, or anybody else! You are tempted too much—too much; but don't—go you must—but go carefully, prudently; pray God to help you."

"Well, then, Eliza, hear my plan. Mas'r took it into his head to send me right by here, with a note to Mr. Symmes, that lives a mile past. I believe he expected I should come here to tell you what I have. It would please him, if he thought it would aggravate 'Shelby's folks,' as he calls 'em. I'm going home quite resigned, you understand, as if all was over. I've got some preparations made,—and there are those that will help me; and, in the course of a week or so, I shall be among the missing, some day. Pray for me, Eliza; perhaps the good Lord will hear *you*."

"O, pray yourself, George, and go trusting in him; then you won't do anything wicked."

"Well, now, *good-bye*," said George, holding Eliza's hands, and gazing into her eyes, without moving. They stood silent; then there were last words, and sobs, and bitter weeping,—such parting as those may make whose hope to meet again is as the spider's web,—and the husband and wife were parted.

# Fathers and Sons

# THE HOLY BIBLE

(Authorized King James Version)

⚔ ⚔

*The Old Testament records the lament of King David*
*for his rebellious but beloved son.*

## The Second Book of Samuel, Chapter 18, Verses 29–33

And the king said, Is the young man Absalom safe? And Ahimaaz answered, When Joab sent the king's servant, and me thy servant, I saw a great tumult, but I knew not what it was.

And the king said unto him, Turn aside, and stand here. And he turned aside, and stood still.

And, behold, Cushi came; and Cushi said, Tidings, my lord the king: for the LORD hath avenged thee this day of all them that rose up against thee.

And the king said unto Cushi, Is the young man Absalom safe? And Cushi answered, The enemies of my lord the king, and all that rise against thee to do thee hurt, be as that young man is.

And the king was much moved, and went up to the chamber over the gate, and wept: and as he went, thus he said, O my son Absalom, my son Absalom! would God I had died for thee, O Absalom, my son, my son!

# CHARLES DICKENS

☙ ☙

*Countless aspects of middle and lower-class family
life in England during the middle of the nineteenth
century were reflected in the novels of Charles Dickens. Here, from* Dombey and Son, *a prosperous busi-
nessman interviews his young son.*

SOME PHILOSOPHERS tell us that selfishness is at the root of
our best loves and affections. Mr. Dombey's young child was,
from the beginning, so distinctly important to him as a part of his
own greatness, or (which is the same thing) of the greatness of
Dombey and Son, that there is no doubt his parental affection
might have been easily traced, like many a goodly superstructure
of fair fame, to a very low foundation. But he loved his son with
all the love he had. If there were a warm place in his frosty heart,
his son occupied it; if its very hard surface could receive the impression of any image, the image of that son was there; though
not so much as an infant, or as a boy, but as a grown man—the
"Son" of the Firm. Therefore he was impatient to advance into
the future, and to hurry over the intervening passages of his history. Therefore he had little or no anxiety about them, in spite of
his love; feeling as if the boy had a charmed life, and *must* become
the man with whom he held such constant communication in his
thoughts, and for whom he planned and projected, as for an ex-
isting reality, every day.

Thus Paul grew to be nearly five years old. He was a pretty
little fellow; though there was something wan and wistful in his
small face, that gave occasion to many significant shakes of Mrs.
Wickam's head, and many long-drawn inspirations of Mrs.
Wickam's breath. His temper gave abundant promise of being
imperious in after-life; and he had as hopeful an apprehension of

his own importance, and the rightful subservience of all other things and persons to it, as heart could desire. He was childish and sportive enough at times, and not of a sullen disposition; but he had a strange, old-fashioned, thoughtful way, at other times, of sitting brooding in his miniature arm-chair, when he looked (and talked) like one of those terrible little Beings in the Fairy tales, who, at a hundred and fifty or two hundred years of age, fantastically represent the children for whom they have been substituted. He would frequently be stricken with this precocious mood up-stairs in the nursery; and would sometimes lapse into it suddenly, exclaiming that he was tired: even while playing with Florence, or driving Miss Tox in single harness. But at no time did he fall into it so surely, as when, his little chair being carried down into his father's room, he sat there with him after dinner, by the fire. They were the strangest pair at such a time that ever firelight shone upon. Mr. Dombey so erect and solemn, gazing at the blaze; his little image, with an old, old, face, peering into the red perspective with the fixed and rapt attention of a sage. Mr. Dombey entertaining Heaven knows what wild fancies, half-formed thoughts, and wandering speculations. Mr. Dombey stiff with starch and arrogance; the little image by inheritance, and in unconscious imitation. The two so very much alike, and yet so monstrously contrasted.

On one of these occasions, when they had both been perfectly quiet for a long time, and Mr. Dombey only knew that the child was awake by occasionally glancing at his eye, where the bright fire was sparkling like a jewel, little Paul broke silence thus:

"Papa! what's money?"

The abrupt question had such immediate reference to the subject of Mr. Dombey's thoughts, that Mr. Dombey was quite disconcerted.

"What is money, Paul?" he answered. "Money?"

"Yes," said the child, laying his hands upon the elbows of his little chair, and turning the old face up towards Mr. Dombey's; "what is money?"

Mr. Dombey was in a difficulty. He would have liked to give him some explanation involving the terms circulating-medium, currency, depreciation of currency, paper, bullion, rates of exchange, value of precious metals in the market, and so forth; but looking down at the little chair, and seeing what a long way down it was, he answered: "Gold, and silver, and copper. Guineas, shillings, half-pence. You know what they are?"

"Oh yes, I know what they are," said Paul. "I don't mean that, papa. I mean what's money after all."

Heaven and Earth, how old his face was as he turned it up again towards his father's!

"What is money after all!" said Mr. Dombey, backing his chair a little, that he might the better gaze in sheer amazement at the presumptuous atom that propounded such an inquiry.

"I mean, papa, what can it do?" returned Paul, folding his arms (they were hardly long enough to fold), and looking at the fire, and up at him, and at the fire, and up at him again.

Mr. Dombey drew his chair back to its former place, and patted him on the head. "You'll know better by-and-by, my man," he said. "Money, Paul, can do anything." He took hold of the little hand, and beat it softly against one of his own, as he said so.

But Paul got his hand free as soon as he could; and rubbing it gently to and fro on the elbow of his chair, as if his wit were in the palm, and he were sharpening it—and looking at the fire again, as though the fire had been his adviser and prompter— repeated, after a short pause:

"Anything, papa?"

"Yes. Anything—almost," said Mr. Dombey.

"Anything means everything, don't it, papa?" asked his son: not observing, or possibly not understanding, the qualification.

"It includes it: yes," said Mr. Dombey.

"Why didn't money save me my mama?" returned the child. "It isn't cruel, is it?"

"Cruel!" said Mr. Dombey, settling his neckcloth, and seeming to resent the idea. "No. A good thing can't be cruel."

"If it's a good thing, and can do anything," said the little fellow, thoughtfully, as he looked back at the fire, "I wonder why it didn't save me my mama."

He didn't ask the question of his father this time. Perhaps he had seen, with a child's quickness, that it had already made his father uncomfortable. But he repeated the thought aloud, as if it were quite an old one to him, and had troubled him very much; and sat with his chin resting on his hand, still cogitating and looking for an explanation in the fire.

Mr. Dombey having recovered from his surprise, not to say his alarm (for it was the very first occasion on which the child had ever broached the subject of his mother to him, though he had had him sitting by his side, in this same manner, evening after evening), expounded to him how that money, though a very potent spirit, never to be disparaged on any account whatever, could not keep people alive whose time was come to die; and how that we must all die, unfortunately, even in the city, though we were never so rich. But how that money caused us to be honored, feared, respected, courted, and admired, and made us powerful and glorious in the eyes of all men; and how that it could, very often, even keep off death, for a long time together. How, for example, it had secured to his mama the services of Mr. Pilkins, by which he, Paul, had often profited himself; likewise of the great Doctor Parker Peps, whom he had never known. And how it could do all that could be done. This, with more to the same purpose, Mr. Dombey instilled into the mind of his son, who listened attentively, and seemed to understand the greater part of what was said to him.

"It can't make me strong and quite well, either, papa; can it?" asked Paul, after a short silence; rubbing his tiny hands.

"Why, you *are* strong and quite well," returned Mr. Dombey. "Are you not?"

Oh! the age of the face that was turned up again, with an expression, half of melancholy, half of slyness, on it!

"You are as strong and well as such little people usually are? Eh?" said Mr. Dombey.

"Florence is older than I am, but I'm not as strong and well as Florence, I know," returned the child; "but I believe that when Florence was as little as me, she could play a great deal longer at a time without tiring herself. I am so tired sometimes," said little Paul, warming his hands, and looking in between the bars of the grate, as if some ghostly puppet-show were performing there, "and my bones ache so (Wickam says it's my bones), that I don't know what to do."

"Ay! But that's at night," said Mr. Dombey, drawing his own chair closer to his son's, and laying his hand gently on his back; "little people should be tired at night, for then they sleep well."

"Oh, it's not at night, papa," returned the child, "it's in the day; and I lie down in Florence's lap, and she sings to me. At night I dream about such cu-ri-ous things!"

And he went on, warming his hands again, and thinking about them, like an old man or a young goblin.

Mr. Dombey was so astonished, and so uncomfortable, and so perfectly at a loss how to pursue the conversation, that he could only sit looking at his son by the light of the fire, with his hand resting on his back, as if it were detained there by some magnetic attraction. Once he advanced his other hand, and turned the contemplative face towards his own for a moment. But it sought the fire again as soon as he released it; and remained, addressed towards the flickering blaze, until the nurse appeared to summon him to bed.

"I want Florence to come for me," said Paul.

"Won't you come with your poor Nurse Wickam, Master Paul?" inquired that attendant, with great pathos.

"No, I won't," replied Paul, composing himself in his arm-chair again, like the master of the house.

Invoking a blessing upon his innocence, Mrs. Wickam withdrew, and presently Florence appeared in her stead. The child immediately started up with sudden readiness and animation, and raised towards his father in bidding him good night, a countenance so much brighter, so much younger, and so much more child-like altogether, that Mr. Dombey, while he felt greatly reassured by the change, was quite amazed at it.

After they had left the room together, he thought he heard a soft voice singing; and remembering that Paul had said his sister sung to him, he had the curiosity to open the door and listen, and look after them. She was toiling up the great, wide, vacant staircase, with him in her arms; his head was lying on her shoulder, one of his arms thrown negligently round her neck. So they went, toiling up; she singing all the way, and Paul sometimes crooning out a feeble accompaniment. Mr. Dombey looked after them until they reached the top of the staircase—not without halting to rest by the way—and passed out of his sight; and then he still stood gazing upwards, until the dull rays of the moon, glimmering in a melancholy manner through the dim skylight, sent him back to his own room.

# CATHERINE DRINKER BOWEN

※ ※

*John Adams, the second President of the United States, was not only the father of a renowned son who also became President, but himself the son of a worthy father.* John Adams and the American Revolution *reveals some of Adams' feelings in regard to that relationship.*

RIDING TO WORCESTER that May of '61 to attend court, John thought of these things and of what his father had said. The old man had wisdom; there was no doubt of it. Not the wisdom of books but the wisdom of living. Lately, John had paid little attention to his father's advice, which irritated by its caution. Now he felt remorseful; he might at least pay the compliment of pretending to heed. What an awful thing, to grow old, lose control, authority! And yet, thought John as his horse walked the road and the May sun warmed his back—yet his father seemed content. Perhaps age diminished this fierce urge for authority, this desire, this thirst for men to listen to what one had to say.

Today John felt especially uneasy about his father. The old man had seemed poorly. He had risen stiffly from his chair and walked out the little front path to the highway to see John off, holding a hand to his head and complaining of dizziness. He was catching cold, he said. Never mind—it was nothing. They must not alarm John's mother. Whenever there was an epidemic—and there was one now—Mrs. Adams grew panicky, sprinkled the house with sulphur, urged the boys to chew tobacco (which usually she hated), even smoked a pipe herself each evening before she went to bed, walking round and blowing smoke in every cranny, though she made faces and said it tasted rank. This particular epidemic was a throat distemper. It was very serious; fourteen people had died already in Braintree. Dr. Savil had lost two patients. Bleeding didn't help, he said, nor did purging. The disease began with a sore throat and violent pains in the head. If it spread downward to the lungs, hope was gone and the patient died within the week.

John shook himself, urged his horse to a trot. This was no way to be thinking on a fine day of May. Birds sang in the trees, loamy fields spread on either side and the corn showed green between the furrows. The wheat was tall and would soon be heading out.

Eight days later, when John returned home, his mother met him at the door. Her throat was wrapped in flannel. She coughed. Mr. Adams was most fearfully ill, she said. She led John, still in his boots and traveling clothes, upstairs to the sickroom. John's father lay in the four-posted bed. His eyes were closed, his arms outside the covers; his chest moved laboriously with a rapid, shallow breath. As John entered, the sick man opened his eyes, stared at his son, raised a hand and let it fall, then lapsed again into unconsciousness. So shocked was John at the alteration in his father's face and aspect that it was all he could do to refrain from falling on his knees by the bed. Mrs. Adams stood a little apart, by the window, weeping silently. The sight of her tears was awful to John. She had always been quick to laughter, quick also to anger, but John could not remember seeing her weep like this.

All that night and next day, Mr. Adams lay half conscious, his fingers drumming and plucking at the coverlet, his breath coming and going in light, quick gasps. Dr. Savil came and sat by him, holding the sick man's wrist. Peter and Elihu waited in their room across the hall or squatted on the narrow stairs, very much in the way, very desirous to be of help, and, like everyone, terribly helpless in the face of what was coming.

Just after sundown, Mr. Adams died. John was with him, his mother and two brothers were in the room. He went quietly, without struggle or apparent suffering. It was Mrs. Adams who knew first that he was gone. With her eyes fastened on her husband's face, as they had been hour after hour, she seized his hand, and, crying out, fell on her knees by the bed.

Mrs. Adams, for the next two weeks, was a very sick woman. She was put instantly to bed. Before nightfall on the day of her husband's death, she was delirious with fever. She had caught the epidemic; the household feared for her life. Her sister Anne—Uncle Ebenezer's wife—came to care for her. The house seemed suddenly filled with people—aunts, cousins, uncles, offering aid and managing to be always underfoot. John himself took charge of his father's funeral.

Dr. and Mrs. Savil were infinitely kind; so was Parson Wibird. How beloved in this town his father had been! thought John. The neighbors came—farmers, fishermen, millers, squires—from Colonel John Quincy down to old Scant, the town drunkard, who broke blubbering in tears on the doorstep and stumbled off without managing a word beyond "respects." The women brought jellies and soups for Mrs. Adams; their husbands lingered to exchange, in lowered voices, stories about John's father. The famous story of old Levi Haskins and his boundary fence that had been quarreled over so long in town meeting. The story of Widow Crosby and the premium she claimed for her old lame black boar which she swore was sire to half the pigs in town. . . . Deacon Adams had settled that, too. He wasn't a talking man, the mourners said now. But when he had a mind to, Mr. Adams could persuade a person to anything.

Homely stories, with no trace of heroism—but to John they were stories infinitely touching. His father had been given wisdom to deal with people, knew when to be stern and when to be kind. Only once in his life could John remember seeing him lose his temper.

John acted now as attorney to settle Mr. Adams's estate. It was inventoried at £1330.9.8. The homestead where they lived went to Peter, the second son. (This had been determined long ago, when John chose a college education for patrimony.) To Elihu went the South Precinct land. John's portion was the little house next door where the Savils lived, and thirty acres—ten near the house, the rest on the farm.

Everyone was satisfied. The personal estate, indeed, was larger than John had expected. Groping for some way of declaring officially his gratitude—his respect and love for his father—John, in a kind of desperation, ended by turning the will over and writing on the back of it. What he said was stilted, as became a New England man:

This testator had a good education, though not at college, and was a very capable and useful man. In his early life he was an officer of militia, afterwards a deacon of the church, and a selectman of the town, almost all the business of the town being managed by him in that department for twenty years together; a man of strict piety, and great integrity; much esteemed and beloved wherever he was known, which was not far, his sphere of life not being extensive.

Reading what he had written, John knew it said not a tithe of what was due. Yet it was a comfort, somehow, to have set down the plain words.

# LEWIS CARROLL

*Some parental philosophizing from* Alice's Adventures in Wonderland.

## "You Are Old, Father William"

"You are old, Father William," the young man said
    "And your hair has become very white;
And yet you incessantly stand on your head—
    Do you think, at your age, it is right?"

"In my youth," Father William replied to his son,
    "I feared it might injure the brain;

But, now that I'm perfectly sure I have none,
  Why, I do it again and again."

"You are old," said the youth, "as I mentioned before.
  And have grown most uncommonly fat;
Yet you turned a back-somersault in at the door—
  Pray, what is the reason of that?"

"In my youth," said the sage, as he shook his grey locks,
  "I kept all my limbs very supple
By the use of this ointment—one shilling the box—
  Allow me to sell you a couple?"

"You are old," said the youth, "and your jaws are too weak
  For anything tougher than suet;
Yet you finished the goose, with the bones and the beak—
  Pray, how did you manage to do it?"

"In my youth," said his father, "I took to the law,
  And argued each case with my wife;
And the muscular strength, which it gave to my jaw
  Has lasted the rest of my life."

"You are old," said the youth, "one would hardly suppose
  That your eye was as steady as ever;
Yet you balanced an eel on the end of your nose—
  What made you so awfully clever?"

"I have answered three questions, and that is enough,"
  Said his father. "Don't give yourself airs!
Do you think I can listen all day to such stuff?
  Be off, or I'll kick you down-stairs!"

# FYODOR M. DOSTOEVSKY

※ ※

*Dostoevsky was married in 1857 to a widow, with one son to whom he became a generous stepfather. Even after the death of the boy's mother and Dostoevsky's second marriage, the loving relationship continued, as this selection from his* Letters *evidences.*

## To his Stepson, P. A. Issayev

*Geneva,*
*February 19 (March 3), 1868*

DON'T REPROACH ME and don't be angry with me, my ever dear Pasha, because I send Emilie Fyodorovna[1] a hundred roubles, and you only fifty. You are alone, my dear boy, and she is not alone. And you wrote yourself, indeed, that she needed as much as that. And then, she has to support her Fedya; he is at work, and I wish him luck. I love him dearly. I would willingly give all I have, but I have nothing. I must tell you that it is a great joy to me that you have taken that place, and begun to work. I respect you very much for it, Pasha. It was noble of you; the position is not distinguished, but you are still young, and can wait. But remember that you can always count on me. So long as I live, I shall regard you as my dear son. I swore to your mother, the night before she died, that I would never forsake you. When you were still a little child, I used to call you my son. How could I, then, forsake you and forget you? When I married again, you threw out hints that your position would now be a different one; I never answered them, because the idea wounded me deeply; I may confess that to you now. Know once for all that you will always be

---

[1] His brother Michael's widow.

my son, my eldest son; and not duty bids me say so, but my heart. If I have often scolded you, and been cross to you, that was only my evil disposition; I love you as I have but seldom loved anyone. When I come back to Petersburg some day, I shall do all I can to find you a better place; I will also help you with money as long as I live, and have anything at all of my own. Your saying that you don't feel well has alarmed me much. Write to me directly you receive this, if only a few lines. Send the letter unstamped; you must not have any unnecessary expenses. My address is still the same. I set all my hopes on the new novel. If it succeeds, I shall sell the second edition, pay my debts, and return to Russia. I may also get an advance from the paper. But I fear that the novel will miss fire. I greatly like the idea, but the execution—! The novel is called "The Idiot"; the first part has already been printed in the *Roussky Viestnik*. Perhaps you've read it? The great thing is that it should come off—then all will be well. I work day and night; our life is monotonous. Geneva is a terribly dull town. I froze through the whole winter; but now we are having real spring weather. Ten degrees above—Réamur. My health is neither good nor bad. I suffer from incessant poverty. We live on a few groschen, and have pawned everything. Anna Grigorovna may be confined at any moment. I expect it to happen to-night. I am in great anxiety, but must work uninterruptedly. Judge for yourself whether I can answer all your letters punctually. Tell me fully about yourself. Take care of your health.

# LAFCADIO HEARN

☙ ☙

Out of the East, *published in 1895, offers this Japanese reflection on the value of a son.*

"AND THEREFORE," continued Asakichi, "one who has a son can die with a cheerful mind."

"Because the son will make those offerings of food and drink without which the spirit would suffer?" I queried.

"It is not only that. There are duties much more important than the making of offerings. It is because every man needs some one to love him after he is dead. Now you will understand."

# PEARL S. BUCK

卐 卐

*Family attitudes shaped by centuries of Chinese tradition are described in* The Good Earth. *Here a father is forced to re-examine some of those attitudes toward his son.*

SPRING CAME in long, warm days scented with blossoming plum and cherry, and the willow trees sprouted their leaves fully and unfolded them, and the trees were green and the earth was moist and steaming and pregnant with harvest, and the eldest son of Wang Lung changed suddenly and ceased to be a child. He grew moody and petulant and would not eat this and that and he wearied of his books, and Wang Lung was frightened and did not know what to make of it and talked of a doctor.

There was no correction that could be made of the lad at all, for if his father said to him with anything beyond coaxing, "Now eat of the good meat and rice," the lad turned stubborn and melancholy, and if Wang Lung was angry at all, he burst into tears and fled from the room.

Wang Lung was overcome with surprise and he could make nothing of it, so that he went after the lad and he said gently as he was able,

"I am your father and now tell me what is in your heart." But the lad did nothing except sob and shake his head violently.

Moreover, he took a dislike to his old teacher and would not in the mornings rise out of his bed to go to school unless Wang Lung bawled at him or even beat him, and then he went sullenly and sometimes he spent whole days idling about the streets of the town, and Wang Lung only knew it at night, when the younger boy said spitefully,

"Elder Brother was not in school today."

Wang Lung was angry at his eldest son then and he shouted at him,

"And am I to spend good silver for nothing?"

And in his anger he fell upon the boy with a bamboo and beat him until O-lan, the boy's mother, heard it and rushed in from the kitchen and stood between her son and his father so that the blows rained upon her in spite of Wang Lung's turning this way and that to get at the boy. Now the strange thing was that whereas the boy might burst into weeping at a chance rebuke, he stood these beatings under the bamboo without a sound, his face carven and pale as an image. And Wang Lung could make nothing of it, although he thought of it night and day.

He thought of it one evening thus after he had eaten his night's food, because on that day he had beaten his eldest son for not going to the school, and while he thought, O-lan came into the room. She came in silently and she stood before Wang Lung and he saw she had that which she wished to say. So he said,

"Say on. What is it, mother of my son?"

And she said, "It is useless for you to beat the lad as you do. I have seen this thing come upon the young lords in the courts of the great house, and it came on them melancholy, and when it came the Old Lord found slaves for them if they had not found any for themselves and the thing passed easily."

"Now and it need not be so," answered Wang Lung in argument. "When I was a lad I had no such melancholy and no such weepings and tempers, and no slaves, either."

O-lan waited and then she answered slowly, "I have not indeed seen it thus except with young lords. You worked on the land. But he is like a young lord and he is idle in the house."

Wang Lung was surprised, after he had pondered a while, for he saw truth in what she said. It was true that when he himself was a lad there was no time for melancholy, for he had to be up at dawn for the ox and out with the plow and the hoe and at harvest he must needs work until his back broke, and if he wept he could weep for no one heard him, and he could not run away as his son ran away from school, for if he did there was nothing for him to eat on return, and so he was compelled to labor. He remembered all this and he said to himself,

"But my son is not thus. He is more delicate than I was, and his father is rich and mine was poor, and there is no need for his labor, for I have labor in my fields, and besides, one cannot take a scholar such as my son is and set him to the plow."

And he was secretly proud that he had a son like this and so he said to O-lan,

"Well, and if he is like a young lord it is another matter. But I cannot buy a slave for him. I will betroth him and we will marry him early, and there is that to be done."

Then he rose and went in to the inner court.

# CLARENCE DAY

茓 茓

*Here is one of his recollections of* Life with Father *that began delighting readers in 1920.*

## "Father Opens My Mail"

IT HADN'T BEEN HER CHOICE, Mother said. She had suggested all sorts of names to Father, but there seemed to be something wrong with each one. When she had at last spoken of naming me after him, however, he had said at once that that was the best suggestion yet—he said it sounded just right.

Father and I would have had plenty of friction in any case. This identity of names made things worse. Every time that I had been more of a fool than he liked, Father would try to impress on me my responsibilities as his eldest son, and above all as the son to whom he had given his name, as he put it. A great deal was expected, it seemed to me, of a boy who was named after his father. I used to envy my brothers, who didn't have anything expected of them on this score at all.

I envied them still more after I was old enough to begin getting letters. I then discovered that when Father "gave" me his name he had also, not unnaturally, I had to admit, retained it himself, and when anything came for Clarence S. Day he opened it, though it was sometimes for me.

He also opened everything that came addressed to Clarence S. Day, Jr. He didn't do this intentionally, but unless the "Jr." was clearly written, it looked like "Esq.," and anyhow Father was too accustomed to open all Clarence Day letters to remember about looking carefully every time for a "Jr." So far as mail and express went, I had no name at all of my own.

For the most part nobody wrote to me when I was a small boy except firms whose advertisements I had read in the *Youth's Companion* and to whom I had written requesting them to send me their circulars. These circulars described remarkable bargains in magicians' card outfits, stamps and coins, pocket knives, trick spiders, and imitation fried eggs, and they seemed interesting and valuable to me when I got them. The trouble was that Father usually got them and at once tore them up. I then had to write for such circulars again, and if Father got the second one too, he would sometimes explode with annoyance. He became particularly indignant one year, I remember, when he was repeatedly urged to take advantage of a special bargain sale of false whiskers. He said that he couldn't understand why these offerings kept pouring in. I knew why, in this case, but at other times I was often surprised myself at the number he got, not realizing that as a result of my postcard request my or our name had been automatically put on several large general mailing lists.

During this period I got more of my mail out of Father's wastebasket than I did from the postman.

At the age of twelve or thirteen, I stopped writing for these childish things and turned to a new field. Father and I, whichever of us got at the mail first, then began to receive not merely circulars but personal letters beginning:

Dear Friend Day

In reply to your valued request for one of our Mammoth Agents' Outfits, kindly forward post-office order for $1.49 to cover cost of postage and packing, and we will put you in a position to earn a large income in your spare time with absolutely no labor on your part, by taking subscriptions for *The Secret Handbook of Mesmerism*, and our *Tales of Blood* series.

And one spring, I remember, as the result of what I had intended to be a secret application on my part, Father was assigned "the exclusive rights for Staten Island and Hoboken of selling the Gem Home Popper for Pop Corn. Housewives buy it at sight."

After Father had stormily endured these afflictions for a while, he and I began to get letters from girls. Fortunately for our feelings, these were rare, but they were ordeals for both of us. Father had forgotten, if he ever knew, how silly young girls can sound, and I got my first lesson in how unsystematic they were. No matter how private and playful they meant their letters to be, they forgot to put "Jr." on the envelope every once in so often. When Father opened these letters, he read them all the way through, sometimes twice, muttering to himself over and over: "This is very peculiar. I don't understand this at all. Here's a letter to me from some person I never heard of. I can't see what it's about." By the time it had occurred to him that possibly the letter might be for me, I was red and embarrassed and even angrier at the girl than at Father. And on days when he had read some of the phrases aloud to the family, it nearly killed me to claim it.

Lots of fellows whom I knew had been named after their fathers without having such troubles. But although Father couldn't have been kinder-hearted or had any better intentions, when he saw his name on a package or envelope it never dawned on him that it might not be for him. He was too active in his habits to wait until I had a chance to get at it. And as he was also single-minded and prompt to attend to unfinished business, he opened everything automatically and then did his best to dispose of it.

This went on even after I grew up, until I had a home of my own. Father was always perfectly decent about it, but he never changed. When he saw I felt sulky, he was genuinely sorry and said so, but he couldn't see why all this should annoy me, and he was surprised and amused that it did. I used to get angry once in a while when something came for me which I particularly hadn't wished him to see and which I would find lying opened, on the hall table marked "For Jr.?" when I came in; but nobody could stay angry with Father—he was too utterly guiltless of having meant to offend.

He often got angry himself, but it was mostly at things, not at persons, and he didn't mind a bit (as a rule) when persons got angry at him. He even declared, when I got back from college, feeling dignified, and told him that I wished he'd be more careful, that he suffered from these mistakes more than I did. It wasn't *his* fault, he pointed out, if my stupid correspondents couldn't remember my name, and it wasn't any pleasure to him to be upset at his breakfast by finding that a damned lunatic company in Battle Creek had sent him a box of dry bread crumbs, with a letter asserting that this rubbish would be good for his stomach. "I admit I threw it into the fireplace, Clarence, but what else could I do? If you valued this preposterous concoction, my dear boy, I'm sorry. I'll buy another box for you today, if you'll tell me where I can get it. Don't feel badly! I'll buy you a barrel. Only I hope you won't eat it."

In the days when Mrs. Pankhurst and her friends were chaining themselves to lamp-posts in London, in their campaign for the vote, a letter came from Frances Hand trustfully asking "Dear Clarence" to do something to help Woman Suffrage—speak at a meeting, I think. Father got red in the face. "Speak at one of their meetings!" he roared at Mother. "I'd like nothing better! You can tell Mrs. Hand that it would give me great pleasure to inform all those crackpots in petticoats exactly what I think of their antics."

"Now, Clare," Mother said, "you mustn't talk that way. I like that nice Mrs. Hand, and anyhow this letter must be for Clarence."

One time I asked Father for his opinion of a low-priced stock I'd been watching. His opinion was that it was not worth a damn. I thought this over, but I still wished to buy it, so I placed a scale order with another firm instead of with Father's office, and said nothing about it. At the end of the month this other firm sent me a statement, setting forth each of my little transactions in full, and of course they forgot to put the "Jr." at the end of my name. When Father opened the envelope, he thought at first in his excitement that this firm had actually opened an account for him without being asked. I found him telling Mother that he'd like to wring their damned necks.

"That must be for me, Father," I said, when I took in what had happened.

We looked at each other.

"You bought this stuff?" he said incredulously. "After all I said about it?"

"Yes, Father."

He handed over the statement and walked out of the room.

Both he and I felt offended and angry. We stayed so for several days, too, but we then made it up.

Once in a while when I got a letter that I had no time to answer I used to address an envelope to the sender and then put anything in it that happened to be lying around on my desk—a circular about books, a piece of newspaper, an old laundry bill—anything at all, just to be amiable, and yet at the same time to save myself the trouble of writing. I happened to tell several people about this private habit of mine at a dinner one night—a dinner at which Alice Duer Miller and one or two other writers were present. A little later she wrote me a criticism of Henry James and ended by saying that I needn't send her any of my old laundry bills because she wouldn't stand it. And she forgot to put on the "Jr."

"In the name of God," Father said bleakly, "this is the worst yet. Here's a woman who says I'd better not read *The Golden Bowl,* which I have no intention whatever of doing, and she also warns me for some unknown reason not to send her my laundry bills."

The good part of all these experiences, as I realize now, was that in the end they drew Father and me closer together. My brothers had only chance battles with him. I had a war. Neither he nor I relished its clashes, but they made us surprisingly intimate.

# GEORGE MILBURN

🦂 🦂

*A story from* No More Trumpets *illustrates the adage,*
*"The more things change, the more they are the same."*

## "The Apostate"

HARRY, you been jacking me up about how I been neglecting
Rotary here lately, so I'm just going to break down and tell you
something. Now I don't want you to take this personal, Harry,
because it's not meant personal at all. No siree! Not *a*-tall! But,
just between you and I, Harry, I'm not going to be coming out
to Rotary lunches any more. I mean I'm quitting Rotary! . . .

Now whoa there! Whoa! Whoa just a minute and let me get in
a word edgeways. Just let me finish my little say.

Don't you never take it into your head that I haven't been
wrestling with this thing plenty. I mean I've argued it all out with
myself. Now I'm going to tell you the whyfor and the whereof
and the howcome about this, Harry, but kindly don't let what I
say go no further. Please keep it strictly on the Q.T. Because I
guess the rest of the boys would suspicion that I was turning
highbrow on them. But you've always been a buddy to me, Harry,
you mangy old son of a hoss thief, you, so what I'm telling you is
the straight dope.

Harry, like you no doubt remember, up till a few months ago
Rotary was about "the most fondest thing I is of," as the nigger
says. There wasn't nothing that stood higher for me than Rotary.

Well, here, about a year ago last fall I took a trip down to the
university to visit my son and go to a football game. You know
Hubert Junior, my boy. Sure. Well, this is his second year down
at the university. Yes, that boy is getting a college education. I
mean, I'm all for youth having a college education.

Of course I think there is such a thing as too much education
working a detriment. Take, for instance, some of these longhairs

running around knocking the country right now. But what I mean is, a good, sound, substantial college education. I don't mean a string of letters a yard long for a man to write after his John Henry. I just mean that I want my boy to have his sheepskin, they call it, before he starts out in the world. Like the fellow says, I want him to get his A.B. degree, and then he can go out and get his J.O.B.

Now, Harry, I always felt like a father has got certain responsibilities to his son. That's just good Rotary. That's all that is. You know that that's just good Rotary yourself, Harry. Well, I always wanted Hubert to think about me just like I was a pal to him, or say an older brother, maybe. Hubert always knew that all he had to do was come to me, and I would act like a big buddy to him, irregardless.

Well, like I was telling you, Harry, I started Hubert in to the university two years ago, and after he had been there about two months, I thought I would run down and see how he was getting along and go to a football game. So I and Mrs. T. drove over one Friday. We didn't know the town very well, so we stopped at a filling station, and I give Hubert a ring, and he come right on down to where we was to show us the way. Just as soon as he come up, I could see right then that he had something on his mind bothering him.

He called me aside and took me into the filling-station restroom, and says: "For the love of God, Dad, take that Rotary button out of your coat lapel," he says to me.

Harry, that come as a big surprise to me, and I don't mind telling you that it just about took the wind out of my sails. But I wasn't going to let on to him, so I rared back on my dignity, and says, "Why, what do you mean, take that Rotary button out of my lapel, young man?" I says to him.

"Dad," Hubert says to me, serious, "any frat house has always got a few cynics in it. If you was to wear that Rotary button in your lapel out to the frat house, just as soon as you got out of sight, some of those boys at the house would razz the life out of me," he says.

"Hubert," I says, "there's not a thing that this lapel badge represents that any decent, moral person could afford to make fun of. If that's the kind of Reds you got out at your fraternity, the kind that would razz a what you might call sacred thing—yes sir, a sacred thing—like Rotary, well I and your mamma can just go somewheres else and put up. I don't guess the hotels have quit running," I says to him.

By now I was on my high horse right, see?

"Now, Dad," Hubert says, "it's not that. I mean, person'ly I'm awful proud of you. It's just that I haven't been pledged to this fraternity long, see, and when some of those older members found out you was a Rotarian they would deal me a lot of misery, and I couldn't say nothing. Person'ly I think Rotary is all right," he says to me.

"Well, you better, son," I says, "or I'm going to begin to think that you're sick in the head."

The way he explained it, though, Harry, that made it a horse of a different tail, as the saying goes, so I give in and took off my Rotary button right there. Stuck it in my pocket, see? So we went on out and visited at Hubert's fraternity house, and do you know that those boys just got around there and treated we folks like we was princes of the blood. I mean you would of thought that I was an old ex-graduate of that university. And we saw the big pigskin tussle the next day, fourteen to aught, favor us, and we had such a scrumptious time all around I forgot all about what Hubert had said.

Ever'thing would of been all right, except for what happened later. I guess some of those older boys at the frat house begin using their form of psychology on Hubert. I mean they finely got his mind set against Rotary, because when he come home for the summer vacation that was about the size of things.

I mean all last summer, I thought Hubert never would let up. He just kept it up, making sarcastic remarks about Rotary, see? Even when we was on our vacation trip. You know we drove out to California and back last summer, Harry. Come back with the same air in the tires we started out with. Well, I thought it would be kind of nice to drop in and eat with the Hollywood Rotary—you know, just to be able to say I had. Well, do you know that that boy Hubert made so much fun of the idea I just had to give it up? That was the way it was the whole trip. He got his mother around on his side, too. Just to be frank with you, I never got so sick and tired of anything in all my born days.

Well, Harry, I had my dander up there for a while, and all the bickering in the world couldn't of shook me from my stand. But finely Hubert went back to college in September, and I thought I would have a little peace. Then I just got to thinking about it, and it all come over me. "Look here, Mister Man," I says to myself, "your faith and loyalty to Rotary may be a fine thing, and all that, but it's just costing you the fellowship of your own son." Now a man can't practice Rotary in the higher sense, and yet at the same time be letting his own son's fellowship get loose from him. So there it was. Blood's thicker than water, Harry. You'll have to admit that.

Right along in there, Harry, was the first time I begin to attending meetings irregular. I'll tell you—you might not think so—but it was a pretty tough struggle for me. I remember one Monday noon, Rotary-meeting day, I happened to walk past the Hotel Beckman just at lunchtime. The windows of the Venetian Room was open, and I could hear you boys singing a Rotary song. You know that one we sing set to the tune of "Last Night on the Back Porch." It goes:

> I love the Lions in the morning,
> The Exchange Club at night,
> I love the Y's men in the evening,
> And Kiwanis are all right . . .

Well, I couldn't carry a tune if I had it in a sack, but anyway that's the way it goes. So I just stopped in my tracks and stood there listening to that song coming out of the Hotel Beckman dining room. And when the boys come to the last verse,

> I love the Optimists in the springtime,
> The Ad Club in the fall,
> But each day—and in every way—
> I love Rotary best of all. . . .

I tell you, Harry, that just got me. I had a lump in my throat big enough to choke a cow. The tears begin coming up in my eyes, and it might sound ridiculous to hear me tell it now, but I could of broke down and bawled right there on the street. I got a grip on myself and walked on off, but right then I says to myself, "The hell with Hubert and his highbrow college-fraternity ideas; I'm going back to Rotary next week."

Well, I did go back the next week, and what happened decided me on taking the step I decided on. Here's what decided me. You know I never got very well acquainted with Gay Harrison, the new secretary. I mean, of course, I know him all right, but he hasn't been in Rotary only but about a year. Well, on that particular day, I just happened to let my tongue slip and called him Mister Harrison, instead of by his nickname. Well, of course, the boys slapped a dollar fine on me right then and there. I haven't got no kick to make about that, but the point is, I had a letter from Hubert in my pocket right then, telling me that he had run short of money. So I just couldn't help but be struck by the idea "I wish I was giving Hubert this dollar." So that's what decided me on devoting my time and finances to another kind of fellowship, Harry.

I get down to the university to see Hubert more frequent now. I make it a point to. And the boys come to me, and I been helping them a little on their frat building fund. There's a fine spirit of fellowship in an organization like that. Some boys from the best families of the State are members, too. You might think from what I said that they'd be uppish, but they're not. No siree. Not a bit of it. I been down there enough for them to know me, now, and they all pound me on the back and call me H.T., just like I was one of them. And I do them, too. And I notice that when they sit down to a meal, they have some songs they sing just as lively and jolly as any we had at Rotary. Of course, like Hubert said, a few of them might have some wild-haired ideas about Rotary, but they're young yet. And as far as I can see there's not a knocker nor a sourbelly among them. Absolutely democratic.

It puts me in mind of a little incidence that happened last month when the frat threw a big Dad's Day banquet for us down there. All the fathers of the boys from all over the State was there. Well, to promote the spirit of fellowship between dad and son, the fraternity boys all agreed to call their dads by their first name, just treating their dads like big buddies. So at the table Hubert happened to forget for a minute, and says to me "Dad" something. Well sir, the president of the frat flashed right out, "All right, Hubie, we heard you call H.T. 'Dad.' So that'll just cost you a dollar for the ice-cream fund." Ever'body had a good laugh at Hubert getting caught like that, but do you know, that boy of mine just forked right over without making a kick. That shows the stuff, don't it, Harry? Nothing wrong with a boy like that.

And the whole bunch is like that, ever' one of them. I'll tell you, Harry, the boys at that frat of Hubert's are the builders in the coming generation. Any man of vision can see that.

Well, that's that. Now what was you going to say?

# CARL EWALD

🦋 🦋

*One of this Danish writer's vignettes about his son,* My Little Boy, *published soon after the turn of the century.*

THERE IS a battle royal and a great hullabaloo among the children in the courtyard.

I hear them shouting "Jew!" and I go to the window and see my little boy in the front rank of the bandits, screaming, fighting with clenched fists and without his cap.

I sit down quietly to my work again, certain that he will appear before long and ease his heart.

And he comes directly after.

He stands still, as is his way, by my side and says nothing. I steal a glance at him: he is greatly excited and proud and glad, like one who has fearlessly done his duty.

"What fun you've been having down there!"

"Oh," he says, modestly, "it was only a Jew boy whom we were licking."

I jump up so quickly that I upset my chair.

"A Jew boy? Were you licking him? What had he done?"

"Nothing. . . ."

His voice is not very certain, for I look so queer.

And that is only the beginning. For now I snatch my hat and run out of the door as fast as I can and shout:

"Come . . . come . . . we must find him and beg his pardon!"

My little boy hurries after me. He does not understand a word of it, but he is terribly in earnest. We look in the courtyard, we shout and call. We rush into the street and round the corner, so eager are we to come up with him. Breathlessly, we ask three passers-by if they have not seen a poor, ill-used Jew boy.

All in vain: the Jew boy and all his persecutors are blown away into space.

So we go and sit up in my room again, the laboratory where our soul is crystallized out of the big events of our little life. My forehead is wrinkled and I drum disconsolately with my fingers on the table. The boy has both his hands in his pockets and does not take his eyes from my face.

"Well," I say, decidedly, "there is nothing more to be done. I hope you will meet that Jew boy one day, so that you can give him your hand and ask him to forgive you. You must tell him that you did that only because you were stupid. But if, another time, anyone does him any harm, I hope you will help him and lick the other one as long as you can stir a limb."

I can see by my little boy's face that he is ready to do what I wish. For he is still a mercenary, who does not ask under which flag, so long as there is a battle and booty to follow. It is my duty to train him to be a brave recruit, who will defend his fair motherland, and so I continue:

"Let me tell you, the Jews are by way of being quite wonderful people. You remember David, about whom Dirty reads at school: he was a Jewish boy. And the Child Jesus, Whom we worship and love although He died two thousand years ago: He was a little Jew also."

My little boy stands with his arms on my knee and I go on with my story.

The old Hebrews rise before our eyes in all their splendour and power. . . . They ride on their camels in coats of many colours and with long beards: Moses and Joseph and his brethren and Samson and David and Saul. We hear wonderful stories. The walls of Jericho fall at the sound of the trumpet.

"And what next?" says my little boy, using the expression which he employed when he was much smaller and which still comes to his lips whenever he is carried away.

We hear of the destruction of Jerusalem and how the Jews took their little boys by the hand and wandered from place to place, scoffed at, despised and ill-treated. How they were allowed to own neither house nor land, but could only be merchants, and how the Christian robbers took all the money which they had got together. How, nevertheless, they remained true to their God and kept up their old sacred customs in the midst of strangers who hated and persecuted them.

The whole day is devoted to the Jews.

We look at old books on the shelves which I love best to read and which are written by a Jew with a wonderful name, which a little boy can't remember at all. We learn that the most famous man now living in Denmark is a Jew.

And, when evening comes and Mother sits down at the piano and sings the song which Father likes above all other songs, it appears that the words were written by one Jew and the melody composed by another.

My little boy is hot and red when he falls to sleep that night. He turns restlessly in bed and talks in his sleep.

"He is a little feverish," says his mother.

And I bend down and kiss his forehead and answer, calmly:

"That is not surprising. Today I have vaccinated him against the meanest of all mean and vulgar diseases."

# MARJORIE KINNAN RAWLINGS

🐾 🐾

*After the death of his deer, in* The Yearling, *Jody re- turns home to a new understanding of his father and what it means to grow up.*

HE WALKED WEST without plan. There was no other direction in which to go. Baxter's Island drew him like a magnet. There was no reality but the clearing. He trudged on. He wondered if he dared go home. Probably they would not want him. He had caused them a great deal of trouble. Perhaps if he walked into the kitchen, his mother would drive him out as she had driven Flag. He was no good to anybody. He had prowled and played and eaten recklessly. They had put up with his impudence and his appetite. And Flag had destroyed the better part of the year's living. Almost certainly, they would feel they were better off without him, and he would not be welcome.

He loitered along the road. The sun was strong. The winter was over. He thought hazily that it must now be April. Spring had taken over the scrub, and the birds were mating and singing in the bushes. Only he, in all the world, was homeless. He had been out in the world, and the world was a troubled dream, fluid and desolate, flanked by swamps and cypresses. He stopped to rest in mid-morning at the intersection of the main road and the north road. The low vegetation here was open to the heat of the sun. His head began to ache and he got to his feet and headed north toward Silver Glen. He told himself that he did not mean to go home. He would only go to the spring, and go down between the cool dark banks, and lie a little while in the running water. The north road dipped and rose and dipped again. The sand was scalding under his bare feet. The sweat ran down the grime of his face. At the top of a rise, he could look down and see Lake George far below him to the east. It was pitilessly blue. Thin white lines were the implacable choppy waves that had turned him back to the unfriendly shore. He trudged on.

To the east, the vegetation became luxuriant. There was water near. He turned down the trail to Silver Glen. The steep bank dropped to the ribbon of creek that ran south of the great spring itself, and had a kindred source. He ached in all his bones. He was so thirsty that his tongue seemed glued to the roof of his mouth. He stumbled down the bank and fell flat beside the cool shallow water and drank. The water bubbled over his lips and nose. He drank until his belly was swollen. He felt sickened and rolled over on his back and closed his eyes. The nausea passed and he was drowsy. He lay in a stupor of weariness. He hung suspended in a timeless space. He could go neither forward nor back. Something was ended. Nothing was begun.

In the late afternoon, he roused. He sat up. An early magnolia blossom was wax-white over him.

He thought, " 'Tis April."

A memory stirred him. He had come here a year ago, on a bland and tender day. He had splashed in the creek water and lain, as now, among the ferns and grasses. Something had been fine and lovely. He had built himself a flutter-mill. He rose and moved with a quickening of his pulse to the location. It seemed to him that if he found it, he would discover with it all the other things that had vanished. The flutter-mill was gone. The flood had washed it away, and all its merry turning.

He thought stubbornly, "I'll build me another."

He cut twigs for the supports, and the roller to turn across them, from the wild cherry tree. He whittled feverishly. He cut strips from a palmetto frond and made his paddles. He sunk the up-rights in the stream bed and set the paddles turning. Up, over, down. Up, over, down. The flutter-mill was turning. The silver water dripped. But it was only palmetto strips brushing the water. There was no magic in the motion. The flutter-mill had lost its comfort.

He said, "Play-dolly—"

He kicked it apart with one foot. The broken bits floated down the creek. He threw himself on the ground and sobbed bitterly. There was no comfort anywhere.

There was Penny. A wave of homesickness washed over him so that it was suddenly intolerable not to see him. The sound of his father's voice was a necessity. He longed for the sight of his stooped shoulders as he had never, in the sharpest of his hunger, longed for food. He clambered to his feet and up the bank and began to run down the road to the clearing, crying as he ran. His father might not be there. He might be dead. With the crops ruined, and his son gone, he might have packed up in despair and moved away and he would never find him.

He sobbed, "Pa—Wait for me."

The sun was setting. He was in a panic that he would not reach the clearing before dark. He exhausted himself, and was obliged to slow down to a walk. His flesh quivered. His heart pounded. He had to stop entirely and rest. Darkness overtook him half a mile from home. Even in the dusk, landmarks were familiar. The tall pines of the clearing were recognizable, blacker than the creeping night. He came to the slat fence. He felt his way along it. He opened the gate and went into the yard. He passed around the side of the house to the kitchen stoop and stepped up on it. He crept to the window on bare silent feet and peered in.

A fire burned low on the hearth. Penny sat hunched beside it, wrapped in quilts. One hand covered his eyes. Jody went to the door and unlatched it and stepped inside. Penny lifted his head.

"Ory?"

"Hit's me."

He thought his father had not heard him.

"Hit's Jody."

Penny turned his head and looked at him wonderingly, as though the gaunt ragged boy with sweat and tear-streaks down the grime, with hollow eyes under matted hair, were some stranger of whom he expected that he state his business.

He said, "Jody."

Jody dropped his eyes.

"Come close."

He went to his father and stood beside him. Penny reached out for his hand and took it and turned it over and rubbed it slowly between his own. Jody felt drops on his hand like a warm rain.

"Boy—I near about give you out."

Penny felt along his arm. He looked up at him.

"You all right?"

He nodded.

"You all right—You ain't dead nor gone. You all right." A light filled his face. "Glory be."

It was unbelievable, Jody thought. He was wanted.

He said, "I had to come home."

"Why, shore you did."

"I ain't meant what I said. Hatin' you—"

The light broke into the familiar smile.

"Why, shore you ain't. 'When I was a child, I spake as a child.' "

Penny stirred in his chair.

"They's rations in the safe. In the kittle there. You hongry?"

"I ain't et but oncet. Last night."

"Not but oncet? Then now you know. Ol' Starvation—" His eyes shone in the firelight as Jody had pictured them. "Ol' Starvation—he's got a face meaner'n ol' Slewfoot, ain't he?"

"Hit's fearful."

"There's biscuits there. Open the honey. There's due to be milk in the gourd."

Jody fumbled among the dishes. He ate standing, wolfing down the food. He dipped into a dish of cooked cow-peas with his fingers, scooping them into his mouth. Penny stared at him.

He said, "I'm sorry you had to learn it that-a-way."

"Where's Ma?"

"She's drove the wagon to the Forresters to trade for seed-corn. She figgered she'd try to plant a part of a crop agin. She carried the chickens, to trade. It hurted her pride turrible, but she was obliged to go."

Jody closed the door of the cabinet.

He said, "I should of washed. I'm awful dirty."

"There's warm water on the hearth."

Jody poured water in the basin and scrubbed his face and arms and hands. The water was too dark even for his feet. He threw it out of the door and poured more, and sat on the floor and washed his feet.

Penny said, "I'd be proud to know where you been."

"I been on the river. I aimed to go to Boston."

"I see."

He looked small and shrunken inside the quilts.

Jody said, "How you makin' it, Pa? You better?"

Penny looked a long time into the embers on the hearth.

He said, "You jest as good to know the truth. I ain't scarcely wuth shootin'."

Jody said, "When I git the work done, you got to leave me go fetch ol' Doc to you."

Penny studied him.

He said, "You've done come back different. You've takened a punishment. You ain't a yearlin' no longer. Jody—"

"Yes, sir."

"I'm goin' to talk to you, man to man. You figgered I went back on you. Now there's a thing ever' man has got to know. Mebbe you know it a'ready. 'Twa'n't only me. 'Twa'n't only your yearlin' deer havin' to be destroyed. Boy, life goes back on you."

Jody looked at his father. He nodded.

Penny said, "You've seed how things goes in the world o' men. You've knowed men to be low-down and mean. You've seed ol' Death at his tricks. You've messed around with ol' Starvation. Ever' man wants life to be a fine thing, and a easy. 'Tis fine, boy, powerful fine, but 'tain't easy. Life knocks a man down and he gits up and it knocks him down agin. I've been uneasy all my life."

His hands worked at the folds of the quilt.

"I've wanted life to be easy for you. Easier'n 'twas for me. A man's heart aches, seein' his young uns face the world. Knowin' they got to git their guts tore out, the way his was tore. I wanted to spare you, long as I could. I wanted you to frolic with your yearlin'. I knowed the lonesomeness he eased for you. But ever' man's lonesome. What's he to do then? What's he to do when he gits knocked down? Why, take it for his share and go on."

Jody said, "I'm 'shamed I runned off."

Penny sat upright.

He said, "You're near enough growed to do your choosin'. Could be you'd crave to go to sea, like Oliver. There's men seems made for the land, and men seems made for the sea. But I'd be proud did you choose to live here and farm the clearin'. I'd be proud to see the day when you got a well dug, so's no woman here'd be obliged to do her washin' on a seepage hillside. You willin'?"

"I'm willing."

"Shake hands."

He closed his eyes. The fire on the hearth had burned to embers. Jody banked them with the ashes, to assure live coals in the morning.

Penny said, "Now I'll need some he'p, gittin' to the bed. Looks like your Ma's spendin' the night."

Jody put his shoulder under him and Penny leaned heavily on it. He hobbled to his bed. Jody drew the quilt over him.

"Hit's food and drink to have you home, boy. Git to bed and git your rest. 'Night."

The words warmed him through.

" 'Night, Pa."

He went to his room and closed the door. He took off his tattered shirt and breeches and climbed in under the warm quilts. His bed was soft and yielding. He lay luxuriously, stretching his legs. He must be up early in the morning, to milk the cow and bring in wood and work the crops. When he worked them, Flag would not be there to play about with him. His father would no longer take the heavy part of the burden. It did not matter. He could manage alone.

He found himself listening for something. It was the sound of the yearling for which he listened, running around the house or stirring on his moss pallet in the corner of the bedroom. He would never hear him again. He wondered if his mother had thrown dirt over Flag's carcass, or if the buzzards had cleaned it. Flag—He did not believe he should ever again love anything, man or woman or his own child, as he had loved the yearling. He would be lonely all his life. But a man took it for his share and went on.

In the beginning of his sleep, he cried out, "Flag!"

It was not his own voice that called. It was a boy's voice. Somewhere beyond the sink-hole, past the magnolia, under the live oaks, a boy and a yearling ran side by side, and were gone forever.

# MOSS HART

⚔ ⚔

*Act One, the playwright's autobiography, offers a view of a boy and his father on a bleak Christmas Eve.*

IT WAS THE CHRISTMAS after my aunt had left the house, and since it was she who always supplied the tree and the presents for my brother and myself, this first Christmas without her was a bleak and empty one. I remember that I was more or less reconciled to it, because my father had worked only spasmodically throughout the year. Two of our rooms were vacant of boarders and my mother was doing her marketing farther and farther away from our neighborhood. This was always a sign that we were dangerously close to rock bottom, and each time it occurred I came to dread it more. It was one of the vicious landmarks of poverty that I had come to know well and the one I hated the most. As the bills at our regular grocer and butcher went unpaid, and my mother dared not even be seen at the stores lest they come to the doorways and yell after her publicly, she would trudge ten or twelve blocks to a whole new neighborhood, tell the new grocer or butcher that we had just moved in to some fictitious address around the corner, and establish credit for as long as she could. Thus we were able to exist until my father found work again, or all the rooms were rented, and she could pay our own grocer and butcher, and gradually the others. This time, however, they had all of them gone unpaid and my mother was walking twenty blocks or more for a bottle of milk.

Obviously Christmas was out of the question—we were barely staying alive. On Christmas Eve my father was very silent during the evening meal. Then he surprised and startled me by turning to me and saying, "Let's take a walk." He had never suggested such a thing before, and moreover it was a very cold winter's night. I was even more surprised when he said as we left the house, "Let's go down to a Hundred Forty-ninth Street and Westchester Avenue." My heart leapt within me. That was the section where all the big stores were, where at Christmastime open pushcarts full of toys stood packed end-to-end for blocks at a stretch. On other Christmas Eves I had often gone there with my aunt, and from our tour of the carts she had gathered what I wanted the most. My father had known of this, of course, and I joyously concluded that this walk could mean only one thing—he was going to buy me a Christmas present.

On the walk down I was beside myself with delight and an inner relief. It had been a bad year for me, that year of my aunt's going, and I wanted a Christmas present terribly—not a present merely, but a symbol, a token of some sort. I needed some sign from my father or mother that they knew what I was going through and cared for me as much as my aunt and my grandfather did. I am sure they were giving me what mute signs they could, but I did not see them. The idea that my father had managed a Christmas present for me in spite of everything filled me with a sudden peace and lightness of heart I had not known in months.

We hurried on, our heads bent against the wind, to the cluster of lights ahead that was 149th Street and Westchester Avenue, and those lights seemed to me the brightest lights I had ever seen. Tugging at my father's coat, I started down the line of pushcarts. There were all kinds of things that I wanted, but since nothing had been said by my father about buying a present, I would merely pause before a pushcart to say, with as much control as I could muster, "Look at that chemistry set!" or, "There's a stamp album!" or, "Look at the printing press!" Each time my father would pause and ask the pushcart man the price. Then without a word we would move on to the next pushcart. Once or twice he would pick up a toy of some kind and look at it and then at me, as if to suggest this might be something I might like, but I was ten years old and a good deal beyond just a toy; my heart was set on a chemistry set or a printing press. There they were on every pushcart we stopped at, but the price was always the same and soon I looked up and saw we were nearing the end of the line. Only two or three more pushcarts remained. My father looked up, too, and I heard him jingle some coins in his pocket. In a flash I knew it all. He'd gotten together about seventy-five cents to buy me a Christmas present, and he hadn't dared say so in case there was nothing to be had for so small a sum.

As I looked up at him I saw a look of despair and disappointment in his eyes that brought me closer to him than I had ever been in my life. I wanted to throw my arms around him and say, "It doesn't matter . . . I understand . . . this is better than a chemistry set or a printing press . . . I love you." But instead we stood shivering beside each other for a moment—then turned away from the last two pushcarts and started silently back home. I don't know why the words remained choked up within me. I didn't even take his hand on the way home nor did he take mine. We were not on that basis. Nor did I ever tell him how close to him I felt that night—that for a little while the concrete wall between father and son had crumbled away and I knew that we were two lonely people struggling to reach each other.

I came close to telling him many years later, but again the moment passed. Again it was Christmas and I was on my way to visit him in Florida. My father was a bright and blooming ninety-one years of age now and I arrived in Florida with my wife to spend Christmas and New Year's with him. On Christmas Eve we sat in his living room, and while my wife chatted with his nurse and companion, I sat on a sofa across the room with my father, showing him the pictures of his two grandchildren. Suddenly I felt his hand slip into mine. It was the first time in our lives that either of us had ever touched the other. No words were spoken and I went right on turning the pages of the picture album, but my hand remained over his. A few years before I might have withdrawn mine after a moment or two, but now my hand remained; nor did I tell him what I was thinking and feeling. The moment was enough.

# ARTHUR MILLER

♉ ♉

*In* Death of a Salesman, *a man's sons are forced to realize the despair that is engulfing their father.*

BIFF: What is he doing out there?

LINDA: Sh!

BIFF: God Almighty, Mom, how long has he been doing this?

LINDA: Don't, he'll hear you.

BIFF: What the hell is the matter with him?

LINDA: It'll pass by morning.

BIFF: Shouldn't we do anything?

LINDA: Oh, my dear, you should do a lot of things, but there's nothing to do, so go to sleep.

*Happy comes down the stairs and sits on the steps.*

HAPPY: I never heard him so loud, Mom.

LINDA: Well, come around more often; you'll hear him. *She sits down at the table and mends the lining of Willy's jacket.*

BIFF: Why didn't you ever write me about this, Mom?

LINDA: How could I write to you? For over three months you had no address.

BIFF: I was on the move. But you know I thought of you all the time. You know that, don't you, pal?

LINDA: I know, dear, I know. But he likes to have a letter. Just to know that there's still a possibility for better things.

BIFF: He's not like this all the time, is he?

LINDA: It's when you come home he's always the worst.

BIFF: When I come home?

LINDA: When you write you're coming, he's all smiles, and talks about the future, and—he's just wonderful. And then the closer you seem to come, the more shaky he gets, and then, by the time you get here, he's arguing, and he seems angry at you. I think it's just that maybe he can't bring himself to—to open up to you. Why are you so hateful to each other? Why is that?

BIFF, *evasively*: I'm not hateful, Mom.

LINDA: But you no sooner come in the door than you're fighting!

BIFF: I don't know why. I mean to change. I'm tryin', Mom, you understand?

LINDA: Are you home to stay now?

BIFF: I don't know. I want to look around, see what's doin'.

LINDA: Biff, you can't look around all your life, can you?

BIFF: I just can't take hold, Mom. I can't take hold of some kind of life.

LINDA: Biff, a man is not a bird, to come and go with the springtime.

BIFF: Your hair . . . *He touches her hair.* Your hair got so gray.

LINDA: Oh, it's been gray since you were in high school. I just stopped dyeing it, that's all.

BIFF: Dye it again, will ya? I don't want my pal looking old.
*He smiles.*

LINDA: You're such a boy! You think you can go away for a year and . . . You've got to get it into your head now that one day you'll knock on this door and there'll be strange people here—

BIFF: What are you talking about? You're not even sixty, Mom.

LINDA: But what about your father?

BIFF, *lamely*: Well, I meant him too.

HAPPY: He admires Pop.

LINDA: Biff, dear, if you don't have any feeling for him, then you can't have any feeling for me.

BIFF: Sure I can, Mom.

LINDA: No. You can't just come to see me, because I love him. *With a threat, but only a threat, of tears*: He's the dearest man in the world to me, and I won't have anyone making him feel unwanted and low and blue. You've got to make up your mind now, darling, there's no leeway any more. Either he's your father and you pay him that respect, or else you're not to come here. I know he's not easy to get along with—nobody knows that better than me—but . . .

WILLY, *from the left, with a laugh*: Hey, hey, Biffo!

BIFF, *starting to go out after Willy*: What the hell is the matter with him? *Happy stops him.*

LINDA: Don't—don't go near him!

BIFF: Stop making excuses for him! He always, always wiped the floor with you. Never had an ounce of respect for you.

HAPPY: He's always had respect for—

BIFF: What the hell do you know about it?

HAPPY, *surlily*: Just don't call him crazy.

BIFF: He's got no character—Charley wouldn't do this. Not in his own house—spewing out that vomit from his mind.

HAPPY: Charley never had to cope with what he's got to.

BIFF: People are worse off than Willy Loman. Believe me, I've seen them!

LINDA: Then make Charley your father, Biff. You can't do that, can you? I don't say he's a great man. Willy Loman never made a lot of money. His name was never in the paper. He's not the finest character that ever lived. But he's a human being, and a terrible thing is happening to him. So attention must be paid. He's not to be allowed to fall into his grave like an old dog. Attention, attention must be finally paid to such a person. You called him crazy—

BIFF: I didn't mean—

LINDA: No, a lot of people think he's lost his—balance. But you don't have to be very smart to know what his trouble is. The man is exhausted.

HAPPY: Sure!

LINDA: A small man can be just as exhausted as a great man. He works for a company thirty-six years this March, opens up unheard-of territories to their trademark, and now in his old age they take his salary away.

HAPPY, *indignantly*: I didn't know that, Mom.

LINDA: You never asked, my dear! Now that you get your spending money someplace else you don't trouble your mind with him.

HAPPY: But I gave you money last—

LINDA: Christmas time, fifty dollars! To fix the hot water it cost ninety-seven fifty! For five weeks he's been on straight commission, like a beginner, an unknown!

BIFF: Those ungrateful bastards!

LINDA: Are they any worse than his sons? When he brought them business, when he was young, they were glad to see him. But now his old friends, the old buyers that loved him so and always found some order to hand him in a pinch—they're all dead, retired. He used to be able to make six, seven calls a day in Boston. Now he takes his valises out of the car and puts them back and takes them out again and he's exhausted. Instead of walking he talks now. He drives seven hundred miles, and when he gets there no one knows him any more, no one welcomes him. And what goes through a man's mind, driving seven hundred miles home without having earned a cent? Why shouldn't he talk to himself? Why? When he has to go to Charley and borrow fifty dollars a week and pretend to me that it's his pay? How long can that go on? How long? You see what I'm sitting here and waiting for? And you tell me he has no character? The man who never worked a day but for your benefit? When does he get the medal for that? Is this his reward —to turn around at the age of sixty-three and find his sons, who he loved better than his life, one a philandering bum—

HAPPY: Mom!

LINDA: That's all you are, my baby! *To Biff:* And you! What happened to the love you had for him? You were such pals! How you used to talk to him on the phone every night! How lonely he was till he could come home to you!

BIFF: All right, Mom. I'll live here in my room, and I'll get a job. I'll keep away from him, that's all.

LINDA: No, Biff. You can't stay here and fight all the time.

BIFF: He threw me out of this house, remember that.

LINDA: Why did he do that? I never knew why.

BIFF: Because I know he's a fake and he doesn't like anybody around who knows!

LINDA: Why a fake? In what way? What do you mean?

BIFF: Just don't lay it all at my feet. It's between me and him— that's all I have to say. I'll chip in from now on. He'll settle for half my pay check. He'll be all right. I'm going to bed. *He starts for the stairs.*

LINDA: He won't be all right.

BIFF, *turning on the stairs, furiously:* I hate this city and I'll stay here. Now what do you want?

LINDA: He's dying, Biff.

*Happy turns quickly to her, shocked.*

BIFF, *after a pause:* Why is he dying?

LINDA: He's been trying to kill himself.

BIFF, *with great horror:* How?

LINDA: I live from day to day.

BIFF: What're you talking about?

LINDA: Remember I wrote you that he smashed up the car again? In February?

BIFF: Well?

LINDA: The insurance inspector came. He said that they have evidence. That all these accidents in the last year—weren't—weren't—accidents.

HAPPY: How can they tell that? That's a lie.

LINDA: It seems there's a woman . . . *She takes a breath as*

⎰ BIFF, *sharply but contained:* What woman?
⎱ LINDA, *simultaneously:* . . . *and this woman* . . .

LINDA: What?

BIFF: Nothing. Go ahead.

LINDA: What did you say?

BIFF: Nothing. I just said what woman?

HAPPY: What about her?

LINDA: Well, it seems she was walking down the road and saw his car. She says that he wasn't driving fast at all, and that he didn't skid. She says he came to that little bridge, and then deliberately smashed into the railing, and it was only the shallowness of the water that saved him.

BIFF: Oh, no, he probably just fell asleep again.

LINDA: I don't think he fell asleep.

BIFF: Why not?

LINDA: Last month . . . *With great difficulty:* Oh, boys, it's so hard to say a thing like this! He's just a big stupid man to you, but I tell you there's more good in him than in many other people. *She chokes, wipes her eyes.* I was looking for a fuse. The lights blew out, and I went down the cellar. And behind the fuse box—it happened to fall out—was a length of rubber pipe—just short.

HAPPY: No kidding?

LINDA: There's a little attachment on the end of it. I knew right away. And sure enough, on the bottom of the water heater there's a new little nipple on the gas pipe.

HAPPY, *angrily:* That—jerk!

BIFF: Did you have it taken off?

LINDA: I'm—I'm ashamed to. How can I mention it to him? Every day I go down and take away that little rubber pipe. But, when he comes home, I put it back where it was. How can I insult him that way? I don't know what to do. I live from day to day, boys. I tell you, I know every thought in his mind. It sounds so old-fashioned and silly, but I tell you he put his whole life into you and you've turned your backs on him. *She is bent over in the chair, weeping, her face in her hands.* Biff, I swear to God! Biff, his life is in your hands!

HAPPY, *to Biff:* How do you like that damned fool!

BIFF, *kissing her:* All right, pal, all right. It's all settled now. I've been remiss. I know that, Mom. But now I'll stay, and I swear to you, I'll apply myself. *Kneeling in front of her, in a fever of self-reproach:* It's just—you see, Mom, I don't fit in business. Not that I won't try. I'll try, and I'll make good.

# Fathers and Daughters

# WILLIAM SHAKESPEARE

⚚ ⚚

*Cordelia refuses to exaggerate her love for her father,*
*King Lear.*

## From Act I, Scene 1. King Lear

LEAR:                                    . . . Tell me, my daughters,
  Since now we will divest us both of rule,
  Interest of territory, cares of state,
  Which of you shall we say doth love us most?
  That we our largest bounty may extend
  Where nature doth with merit challenge.
    Goneril,
  Our eldest-born, speak first.

GONERIL: Sir, I love you more than words can wield the matter,
  Dearer than eye-sight, space and liberty,
  Beyond what can be valued, rich or rare,
  No less than life, with grace, health, beauty, honor,
  As much as child e'er loved or father found;
  A love that makes breath poor and speech unable;
  Beyond all manner of so much I love you.

CORDELIA: (*Aside*) What shall Cordelia do? Love, and be silent.

LEAR: Of all these bounds, even from this line to this,
  With shadowy forests and with champains rich'd,
  With plenteous rivers and wide-skirted meads,
  We make thee lady. To thine and Albany's issue
  Be this perpetual. What says our second daughter,
  Our dearest Regan, wife to Cornwall? Speak.

REGAN: I am made of that self metal as my sister,
  And prize me at her worth. In my true heart
  I find she names my very deed of love;
  Only she comes too short; that I profess
  Myself an enemy to all other joys
  Which the most precious square of sense possesses,

And find I am alone felicitate
In your dear highness' love.

CORDELIA: *(Aside)* Then poor Cordelia!
And yet not so, since I am sure my love's
More ponderous than my tongue.

LEAR: To thee and thine hereditary ever
Remain this ample third of our fair kingdom,
No less in space, validity and pleasure,
Than that conferr'd on Goneril. Now, our joy,
Although the last, not least, to whose young love
The vines of France and milk of Burgundy
Strive to be interess'd, what can you say to draw
A third more opulent than your sisters? Speak.

CORDELIA: Nothing, my lord.

LEAR: Nothing!

CORDELIA: Nothing.

LEAR: Nothing will come of nothing: speak again.

CORDELIA: Unhappy that I am, I cannot heave
My heart into my mouth: I love your majesty
According to my bond; nor more nor less.

LEAR: How, how, Cordelia! mend your speech a little,
Lest it may mar your fortunes.

CORDELIA: Good my lord,
You have begot me, bred me, loved me: I
Return those duties back as are right fit,
Obey you, love you, and most honour you.
Why have my sisters husbands, if they say
They love you all? Haply, when I shall wed,
That lord whose hand must take my plight shall carry
Half my love with him, half my care and duty:
Sure, I shall never marry like my sisters,
To love my father all.

LEAR: But goes thy heart with this?

CORDELIA: Aye, good my lord.

LEAR: So young, and so untender?

CORDELIA: So young, my lord, and true.

LEAR: Let it be so; thy truth, then, be thy dower:
For, by the sacred radiance of the sun,
The mysteries of Hecate, and the night;
By all the operation of the orbs
From whom we do exist, and cease to be;
Here I disclaim all my paternal care,
Propinquity and property of blood,
And as a stranger to my heart and me
Hold thee, from this, for ever. The barbarous Scythian,
Or he that makes his generation messes
To gorge his appetite, shall to my bosom
Be as well neighbour'd, pitied, and relieved,
As thou my sometime daughter.

## MARTHA FINLEY

*The melodramatic adventures of Elsie Dinsmore, as recorded in one book after another, were extravagantly popular in the last decades of the nineteenth century. Later generations, oriented to a different point of view, can find a period interest in this father-daughter conflict from Elsie's Girlhood.*

ELSIE LONGED FOR, yet dreaded her father's coming. She knew he would not delay one moment longer than necessary after receiving their letters, yet he reached Lansdale almost a day sooner than she expected him.

Sitting alone in her room, she heard his voice and step in the hall below. She flew down to meet him.

"Oh, papa, dear, dear papa!"

"My darling, precious child." And her arms were about his neck, his straining her to his heart. The next moment she lifted her face, and her eyes sought his with a wistful, pleading, questioning look. He drew her into the sitting-room, and Miss Stanhope closed the door, leaving them alone.

"My darling," he said, "you must give him up; he is utterly unworthy of you."

"Oh, papa! would you break my heart!"

"My precious one, I would save you from a life of misery."

"Ah, papa you would never say that if you knew how—how I love him," she murmured, a deep blush suffusing her face.

"Hush! it horrifies me to hear you speak so of so vile a wretch,—a drinking, swearing gambler, swindler, and rake; for I have learned that he is all these."

"Papa, it is not true! I will not hear such things said of him even by you!" she cried, the hot blood dyeing her face and neck, and the soft eyes filling with indignant tears.

He put his finger upon her lips. "My daughter forgets to whom she is speaking," he said with something of the old sternness, though there was tender pity also in his tones.

"Oh, papa, I am so wretched!" she sobbed, hiding her face on his breast. "Oh, don't believe what they say! it isn't, it *can't* be true."

He caressed her silently, then taking the photograph from his pocket, asked, "Do you know that face?"

"Yes, it is his."

"I knew it, and it is also the face of the man whose character I have just described."

"Oh, no, papa," and with breathless eagerness she repeated the story with which Egerton had swept away all her doubts. She read incredulity in her father's face. "You do not believe it, papa?"

"No, my child, no more than I do black is white. See here!" and he produced Egerton's letter to him, and the one to Arthur, made her read and compare them, and gave her the further proofs Walter had furnished.

She grew deathly pale, but was no more ready to be convinced than he. "Oh, papa, there must be some dreadful mistake! I cannot believe he could be guilty of such things. The cousin has been personating him, has forged that letter, perhaps; and the photograph may be his also."

"You are not using your good common-sense, Elsie; the proof is very full and clear to my mind. The man is a fortune-hunter, seeking your wealth, not you; a scoundrel whose vices should shut him out of all decent society. I can hardly endure the thought that he has even known you, or dared to address a word to you and it must never be again."

"Must I give him up?" she asked with pale, quivering lips.

"You must, my daughter; at once and for ever."

A look of anguish swept over her face, then she started, flushed, and trembled, as a voice and step were heard on the porch without.

"It is he?" her father said inquiringly, and her look answered, "Yes."

He rose to his feet, for they had been sitting side by side on the sofa while they talked. She sprang up also, and clinging to his arm, looked beseechingly into his face, pleading in a hoarse whisper, "Papa, you will let me see him, speak to him once more?—just a few words—in your presence—oh, papa!"

"No, my darling, no; his touch, his breath, are contamination; his very look is pollution, and shall never rest upon you again if I can prevent it. Remember you are never to hold any communication with him again—by word, letter, or in any other way; I positively forbid it; you must never look at him, or intentionally allow him a sight of your face. I must go now, and send him away." He held her to his heart as he spoke; his tone was affectionate, but very firm, and decided; he kissed her tenderly, two or three times, placed her in an easy-chair, saying, "Stay here till I come to you," and left the room.

For a moment she lay back against the cushions like one stunned by a heavy blow; then, roused by the sound of the voices of the two she loved best on earth, started and leaned forward in a listening attitude, straining her ear to catch their words. Few of them reached her, but her father's tones were cold and haughty, Egerton's at first persuasive, then loud, angry and defiant.

He was gone, she had heard the last echo of his departing footsteps, and again her father bent over her, his face full of tender pity. She lifted her sad face to his, with the very look that had haunted him for years, that he could never recall without a pang of regret and remorse—that mournful gaze with which she had parted from him in the time of their estrangement.

It almost unmanned him now, almost broke his heart. "Don't,

my darling, don't look at me so," he said in low, moved tones, taking her cold hands in his. "You don't know, precious one, how willingly your father would bear all this pain for you if he could."

She threw herself upon his breast, and folding her close to his heart, he caressed her with exceeding tenderness, calling her by every fond, endearing name.

For many minutes she received it all passively, then suddenly raising her head, she returned one passionate embrace, withdrew herself from his arms, and hurried from the room.

He let her go unquestioned; he knew she went to seek comfort and support from One nearer and dearer, and better able to give it than himself. He rose and walked the room with a sad and troubled countenance, and a heart filled with grief for his child, with anger and indignation toward the wretch who had wrecked her happiness.

Miss Stanhope opened the door and looked in. "You have had no dinner, Horace. It will be ready in a few moments."

"Thank you, aunt. I will go up to my room first and try to get rid of some of the dust and dirt I have brought with me."

"Stay a moment, nephew. I am sorely troubled for the child. You don't approve of her choice?"

"Very far from it. I have forbidden the man ever to come near her again."

"But you won't be hard with her, poor dear?"

"Hard with her, Aunt Wealthy? hard and cruel to my darling whom I love better than my life? I trust not; but it would be the height of cruelty to allow this thing to go on. The man is a vile wretch, guilty of almost every vice, and seeking my child for her wealth, not for herself. I have forbidden her to see or ever to hold the slightest communication with him again."

"Well, it is quite right if your opinion of him is correct; and I hardly think she is likely to refuse submission."

"I have brought up my daughter to habits of strict, unquestioning obedience, Aunt Wealthy," he said, "and I think they will stand her in good stead now. I have no fear that she will rebel."

A half hour with her best Friend had done much to soothe and calm our sweet Elsie; she had cast her burden on the Lord and He sustained her. She knew that no trial could come to her without

His will, that He had permitted this for her good, that in His own good time and way He would remove it, and she was willing to leave it all with Him; for was He not all-wise, all-powerful, and full of tenderest, pitying love for her?

She had great faith in the wisdom and love of her earthly father also, and doubted not that he was doing what he sincerely believed to be for her happiness,—giving her present pain only in order to save her from keener and more lasting distress and anguish in the future.

It was well for her that she had such trust in him and that their mutual love was so deep and strong; well too that she was troubled with no doubts of the duty of implicit obedience to parental authority when not opposed to the higher commands of God. Her heart still clung to Egerton, refusing to credit his utter unworthiness, and she felt it a bitter trial to be thus completely separated from him, yet hoped that at some future, and perhaps not distant day, he might be able to convince her father of his mistake.

Mr. Dinsmore felt it impossible to remain long away from his suffering child; after leaving the table, a few moments only were spent in conversation with his aunt and Mr. Travilla, and then he sought his darling in her room.

"My poor little pet, you have been too long away from your father," he said, taking her in his arms again. "I shall never forgive myself for allowing it. But, daughter, why was this thing suffered to go on? Your letters never spoke of this man in a way to lead me to suppose that he was paying you serious attention; and indeed I did not intend to permit that from any one yet."

"Papa, I did not deceive you intentionally, I did not mean to be disobedient," she said, imploringly. "Lottie and I were almost always together, and I did not think of him as a lover till he spoke."

"Well, dearest, I am not chiding you; your father could never find it in his heart to add one needless pang to what you are already suffering." His tone was full of pitying tenderness.

She made no answer; only hid her face on his breast and wept silently. "Papa," she murmured at length. "I—I do so want to break one of your rules; oh, if you would only let me, just this once!"

"A strange request, my darling," he said, "but which of them is it?"

"That when you have once decided a matter I must never ask you to reconsider. Oh, papa, do, do let me entreat you just this once!"

"I think it will be useless, daughter, only giving me the pain of refusing, and you of being refused; but you may say on."

"Papa, it is that I may write a little note to—to Mr. Egerton," she said, speaking eagerly and rapidly, yet half trembling at her own temerity the while "just to tell him that I cannot do any thing against your will, and that he must not come near me or try to hold any sort of intercourse with me till you give consent; but that I have not lost my faith in him, and if he is innocent and unjustly suspected, we need not be wretched and despairing; for God will surely some day cause it to be made apparent. Oh, papa, may I not? Please, please let me! I will bring it to you when written, and there shall not be one word in it that you do not approve." She had lifted her face, and the soft, beseeching eyes were looking pleadingly into his.

"My dearest child," he said, "it is hard to refuse you, but I cannot allow it. There, there do not cry so bitterly; every tear I see you shed sends a pang to my heart. Listen to me, daughter. Believing what I do of that man, I would not for a great deal have him in possession of a single line of your writing. Have you ever given him one?"

"No, papa, never," she sobbed.

"Or received one from him?"

"No, sir."

"It is well." Then as if a sudden thought had struck him, "Elsie have you ever allowed him to touch your lips?" he asked almost sternly.

"No, papa, not even my cheek. I would not while we were not engaged; and that could not be without your consent."

"I am truly thankful for that!" he exclaimed in a tone of relief; "to know that he had—that these sweet lips had been polluted by contact with his—would be worse to me than the loss of half my fortune." And lifting her face as he spoke, he pressed his own to them again and again.

But for the first time in her life she turned from him as if almost loathing his caresses, and struggled to release herself from the clasp of his arm.

He let her go, and hurrying to the farther side of the room, she stood leaning against the window-frame, with her back toward him, shedding very bitter tears of mingled grief and anger.

But in the pauses of her sobbing a deep sigh struck upon her ear. Her heart smote her at the sound; still more as she glanced back at her father and noted the pained expression of his eye as it met hers. In a moment she was at his side again, down upon the carpet, with her head laid lovingly on his knee.

"Papa, I am sorry." The low sweet voice was tremulous with grief and penitence.

"My poor darling, my poor little pet!" he said, passing his hand with soft, caressing movement over her hair and cheek, "try to keep your love for your father and your faith in his for you, however hard his rule may seem."

"Ah, papa, my heart would break if I lost either," she sobbed. Then lifting her tear-dimmed eyes with tender concern to his face, which was very pale and sad, "Dear papa," she said, "how tired you look! you were up all night, were you not?"

"Last night and the one before it."

"That you might hasten here to take care of me," she murmured in a tone of mingled regret and gratitude. "Do lie down now and take a nap. This couch is soft and pleasant, and I will close the blinds and sit by your side to keep off the flies."

He yielded to her persuasions, saying as he closed his eyes, "Don't leave the room without waking me."

She was still there when he woke, close at his side and ready to greet him with an affectionate look and smile, though the latter was touchingly sad and there were traces of tears on her cheeks.

# FRANCES HODGSON BURNETT

🦋 🦋

*Best known for her novel that related the loving re-
lationship of little Lord Fauntleroy and his mother,
Mrs. Burnett did not neglect other family ties in her
other books. From Louisiana, published in 1880, here
is the reunion between a young woman and her father.*

## "Confessions"

THEY HAD A LONG, quiet evening together afterward. They
sat before the fire, and Louisiana drew her low seat near him
so that she could rest her head upon his knee.

"It's almost like old times," she said. "Let us pretend I never
went away and that everything is as it used to be."

"Would ye like it to be thataway, Louisianny?" he asked.

She was going to say "Yes," but she remembered the changes he
had made to please her, and she turned her face and kissed the
hand her cheek rested against.

"You mustn't fancy I don't think the new house is beautiful,"
she said. "It isn't that I mean. What I would like to bring back
is—is the feeling I used to have. That is all—nothing but the old
feeling. And people can't always have the same feelings, can they?
Things change so as we get older."

He looked at the crackling fire very hard for a minute.

"Thet's so," he said. "Thet's so. Things changes in gin'ral, an'
feelin's, now, they're cur'us. Thar's things as kin be altered an'
things as cayn't—an' feelin's they cayn't. They're cur'us. Ef ye
hurt 'em, now, thar's money; it aint nothin' ye kin buy as 'll set
'em straight. Ef—fer instants—money could buy back them
feelin's of yourn—them as ye'd like to hev back—how ready an'

willin' I'd be to trade fer' em! Lord! how ready an' willin'! But it wont do it. That's whar it is. When they're gone a body hez to larn to git along without 'em."

And they sat silent again for some time, listening to the snapping of the dry wood burning in the great fire-place.

When they spoke next it was of a different subject.

"Ef ye aint a-goin' to Europe—" the old man began.

"And I'm not, father," Louisiana put in.

"Ef ye aint, we must set to work fixin' up right away. This mornin' I was a-layin' out to myself to let it stay tell ye come back an' then hev it all ready fer ye—cheers an' tables—an' sophias— an' merrors—an'—ile paintin's. I laid out to do it slow, Louisi-anny, and take time, an' steddy a heap, an' to take advice from them es knows, afore I traded ary time. I 'lowed it'd be a heap better to take advice from them es knowed. Brown, es owns the Springs, I 'lowed to hev asked him, now,—he's used to furnishin' up an' knows whar to trade an' what to trade fer. The paintin's, now—I've heern it takes a heap o' experience to pick 'em, an' I aint hed no experience. I 'low I shouldn't know a good un when I seen it. Now, them picters as was in the parlor—ye know more than I do, I dessay,—now, them picters," he said, a little un-certainly, "was they to say good, or—or only about middlin'?"

She hesitated a second.

"Mother was fond of them" she broke out, in a burst of simple feeling.

Remembering how she had stood before the simpering, red-cheeked faces and hated them; how she had burned with shame before them, she was stricken with a bitter pang of remorse.

"Mother was fond of them," she said.

"Thet's so," he answered, simply. "Thet's so, she was; an' you a-bein' so soft-hearted an' tender makes it sorter go agin ye to give in as they wasn't—what she took 'em fer. But ye see, thet—though it's nat'ral—it's nat'ral—don't make 'em good or bad, Louisianny, an' Lord! it don't harm *her*. 'Taint what folks knows or what they don't know thet makes the good in 'em. Ianthy she warn't to say 'complished, but I don't see how she could hev ben no better than she was—nor more calc'lated to wear well—in the p'int o' religion. Not hevin' experience in ile paintin's aint what'd hurt her, nor make us think no less of her. It wouldn't hev hurt her when she was livin' an' Lord! she's past it now—she's past it, Ianthy is."

He talked a good deal about his plans and of the things he meant to buy. He was quite eager in his questioning of her and showed such lavishness as went to her heart.

"I want to leave ye well fixed," he said.

"Leave me?" she echoed.

He made a hurried effort to soften the words.

"I'd oughtn't to said it," he said. "It was kinder keerless. Thet thar—it's a long way off—mebbe—an' I'd oughtn't to hev said it. It's a way old folks hev—but it's a bad way. Things git to seem sorter near to 'em—an' ordinary."

The whole day had been to Louisiana a slow approach to a climax. Sometimes when her father talked she could scarcely bear to look at his face as the firelight shone on it.

So, when she had bidden him good-night at last and walked to the door leaving him standing upon the hearth watching her as she moved away, she turned round suddenly and faced him again, with her hand upon the latch.

"Father," she cried, "I want to tell you—I want to tell you—"

"What?" he said. "What, Louisianny?"

She put her hand to her side and leaned against the door—a slender, piteous figure.

"Don't look at me kindly," she said. "I don't deserve it. I deserve nothing. I have been ashamed—"

He stopped her, putting up his shaking hand and turning pale.

"Don't say nothin' as ye'll be sorry fer when ye feel better, Louisianny," he said. "Don't git carried away by yer feelin's into sayin' nothin' es is hard on yerself. Don't ye do it, Louisianny. Thar aint no need fer it, honey. Yer kinder wrought up, now, an' ye cayn't do yerself jestice."

But she would not be restrained.

"I *must* tell you," she said. "It has been on my heart too long. I ought never to have gone away. Everybody was different from us—and had new ways. I think they laughed at me, and it made me bad. I began to ponder over things until at last I hated myself and everything, and was ashamed that I had been content. When I told you I wanted to play a joke on the people who came here, it was not true. I wanted them to go away without knowing that this was my home. It was only a queer place, to be laughed at, to them, and I was ashamed of it, and bitter and angry. When they went into the parlor they laughed at it and at the pictures, and everything in it, and I stood by with my cheeks burning. When I saw a strange woman in the kitchen it flashed into my mind that I had no need to tell them that all these things that they laughed at had been round me all my life. They were not sneering at them—it was worse than that—they were only interested and amused and curious, and were not afraid to let me see. The—gentleman had been led by his sister to think I came from some city. He thought I was—was pretty and educated,—his equal, and I knew how amazed he would be and how he would say he could not believe that I had lived here, and wonder at me and talk me over. And I could not bear it. I only wanted him to go away without knowing, and never, never see me again!"

Remembering the pain and fever and humiliation of the past, and of that dreadful day above all, she burst into sobbing.

"You did not think I was that bad, did you?" she said. "But I was! I was!"

"Louisianny," he said, huskily, "come yere. Thar aint no need fer ye to blame yerself thataway. Yer kinder wrought up."

"Don't be kind to me!" she said. "Don't! I want to tell you all—every word! I was so bad and proud and angry that I meant to carry it out to the end, and tried to—only I was not quite bad enough for one thing, father—I was not bad enough to be ashamed of *you*, or to bear to sit by and see them cast a slight upon you. They didn't mean it for a slight—it was only their clever way of looking at things—but *I* loved you. You were all I had left, and I knew you were better than they were a thousand times! Did they think I would give your warm, good heart—your kind, faithful heart—for all they had learned, or for all they could ever learn? It killed me to see and hear them! And it seemed as if I was on fire. And I told them the truth—that you were *my* father and that I loved you and was proud of you—that I might be ashamed of myself and all the rest, but not of you—never of you—for I wasn't worthy to kiss your feet!"

For one moment her father watched her, his lips parted and trembling. It seemed as if he meant to try to speak, but could not. Then his eyes fell with an humble, bewildered, questioning glance upon his feet, encased in their large, substantial brogans—the feet she had said she was not worthy to kiss. What he saw in them to touch him so it would be hard to tell—for he broke down utterly, put out his hand, groping to feel for his chair, fell into it with head bowed on his arm, and burst into sobbing too.

She left her self-imposed exile in an instant, ran to him, and knelt down to lean against him.

"Oh!" she cried, "have I broken your heart? Have I broken your heart? Will God ever forgive me? I don't ask you to forgive me, father, for I don't deserve it."

At first he could not speak, but he put his arm round her and drew her head up to his breast—and, with all the love and tenderness he had lavished upon her all her life, she had never known such love and tenderness as he expressed in this one movement.

"Louisianny," he said, brokenly, when he had found his voice, "it's you as should be a-forgivin' me."

"I!" she exclaimed.

He held her in his trembling arm so close that she felt his heart quivering.

"To think," he almost whispered, "as I should not hev ben doin' ye jestice! To think as I didn't know ye well enough to do ye jestice! To think yer own father, thet's knowed ye all yer life, could hev give in to its bein' likely as ye wasn't—what he'd allers thought, an' what yer mother 'd thought, an' what ye was, honey."

"I don't—" she began falteringly.

"It's me as oughter be a-standin' agin the door," he said. "It's me! I knowed every word of the first part of what ye've told me, Louisianny. I've been so sot on ye thet I've got into a kinder noticin' way with ye, an' I guessed it out. I seen it in yer face when ye stood thar tryin' to laugh on the porch while them people was a-waitin'. 'Twa'n't no nat'ral gal's laugh ye laughed, and when ye thought I wasn't a-noticin' I was a-noticin' an' a-thinkin' all the time. But I seen more than was thar, honey, an' I didn't do ye jestice—an' I've ben punished fer it. It come agin me like a slungshot. I ses to myself, 'She's ashamed o' *me!* It's *me* she's ashamed of—an' she wants to pass me off fer a stranger!' "

The girl drew off from him a little and looked up into his face wonderingly.

"You thought that!" she said. "And never told me—and humored me, and—"

"I'd oughter knowed ye better," he said; "but I've suffered fer it, Louisianny. I ses to myself, 'All the years thet we've ben sot on each other an' nussed each other through our little sick spells, an' keered fer each other, hes gone fer nothin'. She wants to pass me off fer a stranger.' Not that I blamed ye, honey. Lord! I knowed the difference betwixt us! I'd knowed it long afore you did. But somehow it warn't eggsakly what I looked fer an' it was kinder hard on me right at the start. An' then the folks went away an' ye didn't go with 'em, an' thar was somethin' workin' on ye as I knowed ye wasn't ready to tell me about. An' I sot an' steddied it over an' watched ye, an' I prayed some, an' I laid wake nights a-steddyin'. An' I made up my mind thet es I'd ben the cause o' trouble to ye I'd oughter try an' sorter balance the thing. I allers 'lowed parents hed a duty to their child'en. An' I ses, 'Thar's some things thet kin be altered an' some thet cayn't. Let's alter them es kin!'"

She remembered the words well, and now she saw clearly the dreadful pain they had expressed; they cut her to her soul.

"Oh! father," she cried. "How could you?"

"I'd oughter knowed ye better, Louisianny," he repeated. "But I didn't. I ses, 'What money an' steddyin' an' watchin'll do fer her to make up, shell be done. I'll try to make up fer the wrong I've did her onwillin'ly—onwillin'ly.'

"An' I went to the Springs an' I watched an' steddied thar, an' I come home an' I watched an' steddied thar—an' I hed the house fixed, an' I laid out to let ye go to Europe—though what I'd heern o' the habits o' the people, an' the brigands an' sich, went powerful agin me makin' up my mind easy. An' I never lost sight nary minnit o' what I'd laid out fer to do—but I wasn't doin' ye jestice an' didn't suffer no more than I'd oughter. An' when ye stood up thar agen the door, honey, with yer tears a-streamin' an' yer eyes a-shinin', an' told me what ye'd felt an' what ye'd said about—wa'l," (delicately) "about thet thar as ye thought ye wasn't worthy to do, it set my blood a-tremblin' in my veins—an' my heart a-shakin' in my side, an' me a-goin' all over—an' I was struck all of a heap, an' knowed thet the Lord hed ben better to me than I thought, an'— an' even when I was fondest on ye, an' proudest on ye, I hadn't done ye no sort o' jestice in the world—an' never could!"

There was no danger of their misunderstanding each other again. When they were calmer they talked their trouble over simply and confidingly, holding nothing back.

"When ye told me, Louisianny," said her father, "that ye wanted nothin' but me, it kinder went agin me more than all the rest, fer I thinks, ses I to myself, 'It aint true, an' she must be a-gettin' sorter hardened to it, or she'd never said it.' It seemed like it was kinder onnecessary. Lord! the onjestice I was a-doin' ye!"

They bade each other good-night again, at last.

"Fer ye're a-lookin' pale," he said. "An' I've been kinder out o' sorts myself these last two or three weeks. My dyspepsy's bin back on me agin an' thet thar pain in my side's bin a-workin' on me. We must take keer o' ourselves, bein' es thar's on'y us two, an' we're so sot on each other."

He went to the door with her and said his last words to her there.

"I'm glad it come to-night," he said, in a grateful tone. "Lord! how glad I am it come to-night! S'posin' somethin' hed happened to ary one of us an' the other hed ben left not a-knowin' how it was. I'm glad it didn't last no longer, Louisianny."

And so they parted for the night.

# BOOTH TARKINGTON

菱 菱

*From* Growth *comes this picture of a father facing financial ruin and the perceptive daughter who is willing to rescue him.*

MR. VERTREES, having watched their departure with the air of a man who had something at hazard upon the expedition, turned from the window and began to pace the library thought-fully, pending their return. He was about sixty; a small man, withered and dry and fine, a trim little sketch of the elderly dandy. His lambrequin moustache—relic of a forgotten Anglomania—had been profoundly black, but now, like his smooth hair, it was approaching an equally sheer whiteness; and though his clothes were old, they had shapeliness and a flavour of mode. And for greater spruceness there were some jaunty touches: gray spats, a narrow black ribbon across the gray waistcoat to the eye-glasses in a pocket, a fleck of colour from a button in the lapel of the black coat, labelling him the descendant of patriot warriors.

The room was not like him, being cheerful and hideous, whereas Mr. Vertrees was anxious and decorative. Under a mantel of imitation black marble a merry little coal-fire beamed forth upon high and narrow "Eastlake" bookcases with long glass doors, and upon comfortable, incongruous furniture, and upon meaning-less "woodwork" everywhere, and upon half a dozen Landseer engravings which Mr. and Mrs. Vertrees sometimes mentioned to each other, after thirty years of possession, as "very fine things." They had been the first people in town to possess Landseer engravings, and there, in art, they had rested, but they still had a feeling that in all such matters they were in the van; and when Mr. Vertrees discovered Landseers upon the walls of other people's houses he thawed, as a chieftain to a trusted follower; and if he found an edition of Bulwer Lytton accompanying the Landseers as a final corroboration of culture, he would say, inevitably, "Those people know good pictures and they know good books."

The growth of the city, which might easily have made him a millionaire, had ruined him because, like Major Amberson, he had failed to understand it. When towns begin to grow they have whims, and the whims of a town always ruin somebody. Mr. Vertrees had been most strikingly the somebody in this case. At about the time he bought the Landseers, he owned, through inheritance, an office-building and a large house not far from it, where he spent the winter; and he had a country place—a farm of four hundred acres—where he went for the summers to the comfortable, ugly old house that was his home now, perforce, all the year round. If he had known how to sit still and let things happen he would have prospered miraculously; but, strangely enough, the dainty little man was one of the first to fall down and worship Bigness, the which proceeded straightway to enact the role of Juggernaut for his better education. He was a true prophet of the prodigious growth, but he had a fatal gift for selling good and buying bad. He should have stayed at home and looked at his Landseers and read his Bulwer, but he took his cow to market, and the trained milkers milked her dry and then ate her. He sold the office-building and the house in town to buy a great tract of lots in a new suburb; then he sold the farm, except the house and the ground about it, to pay the taxes on the suburban lots and to "keep them up." The lots refused to stay up; but he had to do something to keep himself and his family up, so in despair he sold the lots (which went up beautifully the next year) for "traction stock" that was paying dividends; and thereafter he ceased to buy and sell. Thus he disappeared altogether from the commercial surface at about the time that his wife's great relatives, the Ambersons, disappeared from all surfaces. A little later James Sheridan came out securely on top; and Sheridan, until Mrs. Vertrees called upon him with her "anti-smoke" committee, had never heard her name.

Mr. Vertrees, pinched, retired to his Landseers, and Mrs. Vertrees "managed somehow" on the dividends, though "managing" became more and more difficult as the years went by and money bought less and less. But there came a day when three servitors of Bigness in Philadelphia took greedy counsel with four fellow-worshippers from New York, and not long after that there were no more dividends for Mr. Vertrees.

In fact, there was nothing for Mr. Vertrees, because the "traction stock" henceforth was no stock at all, and he had mortgaged his house long ago to help "manage somehow" according to his conception of his "position in life"—one of his own old-fashioned phrases. Six months before the completion of the New House next door, Mr. Vertrees had sold his horses and the worn Victoria and "station-wagon," to pay the arrears of his two servants and re-establish credit at the grocer's and butcher's—and a pair of elderly carriage-horses with such accoutrements are not very ample barter, in these days, for six months' food and fuel and service. Mr. Vertrees had discovered, too, that there was no salary for him in all the buzzing city—he could do nothing.

It may be said that he was at the end of his string. Such times do come in all their bitterness, finally, to the man with no trade or craft, if his feeble clutch on that slippery ghost, Property, shall fail.

The windows grew black while he paced the room, and smoky twilight closed round about the house, yet not more darkly than what closed round about the heart of the anxious little man patrolling the fan-shaped zone of firelight. But as the mantel clock struck wheezily six there was the rattle of an outer door, and a rich and beautiful peal of laughter went ringing through the house. Thus cheerfully did Mary Vertrees herald her return with her mother from their expedition among the barbarians.

She came rushing into the library and threw herself into a deep chair by the hearth, laughing so uncontrollably that tears were in her eyes. Mrs. Vertrees followed decorously, no mirth about her; on the contrary, she looked vaguely disturbed, as if she had eaten something not quite certain to agree with her, and regretted it.

"Papa! Oh, oh!" And Miss Vertrees was fain to apply a handkerchief upon her eyes. "I'm *so* glad you made us go! I wouldn't have missed it—"

Mrs. Vertrees shook her head. "I suppose I'm very dull," she said, gently. "I didn't see anything amusing. They're most ordinary, and the house is altogether in bad taste, but we anticipated that, and—"

"Papa!" Mary cried, breaking in. "They asked us to *dinner!*"

"What!"

"And I'm *going!*" she shouted, and was seized with fresh paroxysms. "Think of it! Never in their house before; never met any of them but the daughter—and just *barely* met her—"

"What about you?" interrupted Mr. Vertrees, turning sharply upon his wife.

She made a little face, as if positive now that what she had eaten would not agree with her. "I couldn't!" she said. "I—"

"Yes, that's just—just the way she—she looked when they asked her!" cried Mary, choking. "And then she—she realized it, and tried to turn it into a cough, and she didn't know how, and it sounded like—like a squeal!"

"I suppose," said Mrs. Vertrees, much injured, "that Mary will have an uproarious time at my funeral. She makes fun of—"

Mary jumped up instantly and kissed her; then she went to the mantel and, leaning an elbow upon it, gazed thoughtfully at the buckle of her shoe, twinkling in the firelight.

"*They* didn't notice anything," she said. "So far as they were concerned, mamma, it was one of the finest coughs you ever coughed."

"Who were 'they'?" asked her father. "Whom did you see?"

"Only the mother and daughter," Mary answered. "Mrs. Sheridan is dumpy and rustly; and Miss Sheridan is pretty and pushing—dresses by the fashion magazines and talks about New York people that have their pictures in 'em. She tutors the mother, but not very successfully—partly because her own foundation is too flimsy and partly because she began too late. They've got an enormous Moor of painted plaster or something in the hall, and the girl evidently thought it was to her credit that she selected it!"

"They have oil-paintings, too," added Mrs. Vertrees, with a glance of gentle pride at the Landseers. "I've always thought oil-paintings in a private house the worst of taste."

"Oh, if one owned a Raphael or a Titian!" said Mr. Vertrees, finishing the implication, not in words, but with a wave of his hand. "Go on, Mary. None of the rest of them came in? You didn't meet Mr. Sheridan or—" He paused and adjusted a lump of coal in the fire delicately with the poker. "Or one of the sons?"

Mary's glance crossed his, at that, with a flash of utter comprehension. He turned instantly away, but she had begun to laugh again.

"No," she said, "no one except the women, but mamma inquired about the sons thoroughly!"

"Mary!" Mrs. Vertrees protested.

"Oh, most adroitly, too!" laughed the girl. "Only she couldn't help unconsciously turning to look at me—when she did it!"

"Mary Vertrees!"

"Never mind, mamma! Mrs. Sheridan and Miss Sheridan neither of *them* could help unconsciously turning to look at me—speculatively—at the same time! They all three kept looking at me and talking about the oldest son, Mr. James Sheridan, Junior. Mrs. Sheridan said his father is very anxious 'to get Jim to marry and settle down,' and she assured me that 'Jim is right cultivated.' Another of the sons, the youngest one, caught me looking in the window this afternoon; but they didn't seem to consider him quite one of themselves, somehow, though Mrs. Sheridan mentioned that a couple of years or so ago he had been 'right sick,' and had been to some cure or other. They seemed relieved to bring the subject back to 'Jim' and his virtues—and to look at me! The other brother is the middle one, Roscoe; he's the one that owns the new house across the street, where that young blacksheep of the Lamhorns, Robert, goes so often. I saw a short, dark young man standing on the porch with Robert Lamhorn there the other day, so I suppose that was Roscoe. 'Jim' still lurks in the mists, but I shall meet him to-night. Papa—" She stepped nearer to him so that he had to face her, and his eyes were troubled as he did. There may have been a trouble deep within her own, but she kept their surface merry with laughter. "Papa, Bibbs is the youngest one's name, and Bibbs—to the best of our information—is a lunatic. Roscoe is married. Papa, does it have to be Jim?"

"Mary!" Mrs. Vertrees cried, sharply. "You're outrageous! That's a perfectly horrible way of talking!"

"Well, I'm close to twenty-four," said Mary, turning to her. "I haven't been able to like anybody yet that's asked me to marry him, and maybe I never shall. Until a year or so ago I've had everything I ever wanted in my life—you and papa gave it all to me—and it's about time I began to pay back. Unfortunately, I don't know how to do anything—but something's got to be done."

"But you needn't talk of it like *that!*" insisted the mother, plaintively. "It's not—it's not—"

"No, it's not," said Mary. "I know that!"

"How did they happen to ask you to dinner?" Mr. Vertrees inquired, uneasily. " 'Stextrawdn'ry thing!"

"Climbers' hospitality," Mary defined it. "We were so very cordial and easy! I think Mrs. Sheridan herself might have done it just as any kind old woman on a farm might ask a neighbour, but it was Miss Sheridan who did it. She played around it awhile; you could see she wanted to—she's in a dreadful hurry to get into things!—and I fancied she had an idea it might impress that Lamhorn boy to find us there to-night. It's a sort of house-warming dinner, and they talked about and talked about it—and then the girl got her courage up and blurted out the invitation. And mamma—" Here Mary was once more a victim to incorrigible merriment. "Mamma tried to say yes, and *couldn't!* She swallowed and squealed—I mean you coughed, dear! And then, papa, she said that you and she had promised to go to a lecture at the Emerson Club to-night, but that her daughter would be delighted to come to the Big Show! So there I am, and there's Mr. Jim Sheridan—and there's the clock! Dinner's at seven-thirty!"

And she ran out of the room, scooping up her fallen furs with a gesture of flying grace as she sped.

When she came down, at twenty minutes after seven, her father stood in the hall, at the foot of the stairs, waiting to be her escort through the dark. He looked up and watched her as she descended, and his gaze was fond and proud—and profoundly disturbed. But she smiled and nodded gaily, and, when she reached the floor, put a hand on his shoulder.

"At least no one could suspect me to-night," she said. "I *look* rich, don't I, papa?"

She did. She had a look that worshipful girl friends bravely called "regal." A head taller than her father, she was as straight and jauntily poised as a boy athlete, and her brown hair and her brown eyes were like her mother's, but for the rest she went back to some stronger and livelier ancestor than either of her parents.

"Don't I look too rich to be suspected?" she insisted.

"You look everything beautiful, Mary," he said, huskily.

"And my dress?" She threw open her dark velvet cloak, showing a splendour of white and silver. "Anything better at Nice next winter, do you think?" She laughed, shrouding her glittering figure in the cloak again. "Two years old, and no one would dream it! I did it over."

"You can do anything, Mary."

There was a curious humility in his tone, and something

more—a significance not veiled and yet abysmally apologetic. It was as if he suggested something to her and begged her forgiveness in the same breath.

And upon that, for the moment, she became as serious as he. She lifted her hand from his shoulder and then set it back more firmly, so that he should feel the reassurance of its pressure.

"Don't worry," she said, in a low voice and gravely. "I know exactly what you want me to do."

# JOHN GALSWORTHY

*In three trilogies of novels about the Forsyte family Galsworthy deals with many aspects of upper and middle-class English life during the Victorian and Edwardian eras. To-Let, Book III of The Forsyte Saga, shows Soames Forsyte as the unwitting instrument of his daughter's unhappiness.*

AT A QUARTER TO EIGHT he heard the car. A great weight lifted from off his heart; he hurried down. She was getting out— pale and tired-looking, but nothing wrong. He met her in the hall.

"You've frightened me. Where have you been?"

"To Robin Hill. I'm sorry, dear. I had to go; I'll tell you afterwards." And, with a flying kiss, she ran up-stairs.

Soames waited in the drawing-room. To Robin Hill! What did that portend?

It was not a subject they could discuss at dinner—consecrated to the susceptibilities of the butler. The agony of nerves Soames had been through, the relief he felt at her safety, softened his power to condemn what she had done, or resist what she was going to do; he waited in a relaxed stupor for her revelation. Life was a queer business. There he was at sixty-five and no more in command of things than if he had not spent forty years in building up security—always something one couldn't get on terms with! In the pocket of his dinner-jacket was a letter from Annette. She was coming back in a fortnight. He knew nothing of what she had been doing out there. And he was glad that he did not. Her absence had been a relief. Out of sight was out of mind! And now she was coming back. Another worry! And the Bolderby Old Crome was gone—Dumetrius had got it—all because that anonymous letter had put it out of his thoughts. He furtively remarked the strained look on his daughter's face, as if she too were gazing at a picture that she couldn't buy. He almost wished the war back. Worries didn't seem, then, quite so worrying. From the caress in her voice, the look on her face, he became certain that she wanted something from him, uncertain whether it would be wise of him to give it her. He pushed his savoury away uneaten, and even joined her in a cigarette.

After dinner she set the electric piano-player going. And he augured the worst when she sat down on a cushion footstool at his knee, and put her hand on his.

"Darling, be nice to me. I had to see Jon—he wrote to me. He's going to try what he can do with his mother. But I've been thinking. But it's really in *your* hands, Father. If you'd persuade her that it doesn't mean renewing the past in any way! That I shall stay yours, and Jon will stay hers; that you need never see him or her, and she need never see you or me! Only you could persuade her, because only you could promise. One can't promise for other people. Sure it wouldn't be too awkward for you to see her just this once—now that Jon's father is dead?"

"Too awkward?" Soames repeated. "The whole thing's preposterous."

"You know," said Fleur, without looking up, "you wouldn't mind seeing her, really."

Soames was silent. Her words had expressed a truth too deep for him to admit. She slipped her fingers between his own—hot, slim, eager, they clung there. This child of his would corkscrew her way into a brick wall!

"What am I to do, if you won't, Father?" she said very softly.

"I'll do anything for your happiness," said Soames; "but this isn't for your happiness."

"Oh! it is; it is!"

"It'll only stir things up," he said grimly.

"But they are stirred up. The thing is to quiet them. To make her feel that this is just *our* lives, and has nothing to do with yours or hers. You can do it, Father, I know you can."

"You know a great deal, then," was Soames' glum answer.

"If you will, Jon and I will wait a year—two years if you like."

"It seems to me," murmured Soames, "that you care nothing about what *I* feel."

Fleur pressed his hand against her cheek.

"I do, darling. But you wouldn't like me to be awfully miserable." How she wheedled to get her ends! And trying with all his might to think she really cared for him—he was not sure—not sure. All she cared for was this boy! Why should he help her to get this boy, who was killing her affection for himself? Why should he? By the laws of the Forsytes it was foolish! There was nothing to be had out of it—nothing! To give her to that boy! To pass her into the enemy's camp, under the influence of the woman who had injured him so deeply! Slowly—inevitably—he would lose this flower of his life! And suddenly he was conscious that his hand was wet. His heart gave a little painful jump. He couldn't bear her to cry. He put his other hand quickly over hers, and a tear dropped on that, too. He couldn't go on like this! "Well, well," he said, "I'll think it over, and do what I can. Come, come!" If she must have it for her happiness—she must; he couldn't refuse to help her. And lest she should begin to thank him he got out of his chair and went up to the piano-player—making that noise! It ran down, as he reached it, with a faint buzz. That musical box of his nursery days: "The Harmonious Blacksmith," "Glorious Port"—the thing had always made him miserable when his mother set it going on Sunday afternoons. Here it was again—the same thing, only larger, more expensive, and now it played: "The Wild Wild Women" and "The Policeman's Holiday," and he was no longer in black velvet with a sky-blue collar. 'Profond's right,' he thought, 'there's nothing in it! We're all progressing to the grave!' And with that surprising mental comment he walked out.

He did not see Fleur again that night. But, at breakfast, her eyes followed him about with an appeal he could not escape—not that he intended to try. No! He had made up his mind to the nerve-racking business. He would go to Robin Hill—to that house of memories. A pleasant memory—the last! Of going down to keep that boy's father and Irene apart by threatening divorce. He had often thought, since, that it had clenched their union. And, now, he was going to clench the union of that boy with his girl. 'I don't know what I've done,' he thought, 'to have such things thrust on me!' He went up by train and down by train, and from the station walked by the long rising lane, still very much as he remembered it over thirty years ago. Funny—so near London! Some one evidently was holding on to the land there. This speculation soothed him, moving between the high hedges slowly, so as not to get overheated, though the day was chill enough. After all was said and done there was something real about land, it didn't shift. Land, and good pictures! The values might fluctuate a bit, but on the whole they were always going up—worth holding on to, in a world where there was such a lot of unreality, cheap building, changing fashions, such a "Here to-day and gone to-morrow" spirit. The French were right, perhaps, with their peasant proprietorship, though he had no opinion of the French. One's bit of land! Something solid in it! He had heard peasant-proprietors described as a pig-headed lot; had heard young Mont call his father a pig-headed *Morning Poster*—disrespectful young devil. Well, there were worse things than being pig-headed or reading *The Morning Post*. There was Profond and his tribe, and all these Labour chaps, and loud-mouthed politicians, and "wild, wild women"! A lot of worse things! And, suddenly, Soames became conscious of feeling weak, and hot, and shaky. Sheer nerves at the meeting before him! As Aunt Juley might have said—quoting "Superior Dosset"—his nerves were "in a proper fantigue." He could see the house now among its trees, the house he had watched being built, intending it for himself and this woman, who, by such strange fate, had lived in it with another after all! He began to think of Dumetrius, Local Loans, and other forms of investment. He could not afford to meet her with his nerves all shaking; he who represented the Day of Judgment for her on earth as it was in heaven; he, legal ownership, personified, meeting lawless beauty, incarnate. His dignity demanded impassivity during this embassy designed to link their offspring, who, if she had behaved herself, would have been brother and sister. That wretched tune: "The Wild Wild Women" kept running in his head, perversely, for tunes did not run there as a rule. Passing the poplars in front of the house, he thought: 'How they've grown; I had them planted!'

A maid answered his ring.

"Will you say—Mr. Forsyte, on a very special matter."

If she realised who he was, quite probably she would not see him. 'By George!' he thought, hardening as the tug came: 'It's a topsy-turvy affair!'

The maid came back. Would the gentleman state his business, please?

"Say it concerns Mr. Jon," said Soames.

And once more he was alone in that hall with the pool of grey-white marble designed by her first lover. Ah! she had been a bad lot—had loved two men, and not himself! He must remember that when he came face to face with her once more. And suddenly he saw her in the opening chink between the long heavy purple curtains, swaying, as if in hesitation; the old perfect poise and line, the old startled dark-eyed gravity; the old calm defensive voice: "Will you come in, please?"

He passed through that opening. As in the picture gallery and the confectioner's shop, she seemed to him still beautiful. And this was the first time—the very first—since he married her five and thirty years ago, that he was speaking to her without the legal right to call her his. She was not wearing black—one of that fellow's radical notions, he supposed.

"I apologise for coming," he said glumly; "but this business must be settled one way or the other."

"Won't you sit down?"

"No, thank you."

Anger at his false position, impatience of ceremony between them, mastered him, and words came tumbling out:

"It's an infernal mischance: I've done my best to discourage it. I consider my daughter crazy, but I've got into the habit of indulging her; that's why I'm here. I suppose you're fond of your son."

"Devotedly."

"Well?"

"It rests with him."

He had a sense of being met and baffled. Always—always she had baffled him, even in those old first married days.

"It's a mad notion," he said.

"It is."

"If you had only—! Well—they might have been—" he did not finish that sentence "brother and sister and all this saved," but he saw her shudder as if he had, and stung by the sight, he crossed over to the window. Out *there* the trees had not grown—they couldn't, they were old!

"So far as I'm concerned," he said, "you may make your mind easy. I desire to see neither you nor your son if this marriage comes about. Young people in these days are—are unaccountable. But I can't bear to see my daughter unhappy. What am I to say to her when I go back?"

"Please say to her, as I said to you, that it rests with Jon."

"You don't oppose it?"

"With all my heart; not with my lips."

Soames stood, biting his finger.

"I remember an evening—" he said suddenly; and was silent. What was there—what was there in this woman that would not fit into the four corners of his hate or condemnation? "Where is he—your son?"

"Up in his father's studio, I think."

"Perhaps you'd have him down."

He watched her ring the bell, he watched the maid come in.

"Please tell Mr. Jon that I want him."

"If it rests with him," said Soames hurriedly, when the maid was gone, "I suppose I may take it for granted that this unnatural marriage will take place; in that case there'll be formalities. Whom do I deal with—Herrings?"

Irene nodded.

"You don't propose to live with them?"

Irene shook her head.

"What happens to this house?"

"It will be as Jon wishes."

"This house," said Soames suddenly: "I had hopes when I began it. If *they* live in it—their children! They say there's such a thing as Nemesis. Do you believe in it?"

"Yes."

"Oh! You do!"

He had come back from the window, and was standing close to her, who, in the curve of her grand piano, was, as it were, embayed.

"I'm not likely to see you again," he said slowly: "Will you shake hands," his lip quivered, the words came out jerkily, "and let the past die?" He held out his hand. Her pale face grew paler, her eyes so dark, rested immovably on his, but her hands remained clasped in front of her. He heard a sound and turned. That boy was standing in the opening of the curtains. Very queer he looked, hardly recognisable as the young fellow he had seen in the Gallery off Cork Street—very queer; much older, no youth in the face at all—haggard, rigid, his hair ruffled, his eyes deep in his head. Soames made an effort, and said with a lift of his lip, not quite a smile nor quite a sneer:

"Well, young man! I'm here for my daughter; it rests with you, it seems—this matter. Your mother leaves it in your hands."

The boy continued staring at his mother's face, and made no answer.

"For my daughter's sake I've brought myself to come," said Soames. "What am I to say to her when I go back?"

Still looking at his mother, the boy said, quietly:

"Tell Fleur that it's no good, please: I must do as my father wished before he died."

"Jon!"

"It's all right, Mother."

In a kind of stupefaction Soames looked from one to the other; then, taking up hat and umbrella, which he had put down on a chair, he walked towards the curtains. The boy stood aside for him to go by. He passed through and heard the grate of the rings as the curtains were drawn behind him. The sound liberated something in his chest.

'So that's that!' he thought, and passed out of the front door.

As Soames walked away from the house at Robin Hill the sun broke through the grey of that chill afternoon, in smoky radiance. So absorbed in landscape-painting that he seldom looked seriously for effects of Nature out-of-doors, he was struck by that moody effulgence—it mourned with a triumph suited to his own feeling. Victory in defeat! His embassy had come to naught. But he was rid of those people, had regained his daughter at the expense of—her happiness. What would Fleur say to him? Would she believe he had done his best? And under that sunlight flaring on the elms, hazels, hollies of the lane and those unexploited fields, Soames felt dread. She would be terribly upset! He must appeal to her pride. That boy had given her up, declared part and lot with the woman who so long ago had given her father up! Soames clenched his hands. Given him up, and why? What had been wrong with him? And once more he felt the *malaise* of one who contemplates himself as seen by another—like a dog who chances on his reflection in a mirror, and is intrigued and anxious at the unseizable thing.

Not in a hurry to get home, he dined in town at the Connoisseurs. While eating a pear it suddenly occurred to him that, if he had not gone down to Robin Hill, the boy might not have so decided. He remembered the expression on his face while his mother was refusing the hand he had held out. A strange, an awkward thought! Had Fleur cooked her own goose by trying to make too sure?

He reached home at half-past nine. While the car was passing in at one drive gate he heard the grinding sputter of a motor-cycle passing out by the other. Young Mont, no doubt, so Fleur had not been lonely. But he went in with a sinking heart. In the cream-panelled drawing-room she was sitting with her elbows on her knees, and her chin on her clasped hands, in front of a white camellia plant which filled the fireplace. That glance at her before she saw him renewed his dread. What was she seeing among those white camellias?

"Well, Father!"

Soames shook his head. His tongue failed him. This was murderous work! He saw her eyes dilate, her lips quivering.

"What? What? Quick, Father!"

"My dear," said Soames, "I—I did my best, but—" And again he shook his head.

Fleur ran to him and put a hand on each of his shoulders.

"She?"

"No," muttered Soames, "he. I was to tell you that it was no use; he must do what his father wished before he died." He caught her by the waist. "Come, child, don't let them hurt you. They're not worth your little finger."

Fleur tore himself from his grasp.

"You didn't—you couldn't have tried. You—you betrayed me, Father!"

Bitterly wounded, Soames gazed at her passionate figure writhing there in front of him.

"You didn't try—you didn't—I was a fool—I won't believe he could—he ever could! Only yesterday he—! Oh! why did I ask you?"

"Yes," said Soames quietly, "why did you? I swallowed my feelings; I did my best for you, against my judgment—and this is my reward. Good-night!"

With every nerve in his body twitching he went towards the door.

Fleur darted after him.

"He gives me up? You mean that? Father!"

Soames turned and forced himself to answer:

"Yes."

"Oh!" cried Fleur. "What did you—what could you have done in those old days?"

The breathless sense of really monstrous injustice cut the power of speech in Soames' throat. What had *he* done! What had they done to him! And with quite unconscious dignity he put his hand on his breast, and looked at her.

"It's a shame!" cried Fleur passionately.

Soames went out. He mounted, slow and icy, to his picture-gallery, and paced among his treasures. Outrageous! Oh! Outrageous! She was spoiled! Ah! and who had spoiled her? He stood still before the Goya copy. Accustomed to her own way in everything—Flower of his life! And now that she couldn't have it.

He turned to the window for some air. Daylight was dying, the moon rising, gold behind the poplars! What sound was that? Why! That piano thing! A dark tune, with a thrum and a throb! She had set it going—what comfort could she get from that? His eyes caught movement down there beyond the lawn, under the trellis of rambler roses and young acacia-trees, where the moon-light fell. There she was, roaming up and down. His heart gave a little sickening jump. What would she do under this blow? How could he tell? What did he know of her—he had only loved her all his life—looked on her as the apple of his eye! He knew nothing—had no notion. There she was—and that dark tune—and the river gleaming in the moonlight!

'I must go out,' he thought.

He hastened down to the drawing-room, lighted just as he had left it, with the piano thrumming out that waltz, or fox-trot, or whatever they called it in these days, and passed through on to the verandah.

Where could he watch, without her seeing him? And he stole down through the fruit garden to the boat-house. He was between her and the river now, and his heart felt lighter. She was his daughter, and Annette's—she wouldn't do anything foolish; but there it was—he didn't know! From the boat-house window he could see the last acacia and the spin of her skirt when she turned in her restless march. That tune had run down at last—thank goodness! He crossed the floor and looked through the farther window at the water slow-flowing past the lilies. It made little bubbles against them, bright where a moon-streak fell. He re-membered suddenly that early morning when he had slept in this boat-house after his father died, and she had just been born—nearly nineteen years ago! Even now he recalled the unaccus-tomed world when he woke up, the strange feeling it had given him. That day the second passion of his life began—for this girl of his, roaming under the acacias. What a comfort she had been to him! And all the soreness and sense of outrage left him. If he could make her happy again, he didn't care! An owl flew, queeking, queeking; a bat flitted by; the moonlight brightened and broadened on the water. How long was she going to roam about like this! He went back to the window, and suddenly saw her coming down to the bank. She stood quite close, on the landing-stage. And Soames watched, clenching his hands. Should he speak to her? His excitement was intense. The stillness of her figure, its youth, its absorption in despair, in longing, in—itself. He would always remember it, moonlit like that; and the faint sweet reek of the river and the shivering of the willow leaves. She had everything in the world that he could give her, except the one thing that she could not have because of him! The perversity of things hurt him at that moment, as might a fishbone in his throat.

Then, with an infinite relief, he saw her turn back towards the house. What could he give her to make amends? Pearls, travel, horses, other young men—anything she wanted—that he might lose the memory of her young figure lonely by the water! There! She had set that tune going again! Why—it was a mania! Dark, thrumming, faint, travelling from the house. It was as though she had said: "If I can't have something to keep me going, I shall die of this!" Soames dimly understood. Well, if it helped her, let her keep it thrumming on all night! And, mousing back through the fruit garden, he regained the verandah. Though he meant to go in and speak to her now, he still hesitated, not knowing what to say, trying hard to recall how it felt to be thwarted in love. He ought to know, ought to remember—and he could not! Gone—all real recollection; except that it had hurt him horribly. In this blank-ness he stood passing his handkerchief over hands and lips, which were very dry. By craning his head he could just see Fleur, standing with her back to that piano still grinding out its tune, her arms tight crossed on her breast, a lighted cigarette between her lips, whose smoke half veiled her face. The expression on it was strange to Soames, the eyes shone and stared, and every feature was alive with a sort of wretched scorn and anger. Once or twice he had seen Annette look like that—the face was too vivid, too naked, not his daughter's at that moment. And he dared not go in, realising the futility of any attempt at consolation. He sat down in the shadow of the inglenook.

Monstrous trick, that Fate had played him! Nemesis! That old unhappy marriage! And in God's name—why? How was he to know, when he wanted Irene so violently, and she consented to be his, that she would never love him? The tune died and was renewed, and died again, and still Soames sat in the shadow, waiting for he knew not what. The fag of Fleur's cigarette, flung through the window, fell on the grass; he watched it glowing, burning itself out. The moon had freed herself above the poplars, and poured her unreality on the garden. Comfortless light, mysterious, withdrawn—like the beauty of that woman who had never loved him—dappling the nemesias and the stocks with a vesture not of earth. Flowers! And his flower so unhappy! Ah, why could one not put happiness into Local Loans, gild its edges, insure it against going down?

Light had ceased to flow out now from the drawing-room window. All was silent and dark in there. Had she gone up? He rose, and, tiptoeing, peered in. It seemed so! He entered. The verandah kept the moonlight out; and at first he could see nothing but the outlines of furniture blacker than the darkness. He groped towards the farther window to shut it. His foot struck a chair, and he heard a gasp. There she was, curled and crushed into the corner of the sofa! His hand hovered. Did she want his consolation? He stood, gazing at that ball of crushed frills and hair and graceful youth, trying to burrow its way out of sorrow. How leave her there? At last he touched her hair, and said:

"Come, darling, better go to bed. I'll make it up to you, somehow." How fatuous! But what could he have said?

# W · B · YEATS

✠ ✠

"A Prayer for My Daughter" *reveals the great Irish poet as a father.*

ONCE MORE the storm is howling, and half hid
Under this cradle-hood and coverlid
My child sleeps on. There is no obstacle
But Gregory's wood and one bare hill

Whereby the haystack- and room-levelling wind,
Bred on the Atlantic, can be stayed;
And for an hour I have walked and prayed
Because of the great gloom that is in my mind.

I have walked and prayed for this young child an hour
And heard the sea-wind scream upon the tower,
And under the arches of the bridge, and scream
In the elms above the flooded stream;
Imagining in excited reverie
That the future years had come,
Dancing to a frenzied drum,
Out of the murderous innocence of the sea.

May she be granted beauty and yet not
Beauty to make a stranger's eye distraught,
Or hers before a looking-glass, for such,
Being made beautiful overmuch,
Consider beauty a sufficient end,
Lose natural kindness and maybe
The heart-revealing intimacy
That chooses right, and never find a friend.

Helen being chosen found life flat and dull
And later had much trouble from a fool,
While that great Queen, that rose out of the spray,
Being fatherless could have her way
Yet chose a bandy-leggèd smith for man.
It's certain that fine women eat
A crazy salad with their meat
Whereby the Horn of Plenty is undone.

In courtesy I'd have her chiefly learned;
Hearts are not had as a gift but hearts are earned
By those that are not entirely beautiful;
Yet many, that have played the fool
For beauty's very self, has charm made wise,
And many a poor man that has roved,

Loved and thought himself beloved,
From a glad kindness cannot take his eyes.

May she become a flourishing hidden tree
That all her thoughts may like the linnet be,
And have no business but dispensing round
Their magnanimities of sound,
Nor but in merriment begin a chase,
Nor but in merriment a quarrel.
O may she live like some green laurel
Rooted in one dear perpetual place.

My mind, because the minds that I have loved,
The sort of beauty that I have approved,
Prosper but little, has dried up of late,
Yet knows that to be choked with hate
May well be of all evil chances chief.
If there's no hatred in a mind
Assault and battery of the wind
Can never tear the linnet from the leaf.

An intellectual hatred is the worst,
So let her think opinions are accursed.
Have I not seen the loveliest woman born
Out of the mouth of Plenty's horn,
Because of her opinionated mind
Barter that horn and every good
By quiet natures understood
For an old bellows full of angry wind?

Considering that, all hatred driven hence,
The soul recovers radical innocence
And learns at last that it is self-delighting,
Self-appeasing, self-affrighting,
And that its own sweet will is Heaven's will;
She can, though every face should scowl
And every windy quarter howl
Or every bellows burst, be happy still.

And may her bridegroom bring her to a house
Where all's accustomed, ceremonious;
For arrogance and hatred are the wares
Peddled in the thoroughfares.
How but in custom and in ceremony
Are innocence and beauty born?
Ceremony's a name for the rich horn,
And custom for the spreading laurel tree.

*June 1919*

# F. SCOTT FITZGERALD

*After his wife became ill, Fitzgerald undertook to be
both mother and father to his young daughter. From
his Letters, here is one of many counseling her when
she was away at school.*

## Letter to Frances Scott Fitzgerald

*Grove Park Inn
Asheville, North Carolina
[Summer, 1935]*

Scottina:

It was fine seeing you, and I liked you a lot (this is aside from
loving you which I always do). You are nicer to adults—you are
emerging from that rather difficult time in girls, 12–15 usually,
but you are emerging I think rather early—probably at 14 or so.
You have one good crack coming but—well:

"Daddy the prophet!" I can hear you say in scorn. I wish to God
I wasn't so right usually about you. When I wrote that "news-
sheet" with events left out, you know—the letter that puzzled
you—and headed it "Scottie Loses Head," it was because I saw it

coming. I knew that your popularity with two or three dazed adolescent boys would convince you that you were at least the Queen of Sheba, and that you would "lose your head." What shape this haywire excursion would take I didn't know—I couldn't have guessed it would be writing a series of indiscreet letters to a gossipy and indiscreet boy who would show them to the persons for whom they were not meant (Understand: I don't blame Andrew[1] too much—the fault was yours—he didn't, will you notice, put into writing an analysis of his best friends of his own sex!).

However, that's of no seriousness. But I think that the next kick will be a bad one—but you will survive, and after that you will manage your affairs better. To avoid such blows you almost *have* to have them yourself so you can begin to think of others as valuing themselves, possibly, quite as much as you do yourself. So I'm not afraid of it for you. I don't want it to be so bad that it will break your self-confidence, which is attractive and is fine [if] founded on positive virtues, work, courage, etc., but if you are selfish it had better be broken early. If you are unselfish you can keep it always—and it is a nice thing to have. I didn't know till 15 that there was anyone in the world except me, and it cost me *plenty*.

Signs and portents of your persistent conceit: Mrs. Owens[2] said to me (and Mrs. Owens loves you), "For the first time in a long while Scottie was *nice,* and not a burden as I expected. It was really nice to be with her."

Because, I guess, for the first time you entered into their lives, humble lives of struggling people, instead of insisting that they enter into yours—a chance they never had, of belonging to "high society." Before, you had let them be aware of what *you* were doing (not in any snobbish sense, because heaven knows I'd have checked you on that)—but because you never considered or pretended to consider their lives, their world at all—your own activities seemed of so much more overwhelming importance to you! *You did not use one bit of your mind, one little spot!* to think what *they* were thinking, or help *them!*

You went to Norfolk and gave out the information (*via* the

---

[1] Andrew Turnbull.
[2] Mrs. Allein Owens had been Fitzgerald's secretary since May 1932.

Taylors, *via* Annabel, *via* mother) that you were going to Dobbs.
That doesn't matter save as indicative of a show-off frame of mind.
You know it was highly tentative. It was a case, again, of boasting,
of "promoting yourself." But those signs of one big catastrophe
(it'll come—I want to minimize it for you, but it can't be
prevented because only experience can teach) are less important
than your failure to realize that you are *a young member of the
human race,* who has not proved itself in any but the most
superficial manner. (I have seen "popular girls" of 15 become
utterly *déclassé* in six months because they were essentially selfish.) You and Peaches[3] (who isn't selfish, I think) had a superficial headstart with prettiness, but you will find more and more
that less pretty girls will be attaching the solider, more substantial
boys as the next two years will show. Both you and Peaches are
intelligent but both of you will be warped by this early attention,
*and something tells me she won't lose her head*; she hasn't the
"gift of gab" as you have—her laughter and her silence takes the
place of much. That's why I wish to God you would write
something when you have time—if only a one act play about how
girls act in the bath house, in a tent, on a train going to camp.

I grow weary, but I probably won't write again for a month.
Don't answer this, justifying yourself—of *course* I know you're
doing the best you "can."

The points of the letter are:

1st   You did spill over, rashly!

2nd  You are getting over the self period—thank God!

3rd   But it'll take one more big kick, and I want it to be mild,
so your backside won't suffer too much.

4th   I wish you'd get your mind off your precious self enough
to write me a one act play about other people—what they
say and how they behave.

> With *dearest* love,
> Your simply so-perfect too-too
> Daddy

*Please,* turn back and read this letter over! It is too packed with
considered thought to digest the first time. Like Milton—oh yeah!

---

[3] Peaches Finney, a close friend of Scottie's.

# BETTY SMITH

## 𝕏 𝕏

*A young girl overhears what her father's contemporaries think of him in* A Tree Grows in Brooklyn.

FRANCIE THOUGHT of the Union Headquarters. One time she had gone there to bring him an apron and carfare to go to a job. She saw him sitting with some men. He wore his tuxedo all the time. It was the only suit he had. His black derby was cocked jauntily and he was smoking a cigar. He took his hat off and threw the cigar away when he saw Francie come in.

"My daughter," he said proudly. The waiters looked at the thin child in her ragged dress and then exchanged glances. They were different from Johnny Nolan. They had regular waiter jobs during the week and picked up extra money on Saturday night jobs. Johnny had no regular job. He worked at one-night places here and there.

"I want to tell you fellows," he said, "that I got a couple of fine children home and a pretty wife. And I want to tell you that I'm not good enough for them."

"Take it easy," said a friend and patted him on the shoulder.

Francie overheard two men outside the group talking about her father. The short man said,

"I want you to hear this fellow talk about his wife and his kids. It's rich. He's a funny duck. He brings his wages home to his wife but keeps his tips for booze. He's got a funny arrangement at McGarrity's. He turns all his tips over to him and McGarrity supplies him with drinks. He don't know whether McGarrity owes him money or whether he owes McGarrity. The system must work out pretty good for him, though. He's always carrying a load." The men walked away.

There was a pain around Francie's heart but when she saw how the men standing around her father liked him, how they smiled and laughed at what he said and how eagerly they listened to him, the pain lessened. Those two men were exceptions. She knew that everyone loved her father.

Yes, everyone loved Johnny Nolan. He was a sweet singer of sweet songs. Since the beginning of time, everyone, especially the Irish, had loved and cared for the singer in their midst. His brother waiters really loved him. The men he worked for loved him. His wife and children loved him. He was still gay and young and handsome. His wife had not turned bitter against him and his children did not know that they were supposed to be ashamed of him.

# COLETTE

愛 愛

*A gay and teasing father who scandalized a neighbor is recalled in "Father and Madame Bruneau" from* My Mother's House.

NINE O'CLOCK; summer; a garden looking larger in the evening shadows; rest before sleep. Hurried steps on the gravel from the terrace to the pump, from the pump to the kitchen. Sitting close to the ground upon an uncomfortable little foot-stool, I rest my head, as I do every evening, against my mother's knees, and guess with my eyes closed; 'That's Morin's heavy step, on his way back from watering the tomatoes. That's Mélie emptying the potato parings. A little high-heeled step: here's Madame Bruneau come to have a chat with Mother.'

A charming voice reaches me from above:

"Minet-Chéri, what about saying good evening nicely to Madame Bruneau?"

"She's half asleep, the little darling, let her be."

"Minet-Chéri, if you really are asleep you'd better go to bed."

"Not just yet, mother, not till a little later! I'm not a bit sleepy."

A slender hand strokes my hair and pinches my ear. How dearly I love its three little hard lumps caused by the rake, the secateur and the dibble.

"Of course not, children of eight are never sleepy."

In failing light I remain leaning against my mother's knees. Wide awake, I close my useless eyes. The linen frock under my cheek smells of household soap, of the wax that is used to polish the iron, and of violets. If I move my face a little away from the fragrant gardening frock, my head plunges into a flood of scents that flows over us like an unbroken wave: the white tobacco plant opens to the night its slender scented tubes and its starlike petals. A ray of light strikes the walnut tree and wakens it; it rustles, stirred to its lowest branches by a slim shaft of moonshine, and the breeze overlays the scent of the white tobacco with the bitter, cool smell of the little worm-eaten walnuts that fall on the grass.

The ray of moonlight reaches down to the flagged terrace and there gives rise to a mellow baritone voice: my father's voice, singing "Page, Squire and Captain." Presently, no doubt, he will change to:

> *I think of thee, I see thee, I adore thee,*
> *At every moment, always, everywhere . . .*

Or perhaps, since Madame Bruneau loves melancholy music, he will give us:

> *Weary of battle, his song arose*
> *From the banks where fatal Dnieper flows.*

But this evening the voice is full of inflexions, agile and awesomely deep, as it broods over scenes of the past.

> *When the fair queen her crown and state forgot*
> *All for the love of her comely page!*

"The Captain's voice would really grace any theatre," sighs Madame Bruneau.

"If he'd only had a mind to . . ." replies my mother proudly. "He is so talented."

The rays of the rising moon fall at last on the angular silhouette of a man standing on the terrace. One hand, so white that it appears green in the moonlight, grips a bar of the railing. His crutch and stick lean against the wall, discarded. My father rests like a heron upon his one leg and sings.

"Ah!" Madame Bruneau sighs again, "every time I hear the Captain sing, I feel sad. You can have no idea what it means to lead such a life as mine. To grow old beside a husband like my poor husband. To tell myself that I shall die without ever having known love."

"Madame Bruneau," the stirring voice interrupts her, "you know that my offer still holds good?"

In the shadows I know that Madame Bruneau gives a start and I hear the shifting of her feet on the gravel.

"The wicked man! The wicked man! Captain, you will force me to run away!"

"Sixpence and a packet of tobacco," says the placid, beautiful voice, "because it is you. Sixpence and a packet of tobacco as payment for teaching you the meaning of love; d'you really think it excessive? Don't be stingy, Madame Bruneau! When my prices go up, you'll regret the present terms. Sixpence and a packet of tobacco."

I hear the scandalised exclamations of Madame Bruneau, her hurried flight, the plump, flabby little woman with greying temples, and I hear my mother's words of indulgent reproof, calling my father, as always, by our surname:

"Oh, Colette! Colette!"

My father's voice launches one more romantic couplet at the moon and gradually I cease to hear him, forgetting, as I sleep against the knees so careful of my repose, both Madame Bruneau, and the risky pleasantries that she comes here to seek on fine summer nights.

But next day, and on all the days that follow, our neighbour, Madame Bruneau, no matter how careful a watch she keeps, peering out before dashing across the road as though under a shower, will not escape her enemy, her idol.

Proudly erect upon his solitary leg, or seated and rolling a cigarette with one hand, or ambushed treacherously behind the unfolded pages of *Le Temps*, he is always there. She may run past, gathering her skirts in both hands as for a country dance, or she may creep noiselessly along by the houses, sheltering under her violet sunshade, but he will challenge her, light-hearted and attractive.

"Sixpence and a packet of tobacco!"

There are souls with an almost endless capacity for hiding their suffering and their trembling responsiveness to the lure of sin. Madame Bruneau was one of these. As long as she could, she bore with my father's scandalous suggestions and cynical glances, pretending to laugh at them. Then, one fine day, deserting her little house, and removing her furniture and her ludicrous husband, she departed to live far away from us, up in the hills, at Bel-Air.

# THEODORE C. SORENSEN

🐝 🐝

*From the book* Kennedy, *here is a side-glance at President John F. Kennedy's way with his daughter, Caroline.*

PRESIDENT KENNEDY, that intellectual, sophisticated man, considered cold by his critics and complicated by his admirers, possessed a gift for communicating with children—with his children, with my children, with all children. He never talked down to them, and they always understood him. "He talked to me," confided one aide's thirteen-year-old son to his diary, "with an air of business-like equality." At the same time he was realistically aware of how limited an adult's influence is in the small child's world. Secretary McNamara liked to tell of the time he saw the President accost Caroline in the midst of the Cuban crisis just before her supper hour. "Caroline," he said, "have you been eating candy?" She ignored him. The question was repeated and it was again ignored. Finally, summoning up his full dignity as

Commander in Chief, he asked his daughter, "Caroline, answer me. Have you been eating candy—yes, no or maybe?"

## PHYLLIS McGINLEY

*A lyrical comment on fathers and daughters comes from* Times Three.

### "First Lesson"

THE THING TO REMEMBER about fathers is, they're men.
A girl has to keep it in mind.
They are dragon-seekers, bent on improbable rescues.
Scratch any father, you find
Someone chock-full of qualms and romantic terrors,
Believing change is a threat—
Like your first shoes with heels on, like your first bicycle
It took such months to get.

Walk in strange woods, they warn you about the snakes there.
Climb, and they fear you'll fall.
Books, angular boys, or swimming in deep water—
Fathers mistrust them all.
Men are the worriers. It is difficult for them
To learn what they must learn:
How you have a journey to take and very likely,
For a while, will not return.

# Mothers and Sons

# J. M. BARRIE

茉 茉

*A touching tribute to this author's mother is found in* Margaret Ogilvy: *"How My Mother Got Her Soft Face."*

ON THE DAY I WAS BORN we bought six hair-bottomed chairs, and in our little house it was an event, the first great victory in a woman's long campaign; how they had been laboured for, the pound-note and the thirty threepenny bits they cost, what anxiety there was about the purchase, the show they made in possession of the west room, my father's unnatural coolness when he brought them in (but his face was white)—I so often heard the tale afterwards, and shared as boy and man in so many similar triumphs, that the coming of the chairs seems to be something I remember, as if I had jumped out of bed on that first day, and run ben to see how they looked. I am sure my mother's feet were ettling to be ben long before they could be trusted, and that the moment after she was left alone with me she was discovered barefooted in the west room, doctoring a scar (which she had been the first to detect) on one of the chairs, or sitting on them regally or withdrawing and re-opening the door suddenly to take the six by surprise. And then, I think, a shawl was flung over her (it is strange to me to think it was not I who ran after her with the shawl), and she was escorted sternly back to bed and reminded that she had promised not to budge, to which her reply was probably that she had been gone but an instant, and the implication that therefore she had not been gone at all. Thus was one little bit of her revealed to me at once: I wonder if I took note of it. Neighbours came in to see the boy and the chairs. I wonder if she deceived me when she affected to think that there were others like us, or whether I saw through her from the first, she was so easily seen through. When she seemed to agree with them that it would be impossible to give me a college education, was I so easily taken in, or did I know already what ambitions burned behind that dear face? When they spoke of the chairs as the goal quickly reached, was I such a newcomer that her timid lips must say 'They are but a beginning' before I heard the words? And when we were left together, did I laugh at the great things that were in her mind, or had she to whisper them to me first, and then did I put my arm round her and tell her that I would help? Thus it was for such a long time: it is strange to me to feel that it was not so from the beginning.

It is all guess-work for six years, and she whom I see in them is the woman who came suddenly into view when they were at an end. Her timid lips I have said, but they were not timid then, and when I knew her the timid lips had come. The soft face—they say the face was not so soft then. The shawl that was flung over her—we had not begun to hunt her with a shawl, nor to make our bodies a screen between her and the draughts, nor to creep into her room a score of times in the night to stand looking at her as she slept. We did not see her becoming little then, nor sharply turn our heads when she said wonderingly how small her arms had grown. In her happiest moments—and never was a happier woman—her mouth did not of a sudden begin to twitch, and tears to lie on the mute blue eyes in which I have read all I know and would ever care to write. For when you looked into my mother's eyes you knew, as if He had told you, why God sent her into the world—it was to open the minds of all who looked to beautiful thoughts. And that is the beginning and end of literature. Those eyes that I cannot see until I was six years old have guided me through life, and I pray God they may remain my only earthly judge to the last. They were never more my guide than when I helped to put her to earth, not whimpering because my mother had been taken away after seventy-six glorious years of life, but exulting in her even at the grave.

She had a son who was far away at school. I remember very little about him, only that he was a merry-faced boy who ran like a squirrel up a tree and shook the cherries into my lap. When he was thirteen and I was half his age the terrible news came, and I have been told the face of my mother was awful in its calmness as she set off to get between Death and her boy. We trooped with her down the brae to the wooden station, and I think I was envying her the journey in the mysterious waggons; I know we played around her, proud of our right to be there, but I do not recall it, only speak from hearsay. Her ticket was taken, she had bidden us good-bye with that fighting face which I cannot see, and then my father came out of the telegraph-office and said huskily 'He's gone!' Then we turned very quietly and went home again up the little brae. But I speak from hearsay no longer; I know my mother for ever now.

That is how she got her soft face and her pathetic ways and her large charity, and why other mothers ran to her when they had lost a child. 'Dinna greet, poor Janet,' she would say to them, and they would answer, 'Ah, Margaret, but you're greeting yoursel.' Margaret Ogilvy had been her maiden name, and after the Scotch custom she was still Margaret Ogilvy to her old friends. Margaret Ogilvy I loved to name her. Often when I was a boy, 'Margaret Ogilvy, are you there?' I would call up the stair.

She was always delicate from that hour, and for many months she was very ill. I have heard that the first thing she expressed a wish to see was the christening robe, and she looked long at it and then turned her face to the wall. That was what made me as a boy think of it always as the robe in which he was christened, but I knew later that we had all been christened in it, from the oldest of the family to the youngest, between whom stood twenty years. Hundreds of other children were christened in it also, such robes being then a rare possession, and the lending of ours among my mother's glories. It was carried carefully from house to house, as if it were itself a child; my mother made much of it, smoothed it out, petted it, smiled to it before putting it into the arms of those to whom it was being lent; she was in our pew to see it borne magnificently (something inside it now) down the aisle to the pulpit side, when a stir of expectancy went through the church and we kicked each other's feet beneath the book-board but were reverent in the face; and however the child might behave, laughing brazenly or skirling to its mother's shame, and whatever the father as he held it up might do, look doited probably and bow at the wrong time, the christening robe of long experience helped them through. And when it was brought back to her she took it in her arms as softly as if it might be asleep, and unconsciously pressed it to her breast: there was never anything in the house that spoke to her quite so eloquently as that little white robe; it was one of her children that always remained a baby. And she had not made it herself, which was the most wonderful thing about it to me, for she seemed to have made all other things. All the clothes in the house were of her making, and you don't know her in the least if you think they were out of the fashion; she turned them and made them new again, she beat them and made them new again, and then she coaxed them into being new again just for the last time, she let them out and took them in and put on new braid, and added a piece up the back, and thus they passed from one member of the family to another until they reached the youngest, and even when we were done with them they re-appeared as something else. In the fashion! I must come back to this. Never was a woman with such an eye for it. She had no fashion-plates; she did not need them. The minister's wife (a cloak), the banker's daughters (the new sleeve)—they had but to pass our window once, and the scalp, so to speak, was in my mother's hands. Observe her rushing, scissors in hand, thread in mouth, to the drawers where her daughters' Sabbath clothes were kept. Or go to church next Sunday, and watch a certain family filing in, the boy lifting his legs high to show off his new boots, but all the others demure, especially the timid, unobservant looking little woman in the rear of them. If you were the minister's wife that day or the banker's daughters you would have got a shock. But she bought the christening robe, and when I used to ask why, she would beam and look conscious, and say she wanted to be extravagant once. And she told me, still smiling, that the more a woman was given to stitching and making things for herself, the greater was her passionate desire now and again to rush to the shops and 'be foolish.' The christening robe with its pathetic frills is over half a century old now, and has begun to droop a little, like a daisy whose time is past, but it is as fondly kept together as ever: I saw it in use again only the other day.

My mother lay in bed with the christening robe beside her, and I peeped in many times at the door and then went to the stair and sat on it and sobbed. I know not if it was that first day, or many days afterwards, that there came to me my sister, the daughter my mother loved the best, yes, more I am sure even than she loved me, whose great glory she has been since I was six years old. This sister, who was then passing out of her teens, came to me with a very anxious face and wringing her hands, and she told me to go ben to my mother and say to her that she still had another boy. I went ben excitedly, but the room was dark, and when I heard the door shut and no sound come from the bed I was afraid, and I stood still. I suppose I was breathing hard, or perhaps I was crying, for after a time I heard a listless voice that had never been listless before say, 'Is that you?' I think the tone hurt me, for I made no answer, and then the voice said more anxiously, 'Is that you?' again. I thought it was the dead boy she was speaking to, and I said in a little lonely voice, 'No, it's no him, it's just me.' Then I heard a cry, and my mother turned in bed, and though it was dark I knew that she was holding out her arms.

After that I sat a great deal in her bed trying to make her forget him, which was my crafty way of playing physician, and if I saw any one out of doors do something that made the others laugh I immediately hastened to that dark room and did it before her. I suppose I was an odd little figure; I have been told that my anxiety to brighten her gave my face a strained look and put a tremor into the joke (I would stand on my head in the bed, my feet against the wall, and then cry excitedly, 'Are you laughing, mother?')— and perhaps what made her laugh was something I was unconscious of, but she did laugh suddenly now and then, whereupon I screamed exultantly to that dear sister, who was ever in waiting, to come and see the sight, but by the time she came the soft face was wet again. Thus I was deprived of some of my glory, and I remember once only making her laugh before witnesses. I kept a record of her laughs on a piece of paper, a stroke for each, and it was my custom to show this proudly to the doctor every morning. There were five strokes the first time I slipped it into his hand, and when their meaning was explained to him, he laughed so boisterously that I cried, 'I wish that was one of hers!' Then he was sympathetic, and asked me if my mother had seen the paper yet, and when I shook my head he said that if I showed it to her now and told her that these were her five laughs he thought I might win another. I had less confidence, but he was the mysterious man whom you ran for in the dead of night (you flung sand at his window to waken him, and if it was only toothache he extracted the tooth through the open window, but when it was something sterner he was with you in the dark square at once, like a man who slept in his topcoat), so I did as he bade me, and not only did she laugh then but again when I put the laugh down, so that though it was really one laugh with a tear in the middle I counted it as two.

It was doubtless that same sister who told me not to sulk when my mother lay thinking of him, but to try instead to get her to talk about him. I did not see how this could make her the merry mother she used to be, but I was told that if I could not do it nobody could, and this made me eager to begin. At first, they say, I was often jealous, stopping her fond memories with the cry, 'Do you mind nothing about me?' but that did not last; its place was taken by an intense desire (again, I think, my sister must have breathed it into life) to become so like him that even my mother should not see the difference, and many and artful were the questions I put to that end. Then I practised in secret, but after a whole week had passed I was still rather like myself. He had such a cheery way of whistling, she had told me, it had always brightened her at her work to hear him whistling, and when he whistled he stood with his legs apart, and his hands in the pockets of his knickerbockers. I decided to trust to this, so one day after I had learned his whistle (every boy of enterprise invents a whistle of his own) from boys who had been his comrades, I secretly put on a suit of his clothes, dark grey they were, with little spots, and they fitted me many years afterwards, and thus disguised I slipped, unknown to the others, into my mother's room. Quaking, I doubt not, yet so pleased, I stood still until she saw me, and then—how it must have hurt her! 'Listen!' I cried in a glow of triumph, and I stretched my legs wide apart and plunged my hands into the pockets of my knickerbockers, and began to whistle.

She lived twenty-nine years after his death, such active years until toward the end, that you never knew where she was unless you took hold of her, and though she was frail henceforth and ever growing frailer, her housekeeping again became famous, so that brides called as a matter of course to watch her ca'ming and sanding and stitching: there are old people still, one or two, to tell with wonder in their eyes how she could bake twenty-four bannocks in the hour, and not a chip in one of them. And how many she gave away, how much she gave away of all she had, and what pretty ways she had of giving it! Her face beamed and rippled with mirth as before, and her laugh, that I had tried so hard to force, came running home again. I have heard no such laugh as hers save from merry children; the laughter of most of us ages, and wears out with the body, but hers remained gleeful to the last, as if it were born afresh every morning. There was always something of the child in her, and her laugh was its voice, as eloquent of the past to me as was the christening robe to her. But I I had not made her forget the bit of her that was dead; in those nine and twenty years he was not removed one day farther from her. Many a time she fell asleep speaking to him, and even while she slept her lips moved and she smiled as if he had come back to her, and when she woke he might vanish so suddenly that she started up bewildered and looked about her, and then said slowly, 'My David's dead!' or perhaps he remained long enough to whisper why he must leave her now, and then she lay silent with filmy eyes. When I became a man and he was still a boy of thirteen, I wrote a little paper called 'Dead this Twenty Years,' which was about a similar tragedy in another woman's life, and it is the only thing I have written that she never spoke about, not even to that daughter she loved the best. No one ever spoke of it to her, or asked her if she had read it: one does not ask a mother if she knows that there is a little coffin in the house. She read many times the book in which it is printed, but when she came to that chapter she would put her hands to her heart or even over her ears.

# ARNOLD BENNETT

❦ ❦

*In* The Old Wives' Tale *Arnold Bennett describes how*
*a son's achievement may result in conflicting emotions*
*for a mother.*

"WELL, MATER," he said, in a voice of factitious calm, "I've
got it." He was looking up at the ceiling.

"Got what?"

"The National Scholarship. Swynnerton says it's a sheer fluke.
But I've got it. Great glory for the Bursley School of Art!"

"National Scholarship?" she said. "What's that? What is it?"

"Now, mother!" he admonished her, not without testiness.
"Don't go and say I've never breathed a word about it!"

He lit a cigarette, to cover his self-consciousness, for he perceived that she was moved far beyond the ordinary.

Never, in fact, not even by the death of her husband, had she
received such a frightful blow as that which the dreamy Cyril had
just dealt her.

It was not a complete surprise, but it was nearly a complete
surprise. A few months previously he certainly had mentioned in
his incidental way, the subject of a National Scholarship. Apropos
of a drinking-cup which he had designed, he had said that the
director of the School of Art had suggested that it was good
enough to compete for the National, and that as he was otherwise
qualified for the competition he might as well send the cup to
South Kensington. He had added that Peel-Swynnerton had
laughed at the notion as absurd. On that occasion she had
comprehended that a National Scholarship involved residence in
London. She ought to have begun to live in fear, for Cyril had a
most disturbing habit of making a mere momentary reference to
matters which he deemed very important and which occupied a

large share of his attention. He was secretive by nature, and the rigidity of his father's rule had developed this trait in his character. But really he had spoken of the competition with such an extreme casualness that with little effort she had dismissed it from her anxieties as involving a contingency so remote as to be negligible. She had, genuinely, almost forgotten it. Only at rare intervals had it wakened in her a dull transitory pain—like the herald of a fatal malady. And, as a woman in the opening stage of disease, she had hastily reassured herself: "how silly of me! This can't possibly be anything serious!"

And now she was condemned. She knew it. She knew there could be no appeal. She knew that she might as usefully have besought mercy from a tiger as from her good, industrious, dreamy son.

"It means a pound a week," said Cyril, his self-consciousness intensified by her silence and by the dreadful look on her face. "And of course free tuition."

"For how long?" she managed to say.

"Well," said he, "that depends. Nominally for a year. But if you behave yourself it's always continued for three years."

If he stayed for three years he would never come back: that was a certainty.

How she rebelled, furious and despairing, against the fortuitous cruelty of things! She was sure that he had not, till then, thought seriously of going to London. But the fact that the Government would admit him free to its classrooms and give him a pound a week besides, somehow forced him to go to London. It was not the lack of means that would have prevented him from going. Why, then, should the presence of means induce him to go? There was no logical reason. The whole affair was disastrously absurd. The art-master at the Wedgwood Institution had chanced, merely chanced, to suggest that the drinking-cup should be sent to South Kensington. And the result of this caprice was that she was sentenced to solitude for life! It was too monstrously, too incredibly wicked!

With what futile and bitter execration she murmured in her heart the word 'If.' If Cyril's childish predilections had not been encouraged! If he had only been content to follow his father's trade! If she had flatly refused to sign his indenture at Peel's and pay the premium! If he had not turned from colour to clay! If the art-master had not had that fatal 'idea'! If the judges for the competition had decided otherwise! If only she had brought Cyril up in habits of obedience, sacrificing temporary peace to permanent security!

For after all he could not abandon her without her consent. He was not of age. And he would want a lot more money, which he could obtain from none but her. She could refuse. . . . No! She could not refuse. He was the master, the tyrant. For the sake of daily pleasantness she had weakly yielded to him at the start! She had behaved badly to herself and to him. He was spoiled. She had spoiled him. And he was about to repay her with lifelong misery, and nothing would deflect him from his course. The usual conduct of the spoilt child! Had she not witnessed it, and moralized upon it, in other families?

"You don't seem very chirpy over it, mater!" he said.

She went out of the room. His joy in the prospect of departure from the Five Towns, from her, though he masked it, was more manifest than she could bear.

The *Signal*, the next day, made a special item of the news. It appeared that no National Scholarship had been won in the Five Towns for eleven years. The citizens were exhorted to remember that Mr. Povey had gained his success in open competition with the cleverest young students of the entire kingdom—and in a branch of art which he had but recently taken up; and further, that the Government offered only eight scholarships each year. The name of Cyril Povey passed from lip to lip. And nobody who met Constance, in street or shop, could refrain from informing her that she ought to be a proud mother, to have such a son, but that truly they were not surprised . . . and how proud his poor father would have been! A few sympathetically hinted that maternal pride was one of those luxuries that may cost too dear.

# ALICE HEGAN RICE

※ ※

*Mrs. Wiggs of the Cabbage Patch, a novel that touched many tender hearts at the beginning of the twentieth century, describes a son's efforts to help his mother in her struggle with poverty.*

## "Ways and Means"

"Ah! well may the children weep before you!
   They are weary ere they run;
They have never seen the sunshine, nor the glory
   Which is brighter than the sun."

THE COLD WAVE that was ushered in that December morning was the beginning of a long series of days that vied with each other as to which could induce the mercury to drop the lowest. The descent of the temperature seemed to have a like effect on the barrel of potatoes and the load of coal in the Wiggses' parlor.

Mrs. Wiggs's untiring efforts to find employment had met with no success, and Jim's exertions were redoubled; day by day his scanty earnings became less sufficient to meet the demands of the family.

On Christmas eve they sat over the stove, after the little ones had gone to bed, and discussed the situation. The wind hurled itself against the house in a very frenzy of rage, shaking the icicles from the window-ledge and hissing through the patched panes. The snow that sifted in through the loose sash lay unmelted on the sill. Jim had a piece of old carpet about him, and coughed with almost every breath. Mrs. Wiggs's head was in her hands, and the tears that trickled through her crooked fingers hissed as they fell on the stove. It was the first time Jim had ever seen her give up.

"Seems like we'll have to ast fer help, Jim" she said. "I can't ast fer credit at Mr. Bagby's; seems like I'd never have the courage to pull agin a debt. What do you think? I guess—it looks like mebbe we'll have to apply to the organization."

Jim's eyes flashed. "Not yet, ma!" he said, firmly. "It 'ud be with us like it was with the Hornbys; they didn't have nothin' to eat, and they went to the organization an' the man asted 'em if they had a bed or a table, an' when they said yes, he said, 'Well, why don't you sell 'em?' No, ma! As long as we've got coal I'll get the vittles some way!" He had to pause, for a violent attack of coughing shook him from head to foot. "I think I can git a night job next week; one of the market-men comes in from the country ever' night to git a early start nex' mornin', an' he ast me if I'd sleep in his wagon from three to six an' keep his vegetables from bein' stole. That 'ud gimme time to git home an' git breakfast, an' be down to the fact'ry by seven."

"But, Jimmy boy," cried his mother, her voice quivering with anxiety, "you never could stan' it night an' day too! No, I'll watch the wagon; I'll—"

A knock on the parlor door interrupted her. She hastily dried her eyes and smoothed her hair. Jim went to the door.

"I've a Christmas basket for you!" cried a cheery voice.

"Is this Christmas?" Jim asked dully.

The girl in the doorway laughed. She was tall and slender, but Jim could only see a pair of sparkling eyes between the brim of the hat and her high fur collar. It was nice to hear her laugh, though; it made things seem warmer somehow. The colored man behind her deposited a large basket on the doorstep.

"It's from the church," she explained; "a crowd of us are out in the omnibus distributing baskets."

"Well, how'd you ever happen to come here?" cried Mrs. Wiggs, who had come to the door.

"There is one for each of the mission-school families; just a little Christmas greeting, you know."

Mrs. Wiggs's spirits were rising every minute. "Well, that certainly is kind an' thoughtful like," she said. "Won't you—" she hesitated; the room she had just left was not in a condition to receive guests, but Mrs. Wiggs was a Kentuckian. "Come right in an' git warm," she said cordially; "the stove's died down some, but you could git thawed out."

"No, thank you, I can't come in," said the young lady, with a side glance at Jim, who was leaning against the door. "Have you plenty of coal?" she asked, in an undertone.

"Oh, yes'm, thank you," said Mrs. Wiggs, smiling reassuringly. Her tone might have been less confident, but for Jim's warning glance. Every fiber of his sensitive nature shrank from asking help.

The girl was puzzled; she noticed the stamp of poverty on everything in sight except the bright face of the little woman before her.

"Well," she said doubtfully, "if you ever want—to come to see me, ask for Miss Lucy Olcott at Terrace Park. Good night, and a happy Christmas!"

She was gone, and the doorway looked very black and lonesome in consequence. But there was the big basket to prove she was not merely an apparition, and it took both Jim and his mother to carry it in. Sitting on the floor, they unpacked it. There were vegetables, oatmeal, fruit, and even tea and coffee. But the surprise was at the very bottom! A big turkey, looking so comical with his legs stuck in his body that Jim laughed outright.

"It's the first turkey that's been in this house fer many a day!" said Mrs. Wiggs, delightedly, as she pinched the fat fowl. "I 'spect Europena'll be skeered of it, it's so big. My, but we'll have a good dinner to-morrow. I'll git Miss Hazy an' Chris to come over an' spend the day, and I'll carry a plate over to Mrs. Schultz, an' take a little o' this here tea to ole Mrs. Lawson."

The cloud had turned inside out for Mrs. Wiggs, and only the silver lining was visible. Jim was doing a sum on the brown paper that came over the basket, and presently he looked up and said slowly:

"Ma, I guess we can't have the turkey this year. I kin sell it fer a dollar seventy-five, and that would buy us hogmeat fer a good while."

Mrs. Wiggs's face fell, and she twisted her apron-string in silence. She had pictured the joy of a real Christmas dinner, the first the youngest children had ever known; she had already thought of half a dozen neighbors to whom she wanted to send "a little snack." But one look at Jim's anxious face recalled their circumstances.

"Of course we'll sell it," she said brightly. "You have got the longest head fer a boy! We'll sell it in the mornin', an' buy sausage fer dinner, an' I'll cook some of these here nice vegetables an' put a orange an' some candy at each plate, an' the children'll never know nothin' 'bout it. Besides," she added, "if you ain't never et turkey meat you don't know how good it is."

But in spite of her philosophy, after Jim had gone to bed she slipped over and took one more look at the turkey.

"I think I wouldn't 'a' minded so much," she said, wistfully, "ef they hadn't 'a' sent the cramberries, too!"

For ten days the basket of provisions and the extra money made by Jim's night work and Mrs. Wiggs's washing supplied the demands of the family; but by the end of January the clouds had gathered thicker than before.

Mrs. Wiggs's heart was heavy, one night, as she tramped home through the snow after a hard day's work. The rent was due, the coal was out, and only a few potatoes were left in the barrel. But these were mere shadow troubles, compared to Jim's illness; he had been too sick to go to the factory that morning, and she dared not think what changes the day may have brought. As she lifted the latch of her rickety door the sobbing of a child greeted her; it was little Europena, crying for food. For three days there had been no bread in the house, and a scanty supply of potatoes and beans had been their only nourishment.

Mrs. Wiggs hastened to where Jim lay on a cot in the corner; his cheeks were flushed, and his thin, nervous fingers picked at the old shawl that covered him.

"Jim," she said, kneeling beside him and pressing his hot hand to her cheek, "Jim, darlin', lemme go fer the doctor. You're worser than you was this mornin', an'—an'—I'm so skeered!" Her voice broke in a sob.

Jim tried to put his arm around her, but something hurt him in his chest when he moved, so he patted her hand instead.

"Never mind, ma," he said, his breath coming short; "we ain't got no money to buy the medicine, even if the doctor did come. You go git some supper, now; an', ma, don't worry; I'm goin' to take keer of you all! Only—only," he added, wearily, "I guess I can't sleep in the wagon to-night."

Slowly the hours passed until midnight. Mrs. Wiggs had pulled Jim's cot close to the stove, and applied vigorous measures to relieve him. Her efforts were unceasing, and one after another the homely country remedies were faithfully administered. At twelve o'clock he grew restless.

"Seems like I'm hot, then agin I'm cold," he said, speaking with difficulty. "Could you find a little somethin' more to put over me, ma?"

Mrs. Wiggs got up and went toward the bed. The three little girls lay huddled under one old quilt, their faces pale and sunken. She turned away abruptly, and looked toward the corner where Billy slept on a pallet. The blankets on his bed were insufficient even for him. She put her hands over her face, and for a moment dry sobs convulsed her. The hardest grief is often that which leaves no trace. When she went back to the stove she had a smile ready for the sick boy.

"Here's the very thing," she said; "it's my dress skirt. I don't need it a mite, settin' up here so clost to the fire. See how nice it tucks in all round!"

For a while he lay silent, then he said: "Ma, are you 'wake?"

"Yes, Jim."

"Well, I bin thinkin' it over. If I ain't better in the mornin', I guess—" the words came reluctantly— "I guess you'd better go see the Christmas lady. I wouldn't mind her knowin' so much. 'T won't be fer long, nohow, cause I kin take keer of you all soon—soon's I kin git up."

The talking brought on severe coughing, and he sank back exhausted.

"Can't you go to sleep, honey?" asked his mother.

"No, it's them ole wheels," he said fretfully, "them wheels at the fact'ry; when I git to sleep they keep on wakin' me up."

Mrs. Wiggs's hands were rough and knotted, but love taught them to be gentle as she smoothed his hot head.

"Want me to tell you 'bout the country, Jim?" she asked.

Since he was a little boy he had loved to hear of their old home in the valley. His dim recollection of it all formed his one conception of heaven.

"Yes, ma; mebbe it will make me fergit the wheels," he said.

"Well," she began, putting her head beside his on the pillow, so he could not watch her face, "it was all jes' like a big front yard without no fences, an' the flowers didn't belong to folks like they do over on the avenue, where you dassent pick a one; but they was God's, an' you was welcome to all you could pull. An' there was trees, Jim, where you could climb up an' git big red apples, an' when the frost 'ud come they'd be persimmons that 'ud jes' melt in yer mouth. An' you could look 'way off 'crost the meaders, an' see the trees a-wavin' in the sunshine, an' up over yer head the birds 'ud be singin' like they was never goin' to stop. An' yer pa an' me 'ud take you out at the harvestin' time, an' you 'ud play on the hay-stacks. I kin remember jes' how you looked, Jim— a fat little boy, with red cheeks a-laughin' all the time."

Mrs. Wiggs could tell no more, for the old memories were too much for her. Jim scarcely knew when she stopped; his eyes were half closed, and a sweet drowsiness was upon him.

"It's nice an' warm in the sunshine," he murmured; "the meaders an' trees—laughin' all the time! Birds singin', singin', singin'."

Then Jim began to sing too, softly and monotonously, and the sorrow that had not come with years left his tired face, and he fearlessly drifted away into the Shadowy Valley where his lost childhood lay.

# MARCEL PROUST

※ ※

*In* Swann's Way, *from his novel sequence* Remembrance of Things Past, *Proust explores the emotions of a little boy obsessed with the need for his mother's good-night kiss.*

I NEVER TOOK MY EYES off my mother, I knew that when they were at table I should not be permitted to stay there for the whole

of dinner-time, and that Mamma, for fear of annoying my
father, would not allow me to give her in public the series of
kisses that she would have had in my room. And so I promised
myself that in the dining-room, as they began to eat and drink
and as I felt the hour approach, I would put beforehand into
this kiss, which was bound to be so brief and stealthy in execution, everything my own efforts could put into it; would look
out very carefully first the exact spot on her cheek where I
would imprint it, and would so prepare my thoughts that I might
be able, thanks to these mental preliminaries, to consecrate the
whole of the minute Mamma would allow me to the sensation
of her cheek against my lips, as a painter who can have his subject for short sittings only prepares his palette, and from what
he remembers and from rough notes does in advance everything
which he possibly can do in the sitter's absence. But tonight,
before the dinner-bell had sounded, my grandfather said with
unconscious cruelty: "The little man looks tired; he'd better go
up to bed. Besides, we are dining late to-night."

And my father, who was less scrupulous than my grandmother
or mother in observing the letter of a treaty, went on: "Yes; run
along; to bed with you."

I would have kissed Mamma then and there, but at that
moment the dinner-bell rang.

"No, no, leave your mother alone. You've said good night quite
enough. These exhibitions are absurd. Go on upstairs."

And so I must set forth without viaticum; must climb each step
of the staircase 'against my heart,' as the saying is, climbing in
opposition to my heart's desire, which was to return to my mother,
since she had not, by her kiss, given my heart leave to accompany
me forth. That hateful staircase, up which I always passed with
such dismay, gave out a smell of varnish which had to some extent
absorbed, made definite and fixed the special quality of sorrow
that I felt each evening, and made it perhaps even more cruel to
my sensibility because, when it assumed this olfactory guise, my
intellect was powerless to resist it. When we have gone to sleep
with a maddening toothache and are conscious of it only as a little
girl whom we attempt, time after time, to pull out of the water, or
as a line of Molière which we repeat incessantly to ourselves, it is
a great relief to wake up, so that our intelligence can disentangle

the idea of toothache from any artificial semblance of heroism or rhythmic cadence. It was the precise converse of this relief which I felt when my anguish at having to go up to my room invaded my consciousness in a manner infinitely more rapid, instantaneous almost, a manner at once insidious and brutal as I breathed in—a far more poisonous thing than any moral penetration—the peculiar smell of varnish upon that staircase.

Once in my room I had to stop every loophole, to close the shutters, to dig my own grave as I turned down the bedclothes, to wrap myself in the shroud of my nightshirt. But before burying myself in the iron bed which had been placed there because, on summer nights, I was too hot among the rep curtains of the four-poster, I was stirred to revolt, and attempted the desperate stratagem of a condemned prisoner. I wrote to my mother begging her to come upstairs for an important reason which I could not put in writing. My fear was that Françoise, my aunt's cook who used to be put in charge of me when I was at Combray, might refuse to take my note. I had a suspicion that, in her eyes, to carry a message to my mother when there was a stranger in the room would appear flatly inconceivable, just as it would be for the doorkeeper of a theatre to hand a letter to an actor upon the stage. For things which might or might not be done she possessed a code at once imperious, abundant, subtle, and uncompromising on points themselves imperceptible or irrelevant, which gave it a resemblance to those ancient laws which combine such cruel ordinances as the massacre of infants at the breast with prohibitions, of exaggerated refinement, against "seething the kid in his mother's milk," or "eating of the sinew which is upon the hollow of the thigh." This code, if one could judge it by the sudden obstinacy which she would put into her refusal to carry out certain of our instructions, seemed to have foreseen such social complications and refinements of fashion as nothing in Françoise's surroundings or in her career as a servant in a village household could have put into her head; and we were obliged to assume that there was latent in her some past existence in the ancient history of France, noble and little understood, just as there is in those manufacturing towns where old mansions still testify to their former courtly days, and chemical workers toil among delicately sculptured scenes of the Miracle of Theophilus or the Quatre Fils Aymon.

In this particular instance, the article of her code which made it highly improbable that—barring an outbreak of fire—Françoise would go down and disturb Mamma when M. Swann was there for so unimportant a person as myself was one embodying the respect she shewed not only for the family (as for the dead, for the clergy, or for royalty), but also for the stranger within our gates; a respect which I should perhaps have found touching in a book, but which never failed to irritate me on her lips, because of the solemn and gentle tones in which she would utter it, and which irritated me more than usual this evening when the sacred character in which she invested the dinner-party might have the effect of making her decline to disturb its ceremonial. But to give myself one chance of success I lied without hesitation, telling her that it was not in the least myself who had to write to Mamma, but Mamma who, on saying good night to me, had begged me not to forget to send her an answer about something she had asked me to find, and that she would certainly be very angry if this note were not taken to her. I think that Françoise disbelieved me, for, like those primitive men whose senses were so much keener than our own, she would immediately detect, by signs imperceptible by the rest of us, the truth or falsehood of anything that we might wish to conceal from her. She studied the envelope for five minutes as though an examination of the paper itself and the look of my handwriting could enlighten her as to the nature of the contents, or tell her to which article of her code she ought to refer the matter. Then she went out with an air of resignation which seemed to imply: "What a dreadful thing for parents to have a child like this!"

A moment later she returned to say that they were still at the ice stage and that it was impossible for the butler to deliver the note at once, in front of everybody; but that when the finger-bowls were put round he would find a way of slipping it into Mamma's hand. At once my anxiety subsided; it was now no longer (as it had been a moment ago) until to-morrow that I had lost my mother, for my little line was going—to annoy her, no doubt, and doubly so because this contrivance would make me ridiculous in Swann's eyes—but was going all the same to admit me, invisibly and by stealth, into the same room as herself, was going to whisper from me into her ear; for that forbidden and unfriendly dining-room, where but a moment ago the ice itself—with burned nuts in it—and the finger-bowls seemed to me to be concealing pleasures that were mischievous and of a mortal sadness because Mamma was tasting of them and I was far away, had opened its doors to me and, like a ripe fruit which bursts through its skin, was going to pour out into my intoxicated heart the gushing sweetness of Mamma's attention while she was reading what I had written. Now I was no longer separated from her; the barriers were down; an exquisite thread was binding us. Besides, that was not all, for surely Mamma would come.

As for the agony through which I had just passed, I imagined that Swann would have laughed heartily at it if he had read my letter and had guessed its purpose; whereas, on the contrary, as I was to learn in due course, a similar anguish had been the bane of his life for many years, and no one perhaps could have understood my feelings at that moment so well as himself; to him, that anguish came through Love, to which it is in a sense predestined, by which it must be equipped and adapted; but when, as had befallen me, such an anguish possesses one's soul before Love has yet entered into one's life, then it must drift, awaiting Love's coming, vague and free, without precise attachment, at the disposal of one sentiment to-day, of another to-morrow, of filial piety or affection for a comrade. And the joy with which I first bound myself apprentice, when Françoise returned to tell me that my letter would be delivered, Swann, too, had known well that false joy which a friend can give us, or some relative of the woman we love, when on his arrival at the house or the theatre where she is to be found, for some ball or party or 'first-night' at which he is to meet her, he sees us wandering outside, desperately awaiting some opportunity of communicating with her. He recognises us, greets us familiarly, and asks what we are doing there. And when we invent a story of having some urgent message to give to his relative or friend, he assures us that nothing could be more simple, takes us in at the door, and promises to send her down to us in five minutes. How much we love him—as at that moment I loved Françoise—the good-natured intermediary who by a single word has made supportable, human, almost propitious the inconceivable, infernal scene of gaiety in the thick of which we had been imagining swarms of enemies, perverse and seductive, beguiling away from us, even making laugh at us, the woman whom we love. If we are to judge of them by him, this relative who has accosted us and who is himself an initiate in those cruel mysteries, then the other guests cannot be so very demoniacal. Those inaccessible and torturing hours into which she had gone to taste of unknown pleasures—behold, a breach in the wall, and we are through it. Behold, one of the moments whose series will go to make up their sum, a moment as genuine as the rest, if not actually more important to ourself because our mistress is more intensely a part of it; we picture it to ourselves, we possess it, we intervene upon it, almost we have created it: namely, the moment in which he goes to tell her that we are waiting there below. And very probably the other moments of the party will not be essentially different, will contain nothing else so exquisite or so well able to make us suffer, since this kind friend has assured us that "Of course, she will be delighted to come down! It will be far more amusing for her to talk to you than to be bored up there." Alas! Swann had learned by experience that the good intentions of a third party are powerless to control a woman who is annoyed to find herself pursued even into a ball-room by a man whom she does not love. Too often, the kind friend comes down again alone.

My mother did not appear, but with no attempt to safe-guard my self-respect (which depended upon her keeping up the fiction that she had asked me to let her know the result of my search for something or other) made Françoise tell me, in so many words "There is no answer"—words I have so often, since then, heard hall-porters in 'mansions' and the flunkeys in gambling-clubs and the like repeat to some poor girl, who replies in bewilderment: "What! he's said nothing? It's not possible. You did give him my letter, didn't you? Very well, I shall wait a little longer." And just as she invariably protests that she does not need the extra gas which the porter offers to light for her, and sits on there, hearing nothing further, except an occasional remark on the weather which the porter exchanges with a messenger whom he will send off suddenly, when he notices the time, to put some customer's wine on the ice; so, having declined Françoise's offer to make me some tea or to stay beside me, I let her go off again to the servants' hall, and lay down and shut my eyes, and tried not to hear the voices of my family who were drinking their coffee in the garden.

But after a few seconds I realised that, by writing that line to Mamma, by approaching—at the risk of making her angry—so near to her that I felt I could reach out and grasp the moment in which I should see her again, I had cut myself off from the possibility of going to sleep until I actually had seen her, and my heart began to beat more and more painfully as I increased my agitation by ordering myself to keep calm and to acquiesce to my ill-fortune. Then, suddenly, my anxiety subsided, a feeling of intense happiness coursed through me, as when a strong medicine begins to take effect and one's pain vanishes: I had formed a resolution to abandon all attempts to go to sleep without seeing Mamma and had decided to kiss her at all costs, even with the certainty of being in disgrace with her for long afterwards, when she herself came up to bed. The tranquillity which followed my anguish made me extremely alert, no less than my sense of expectation, my thirst for and my fear of danger.

Noiselessly I opened the window and sat down on the foot of my bed; hardly daring to move in case they should hear me from below. Things outside seemed also fixed in mute expectation, so as not to disturb the moonlight which, duplicating each of them and throwing it back by the extension, forwards of a shadow denser and more concrete than its substance, had made the whole landscape seem at once thinner and longer, like a map which, after being folded up, is spread out upon the ground. What had to move—a leaf of the chestnut-tree, for instance—moved. But its minute shuddering, complete, finished to the least detail and with utmost delicacy of gesture, made no discord with the rest of the scene, and yet was not merged in it, remaining clearly outlined. Exposed upon this surface of silence, which absorbed nothing from them, the most distant sounds, those which must have come from gardens at the far end of the town, could be distinguished with such exact 'finish' that the impression they gave of coming from a distance seemed due only to their 'pianissimo' execution, like those movements on muted strings so well performed by the orchestra of the Conservatoire that, although one does not lose a single note, one thinks all the same that they are being played somewhere outside, a long way from the concert hall, so that all the old subscribers, and my grandmother's sisters too, when Swann had given them his seats, used to strain their ears as if they had caught the distant approach of an army on the march, which had not yet rounded the corner of the Rue de Trévise.

I was well aware that I had placed myself in a position than which none could be counted upon to involve me in graver consequences at my parents' hands; consequences far graver, indeed, than a stranger would have imagined, and such as (he would have thought) could follow only some really shameful fault. But in the system of education which they had given me faults were not classified in the same order as in that of other children, and I had been taught to place at the head of the list (doubtless because there was no other class of faults from which I needed to be more carefully protected) those in which I can now distinguish the common feature that one succumbs to them by yielding to a nervous impulse. But such words as these last had never been uttered in my hearing; no one had yet accounted for my temptations in a way which might have led me to believe that there was some excuse for my giving in to them, or that I was actually incapable of holding out against them. Yet I could easily recognise this class of transgressions by the anguish of mind which preceded, as well as by the rigour of the punishment which followed them; and I knew that what I had just done was in the same category as certain other sins for which I had been severely chastised, though infinitely more serious than they. When I went out to meet my mother as she herself came up to bed, and when she saw that I had remained up so as to say good night to her again in the passage, I should not be allowed to stay in the house a day longer, I should be packed off to school the next morning; so much was certain. Very good: had I been obliged, the next moment, to hurl myself out of the window, I should still have preferred such a fate. For what I wanted now was Mamma, and to say good night to her. I had gone too far along the road which led to the realisation of this desire to be able to retrace my steps.

I could hear my parents' footsteps as they went out with Swann; and, when the rattle of the gate assured me that he had really gone, I crept to the window. Mamma was asking my father if he had thought the lobster good, and whether M. Swann had had some more of the coffee-and-pistachio ice. "I thought it rather so-so," she was saying; "next time we shall have to try another flavour."

"I can't tell you," said my great-aunt, "what a change I find in Swann. He is quite antiquated!" She had grown so accustomed to seeing Swann always in the same stage of adolescence that it was a shock to her to find him less young than the age she still attributed to him. And the others too were beginning to remark in Swann that abnormal, excessive, scandalous senescence, meet only in a celibate, in one of that class for whom it seems that the great day which knows no morrow must be longer than for other men, since for such a one it is void of promise, and from its dawn the moments steadily accumulate without any subsequent partition among his offspring.

"I fancy he has a lot of trouble with that wretched wife of his, who 'lives' with a certain Monsieur de Charlus, as all Combray knows. It is the talk of the town."

My mother observed that, in spite of this, he had looked much less unhappy of late. "And he doesn't nearly so often do that trick of his, so like his father, of wiping his eyes and passing his hand across his forehead. I think myself that in his heart of hearts he doesn't love his wife any more."

"Why, of course he doesn't," answered my grandfather. "He wrote me a letter about it, ages ago, to which I took care to pay no attention, but it left no doubt as to his feelings, let alone his love for his wife. Hullo! you two; you never thanked him for the Asti!" he went on, turning to his sisters-in-law.

"What! we never thanked him? I think, between you and me, that I put it to him quite neatly," replied my aunt Flora.

"Yes, you managed it very well; I admired you for it," said my aunt Céline.

"But you did it very prettily, too."

"Yes; I liked my expression about 'nice neighbours.'"

"What! Do you call that thanking him?" shouted my grandfather. "I heard that all right, but devil take me if I guessed it was meant for Swann. You may be quite sure he never noticed it."

"Come, come; Swann is not a fool. I am positive he appreciated the compliment. You didn't expect me to tell him the number of bottles, or to guess what he paid for them."

My father and mother were left alone and sat down for a moment; then my father said: "Well, shall we go up to bed?"

"As you wish, dear, though I don't feel in the least like sleeping. I don't know why; it can't be the coffee-ice—it wasn't strong enough to keep me awake like this. But I see a light in the servants' hall: poor Françoise had been sitting up for me, so I will get her to unhook me while you go and undress."

My mother opened the latticed door which led from the hall to the staircase. Presently I heard her coming upstairs to close her window. I went quietly into the passage; my heart was beating so violently that I could hardly move, but at least it was throbbing no longer with anxiety, but with terror and with joy. I saw in the well of the stair a light coming upwards, from Mamma's candle. Then I saw Mamma herself: I threw myself upon her. For an instant she looked at me in astonishment, not realising what could have happened. Then her face assumed an expression of anger. She said not a single word to me and for that matter I used to go for days on end without being spoken to, for far less offences than this. A single word from Mamma would have been an admission that further intercourse with me was within the bounds of possibility, and that might perhaps have appeared to me more terrible still, as indicating that, with such a punishment as was in store for me, mere silence, and even anger, were relatively puerile.

A word from her then would have implied the false calm in which one converses with a servant to whom one has just decided to give notice; the kiss one bestows on a son who is being packed off to enlist, which would have been denied him if it had merely been a matter of being angry with him for a few days. But she heard my father coming from the dressing-room, where he had gone to take off his clothes, and, to avoid the 'scene' which he would make if he saw me, she said, in a voice half-stifled by her anger: "Run away at once. Don't let your father see you standing there like a crazy jane!"

But I begged her again to "Come and say good night to me!" terrified as I saw the light from my father's candle already creeping up the wall, but also making use of his approach as a means of blackmail, in the hope that my mother, not wishing him to find me there, as find me he must if she continued to hold out, would give in to me, and say: "Go back to your room. I will come."

Too late: my father was upon us. Instinctively I murmured, though no one heard me, "I am done for!"

I was not, however. My father used constantly to refuse to let me do things which were quite clearly allowed by the more liberal charters granted me by my mother and grandmother, because he paid no heed to 'Principles,' and because in his sight there were no such things as 'Rights of Man.' For some quite irrelevant reason, or for no reason at all, he would at the last moment prevent me from taking some particular walk, one so regular and consecrated to my use that to deprive me of it was a clear breach of faith; or again, as he had done this evening, long before the appointed hour he would snap out: "Run along up to bed now; no excuses!" But then again, simply because he was devoid of principles (in my grandmother's sense), so he could not, properly speaking, be called inexorable. He looked at me for a moment with an air of annoyance and surprise, and then when Mamma had told him, not without some embarrassment, what had happened, said to her: "Go along with him, then; you said just now that you didn't feel like sleep, so stay in his room for a little. I don't need anything."

"But dear," my mother answered timidly, "whether or not I feel like sleep is not the point; we must not make the child accustomed . . ."

"There's no question of making him accustomed," said my father, with a shrug of his shoulders; "you can see quite well that the child is unhappy. After all, we aren't gaolers. You'll end by making him ill, and a lot of good that will do. There are two beds in his room; tell Françoise to make up the big one for you, and stay beside him for the rest of the night. I'm off to bed, anyhow; I'm not nervous like you. Good night."

It was impossible for me to thank my father; what he called my sentimentality would have exasperated him. I stood there, not daring to move; he was still confronting us, an immense figure in his white nightshirt, crowned with the pink and violet scarf of Indian cashmere in which, since he had begun to suffer from neuralgia, he used to tie up his head, standing like Abraham in the engraving after Benozzo Gozzoli which M. Swann had given me, telling Sarah that she must tear herself away from Isaac. Many years have passed since that night. The wall of the staircase, up which I had watched the light of his candle gradually climb, was long ago demolished. And in myself, too, many things have perished which, I imagined, would last for ever, and new structures have arisen, giving birth to new sorrows and new joys which in those days I could not have foreseen, just as now the old are difficult of comprehension. It is a long time, too, since my father has been able to tell Mamma to "Go with the child." Never again will such hours be possible for me. But of late I have been increasingly able to catch, if I listen attentively, the sound of the sobs which I had the strength to control in my father's presence, and which broke out only when I found myself alone with Mamma. Actually, their echo has never ceased: it is only because life is now growing more and more quiet round about me that I hear them afresh, like those convent bells which are so effectively drowned during the day by the noises of the streets that one would suppose them to have been stopped for ever, until they sound out again through the silent evening air.

Mamma spent that night in my room: when I had just committed a sin so deadly that I was waiting to be banished from the household, my parents gave me a far greater concession than I should ever have won as the reward of a good action. Even at the moment when it manifested itself in this crowning mercy, my father's conduct towards me was still somewhat arbitrary, and regardless of my deserts, as was characteristic of him and due to the fact that his actions were generally dictated by chance expediencies rather than based on any formal plan. And perhaps even what I called his strictness, when he sent me off to bed, deserved that title less, really, than my mother's or grandmother's attitude, for his nature, which in some respects differed more than theirs from my own, had probably prevented him from guessing, until then, how wretched I was every evening, a thing which my mother and grandmother knew well; but they loved me enough to be unwilling to spare me that suffering, which they hoped to teach me to overcome, so as to reduce my nervous sensibility and to strengthen my will. As for my father, whose affection for me was of another kind, I doubt if he would have shewn so much courage, for as soon as he had grasped the fact that I was unhappy he said to my mother: "Go and comfort him."

Mamma stayed all night in my room, and it seemed that she did not wish to mar by recrimination those hours, so different from anything that I had a right to expect; for when Françoise (who guessed that something extraordinary must have happened when she saw Mamma sitting by my side and letting me cry unchecked) said to her: "But, Madame, what is little Master crying for?" she replied: "Why, Françoise, he doesn't know himself: it is his nerves. Make up the big bed for me quickly and then go off to your own." And thus for the first time my unhappiness was regarded no longer as a fault for which I must be punished, but as an involuntary evil which had been officially recognised, a nervous condition for which I was in no way responsible: I had the consolation that I need no longer mingle apprehensive scruples with the bitterness of my tears; I could weep henceforward without sin. I felt no small degree of pride, either, in Françoise's presence at this return to humane conditions which, not an hour after Mamma had refused to come up to my room and had sent the snubbing message that I was to go to sleep, raised me to the dignity of a grown-up person, brought me of a sudden to a sort of puberty of sorrow, to emancipation from tears. I ought then to have been happy; I was not. It struck me that my mother had just made a first concession which must have been painful to her, that it was a first step down from the ideal she had formed for me, and that for the first time she, with all her courage, had to confess herself beaten. It struck me that if I had just scored a victory it was over her; that I had succeeded, as sickness or sorrow or age might have succeeded, in relaxing her will, in altering her judgment; that this evening opened a new era, must remain a black date in the calendar. And if I had dared now, I should have said to Mamma: "No, I don't want you; you mustn't sleep here." But I was conscious of the practical wisdom, of what would be called nowadays the realism with which she tempered the ardent ideal-ism of my grandmother's nature, and I knew that now the mischief was done she would prefer to let me enjoy the soothing pleasure of her company, and not to disturb my father again. Certainly my mother's beautiful features seemed to shine again with youth that evening, as she sat gently holding my hands and trying to check my tears; but, just for that reason, it seemed to me that this should not have happened; her anger would have been less difficult to endure than this new kindness which my childhood had not known; I felt that I had with an impious and secret finger traced a first wrinkle upon her soul and made the first white hair shew upon her head. This thought redoubled my sobs, and then I saw that Mamma, who had never allowed herself to go to any length of tenderness with me, was suddenly overcome by my tears and had to struggle to keep back her own. Then, as she saw that I had noticed this, she said to me, with a smile: "Why, my little buttercup, my little canary-boy, he's going to make Mamma as silly as himself if this goes on. Look, since you can't sleep, and Mamma can't either, we mustn't go on in this stupid way; we must do something; I'll get one of your books." But I had none there. "Would you like me to get out the books now that your grandmother is going to give you for your birthday? Just think it over first, and don't be disappointed if there is nothing new for you then."

I was only too delighted, and Mamma went to find a parcel of books in which I could not distinguish, through the paper in which it was wrapped, any more than its squareness and size, but which, even at this first glimpse, brief and obscure as it was, bade fair to eclipse already the paintbox of last New Year's Day and the silkworms of the year before. It contained *La Mare au Diable*, *François le Champi*, *La Petite Fadette*, and *Les Maîtres Sonneurs*. My grandmother, as I learned afterwards, had at first chosen Musset's poems, a volume of Rousseau, and *Indiana*; for while she considered light reading as unwholesome as sweets and cakes, she did not reflect that the strong breath of genius must have upon the very soul of a child an influence at once more dangerous and less quickening than those of fresh air and country breezes upon his body. But when my father had seemed almost to regard her as insane on learning the names of the books she proposed to give me, she had journeyed back by herself to Jouy-le-Vicomte to the bookseller's, so that there should be no fear of my not having my present in time (it was a burning hot day, and she had come home so unwell that the doctor had warned my mother not to allow her again to tire herself in that way), and had there fallen back upon the four pastoral novels of George Sand.

"My dear," she had said to Mamma, "I could not allow myself to give the child anything that was not well written."

The truth was that she could never make up her mind to purchase anything from which no intellectual profit was to be derived, and, above all, that profit which good things bestowed upon us by teaching us to seek our pleasures elsewhere than in the barren satisfaction of worldly wealth. Even when she had to make some one a present of the kind called "useful," when she had to give an armchair or some table-silver or a walking-stick, she would choose 'antiques,' as though their long desuetude effaced from them any semblance of utility and fitted them rather to instruct us in the lives of the men of other days than to serve the common requirements of our own. She would have liked me to have in my room photographs of ancient buildings or of beautiful places. But at the moment of buying them, and for all that the subject of the picture had an aesthetic value of its own, she would find that vulgarity and utility had too prominent a part in them, through the mechanical nature of their reproduction by photography. She attempted by a subterfuge, if not to eliminate altogether their commercial banality, at least to minimise it, to substitute for the bulk of it what was art still, to introduce, as it might be, several 'thicknesses' of art; instead of photographs of Chartres Cathedral, of the Fountains of Saint-Cloud, or of Vesuvius she would inquire of Swann whether some great painter had not made pictures of them, and preferred to give me photographs of 'Chartres Cathedral' after Corot, of the 'Fountains of Saint-Cloud' after Hubert Robert, and of 'Vesuvius' after Turner, which were a stage higher in the scale of art. But although the photographer had been prevented from reproducing directly the masterpeices of the beauties of nature, and had there been replaced by a great artist, he resumed his odious position when it came to reproducing the artist's interpretation. Accordingly, having to reckon again with vulgarity, my grandmother would endeavour to postpone the moment of contact still further. She would ask Swann if the picture had not been engraved, preferring, when possible, old engravings with some interest of association apart from themselves, such, for example, as shew us a masterpiece in a state which we can no longer see it to-day, as Morghen's print of the 'Cenacolo' of Leonardo before it was spoiled by restoration. It must be admitted that the results of this method of interpreting the art of making presents were not always happy. The idea which I formed of Venice, from a drawing by Titian which is supposed to have the lagoon in the background, was certainly far less accurate than what I have since derived from ordinary photographs. We could no longer keep count in the family (when my great-aunt tried to frame an indictment of my grandmother) of all the armchairs she had presented to married couples, young and old, which on first attempt to sit down upon them had at once collapsed beneath the weight of their recipient. But my grandmother would have thought it sordid to concern herself too closely with the solidity of any piece of furniture in which could still be discerned a flourish, a smile, a brave conceit of the past. And even what in such pieces supplied a material need, since it did so in a manner to which we are no longer accustomed, was as charming to her as one of those old forms of speech in which we can still see traces of a metaphor whose fine point has been worn away by the rough usage of our modern tongue. In precisely the same way the pastoral novels of George Sand, which she was giving me for my birthday, were regular lumber-rooms of antique furniture, full of expressions that have fallen out of use and returned as imagery, such as one finds now only in country dialects. And my grandmother had bought them in preference to other books, just as she would have preferred to take a house that had a gothic dovecot, or some other such piece of antiquity as would have a pleasant effect on the mind, filling it with a nostalgic longing for impossible journeys through the realms of time.

Mama sat down by my bed; she had chosen *François le Champi,* whose reddish cover and incomprehensible title gave it a distinct personality in my eyes and a mysterious attraction. I had not then read any real novels. I had heard it said that George Sand was a typical novelist. That prepared me in advance to imagine that *François le Champi* contained something inexpressibly delicious.

The course of the narrative, where it tended to arouse curiosity or melt pity, certain modes of expression which disturb or sadden the reader, and which, with a little experience, he may recognise as 'common form' in novels, seemed to me then distinctive—for to me a new book was not one of a number of similar objects, but was like an individual man, unmatched, and with no cause of existence beyond himself—an intoxicating whiff of the peculiar essence of *François le Champi*. Beneath the everyday incidents, the commonplace thoughts and hackneyed words, I could hear, or overhear, an intonation, a rhythmic utterance fine and strange. The 'action' began: to me it seemed all the more obscure because in those days, when I read to myself, I used often, while I turned the pages, to dream of something quite different. And to the gaps which this habit made in my knowledge of the story more were added by the fact that when it was Mamma who was reading to me aloud she left all the love-scenes out. And so all the odd changes which take place in the relations between the miller's wife and the boy, changes which only the birth and growth of love can explain, seemed to me plunged and steeped in a mystery, the key to which (as I could readily believe) lay in that strange and pleasant-sounding name of *Champi*, which draped the boy who bore it, I knew not why, in its own bright color, purpurate and charming. If my mother was not a faithful reader, she was, none the less, admirable when reading a work in which she found the note of true feeling by the respectful simplicity of her interpretation and by the sound of her sweet and gentle voice. It was the same in her daily life, when it was not works of art but men and women whom she was moved to pity or admire: it was touching to observe with what deference she would banish from her voice, her gestures, from her whole conversation, now the note of joy which might have distressed some other who had long ago lost a child, now the recollection of an event or anniversary which might have reminded some old gentleman of the burden of his years, now the household topic which might have bored some young man of letters. And so, when she read aloud the prose of George Sand, prose which is everywhere redolent of that generosity and moral distinction which Mamma had learned from my grandmother to place above all other qualities in life, and which I was not to teach her until much later to refrain from placing, in the same way, above all other qualities in literature; taking pains to banish from her voice any weakness or affectation which might have blocked its channel for that powerful stream of language, she supplied all the natural tenderness, all the lavish sweetness which they demanded to the phrases which seemed to have been composed for her voice, and which were all, so to speak, within her compass. She came to them with the tone that they required, with the cordial accent which existed before they were, which dictated them, but which is not to be found in the words themselves, and by these means she smoothed away, as she read on, any harshness there might be or discordance in the tenses of verbs, endowing the imperfect and the preterite with all the sweetness which there is in generosity, all the melancholy which there is in love; guided the sentence that was drawing to an end towards that which was waiting to begin, now hastening, now slackening the pace of the syllables so as to bring them, despite their difference of quantity, into a uniform rhythm, and breathed into this quite ordinry prose a kind of life, continuous and full of feeling.

My agony was soothed; I let myself be borne upon the current of this gentle night on which I had my mother by my side. I knew that such a night could not be repeated; that the strongest desire I had in the world, namely, to keep my mother in my room through the sad hours of darkness, ran too much counter to general requirements and to the wishes of others for such a concession as had been granted me this evening to be anything but a rare and casual exception. Tomorrow night I should again be the vicitm of anguish and Mamma would not stay by my side. But when these storms of anguish grew calm I could no longer realise their existence; besides, to-morrow evening was still a long way off; I reminded myself that I should still have time to think about things, albeit that remission of time could bring me no access of power, albeit the coming event was in no way dependent upon the exercise of my will, and seemed not quite inevitable only because it was still separated from me by this short interval.

# D. H. LAWRENCE

秀 秀

*Sons grow up and their mothers often grieve when they go off to make their way in the world. But sometimes there are happy homecomings, as in* Sons and Lovers.

THEY WERE VERY POOR that autumn. William had just gone away to London, and his mother missed his money. He sent ten shillings once or twice, but he had many things to pay for at first. His letters came regularly once a week. He wrote a good deal to his mother, telling her all his life, how he made friends, and was exchanging lessons with a Frenchman, how he enjoyed London. His mother felt again he was remaining to her just as when he was at home. She wrote to him every week her direct, rather witty letters. All day long, as she cleaned the house, she thought of him. He was in London: he would do well. Almost, he was like her knight who wore *her* favour in the battle.

He was coming at Christmas for five days. There had never been such preparations. Paul and Arthur scoured the land for holly and evergreens. Annie made the pretty paper hoops in the old-fashioned way. And there was unheard-of extravagance in the larder. Mrs. Morel made a big and magnificent cake. Then, feeling queenly, she showed Paul how to blanch almonds. He skinned the long nuts reverently, counting them all, to see not one was lost. It was said eggs whisked better in a cold place. So the boy stood in the scullery, where the temperature was nearly at freezing-point, and whisked and whisked, and flew in excitement to his mother as the white of egg grew stiffer and more snowy.

"Just look, mother! Isn't it lovely?"

And he balanced a bit on his nose, then blew it in the air.

"Now, don't waste it," said the mother.

Everybody was mad with excitement. William was coming on Christmas Eve. Mrs. Morel surveyed her pantry. There was a big plum cake, and a rice cake, jam tarts, lemon tarts and mince-pies—two enormous dishes. She was finishing cooking—Spanish tarts and cheese-cakes. Everywhere was decorated. The kissing-bunch of berried holly hung with bright and glittering things, spun slowly over Mrs. Morel's head as she trimmed her little tarts in the kitchen. A great fire roared. There was a scent of cooked pastry. He was due at seven o'clock, but he would be late. The three children had gone to meet him. She was alone. But at a quarter to seven Morel came in again. Neither wife nor husband spoke. He sat in his armchair, quite awkward with excitement, and she quietly went on with her baking. Only by the careful way in which she did things could it be told how much moved she was. The clock ticked on.

"What time dost say he's coming?" Morel asked for the fifth time.

"The train gets in at half-past six," she replied emphatically.

"Then he'll be here at ten past seven."

"Eh, bless you, it'll be hours late on the Midland," she said indifferently. But she hoped, by expecting him late, to bring him early. Morel went down the entry to look for him. Then he came back.

"Goodness, man!" she said. "You're like an ill-sitting hen."

"Hadna you better be gettin' him summat t' eat ready?" asked the father.

"There's plenty of time," she answered.

"There's not so much as *I* can see on," he answered, turning crossly in his chair. She began to clear her table. The kettle was singing. They waited and waited.

Meantime the three children were on the platform at Sethley Bridge, on the Midland main line, two miles from home. They waited one hour. A train came—he was not there. Down the line the red and green lights shone. It was very dark and very cold.

"Ask him if the London train's come," said Paul to Annie, when they saw a man in a tip cap.

"I'm not," said Annie. "You be quiet—he might send us off."

But Paul was dying for the man to know they were expecting someone by the London train: it sounded so grand. Yet he was much too much scared of broaching any man, let alone one in a peaked cap, to dare to ask. The three children could scarcely go into the waiting-room for fear of being sent away, and for fear something should happen whilst they were off the platform. Still they waited in the dark and cold.

"It's an hour an' a half late," said Arthur pathetically.

"Well," said Annie, "it's Christmas Eve."

They all grew silent. He wasn't coming. They looked down the darkness of the railway. There was London! It seemed the uttermost of distance. They thought anything might happen if one came from London. They were all too troubled to talk. Cold, and unhappy, and silent, they huddled together on the platform.

At last, after more than two hours, they saw the lights of an engine peering round, away down the darkness. A porter ran out. The children drew back with beating hearts. A great train, bound for Manchester, drew up. Two doors opened, and from one of them, William. They flew to him. He handed parcels to them cheerily, and immediately began to explain that this great train had stopped for *his* sake at such a small station as Sethley Bridge: it was not booked to stop.

Meanwhile the parents were getting anxious. The table was set, the chop was cooked, everything was ready. Mrs. Morel put on her black apron. She was wearing her best dress. Then she sat, pretending to read. The minutes were a torture to her.

"H'm!" said Morel. "It's an hour an' a ha'ef."

"And those children waiting!" she said.

"Th' train canna ha' come in yet," he said.

"I tell you, on Christmas Eve they're *hours* wrong."

They were both a bit cross with each other, so gnawed with anxiety. The ash-tree moaned outside in a cold, raw wind. And all that space of night from London home! Mrs. Morel suffered.

The slight click of the works inside the clock irritated her. It was getting so late; it was getting unbearable.

At last there was a sound of voices, and a footstep in the entry.

"Ha's here!" cried Morel, jumping up.

Then he stood back. The mother ran a few steps towards the

door and waited. There was a rush and a patter of feet, the door burst open. William was there. He dropped his Gladstone bag and took his mother in his arms.

"Mater!" he said.

"My boy!" she cried.

And for two seconds, no longer, she clasped him and kissed him. Then she withdrew and said, trying to be quite normal:

"But how late you are!"

"Aren't I!" he cried turning to his father. "Well, dad!"

The two men shook hands.

"Well, my lad!"

Morel's eyes were wet.

"We thought tha'd niver be commin'," he said.

"Oh, I'd come!" exclaimed William.

Then the son turned round to his mother.

"But you look well," she said proudly, laughing.

"Well!" he exclaimed. "I should think so—coming home!"

He was a fine fellow, big, straight, and fearless-looking. He looked round at the evergreens and the kissing bunch, and the little tarts that lay in their tins on the hearth.

"By jove! mother, it's not different!" he said, as if in relief.

Everybody was still for a second. Then he suddenly sprang forward, picked a tart from the hearth, and pushed it whole into his mouth.

"Well, did iver you see such a parish oven!" the father exclaimed.

He had brought them endless presents. Every penny he had he had spent on them. There was a sense of luxury overflowing in the house. For his mother there was an umbrella with gold on the pale handle. She kept it to her dying day, and would have lost anything rather than that. Everybody had something gorgeous, and besides, there were pounds of unknown sweets: Turkish delight, crystallized pineapple, and such-like things which, the children thought, only the splendour of London could provide. And Paul boasted of these sweets among his friends.

"Real pineapple, cut off in slices, and then turned into crystal—fair grand!"

Everybody was mad with happiness in the family. Home was

home, and they loved it with a passion of love, whatever the suffering had been. There were parties, there were rejoicings. People came in to see William, to see what difference London had made to him. And they all found him "such a gentleman, and *such* a fine fellow, my word!"

When he went away again the children retired to various places to weep alone. Morel went to bed in misery, and Mrs. Morel felt as if she were numbed by some drug, as if her feelings were paralyzed. She loved him passionately.

He was in the office of a lawyer connected with a large shipping firm, and at the midsummer his chief offered him a trip in the Mediterranean on one of the boats, for quite a small cost. Mrs. Morel wrote: "Go, go, my boy. You may never have a chance again, and I should love to think of you cruising there in the Mediterranean almost better than to have you at home." But William came home for his fortnight's holiday. Not even the Mediterranean, which pulled at all his young man's desire to travel, and at his poor man's wonder at the glamorous south, could take him away when he might come home. That compensated his mother for much.

# ELEANOR ROOSEVELT

*At the age of thirty-nine, his political career just be-ginning, Franklin D. Roosevelt was stricken with poliomyelitis. In her* Autobiography, *his wife recalls some of the reactions of his mother, Sara Delano Roosevelt.*

. . . FRANKLIN'S MOTHER was really remarkable about this entire illness. It must have been a terrific strain for her, and I am sure that, out of sight, she wept many hours, but with all of us she was very cheerful. She had, however, made up her mind that

Franklin was going to be an invalid for the rest of his life and that he would retire to Hyde Park and live there. Her anxiety over his general health was so great that she dreaded his making any effort whatever. . . .

. . . In many ways this was the most trying winter of my entire life. It was the small personal irritations, as I look back upon them now, that made life so difficult. My mother-in-law thought we were tiring my husband and that he should be kept completely quiet, which made the discussions about his care somewhat acrimonious on occasion. She always thought that she understood what was best, particularly where her child was concerned, regardless of what any doctor might say. I felt that if you placed a patient in a doctor's care you must at least follow out his suggestions and treatment. The house was not overlarge and we were very crowded. . . .

# RICHARD WRIGHT

☙ ☙

*The unhappiness of a mother, helpless to give her sons what they need, is recalled by Richard Wright in his autobiography,* Black Boy.

HUNGER STOLE UPON ME so slowly that at first I was not aware of what hunger really meant. Hunger had always been more or less at my elbow when I played, but now I began to wake up at night to find hunger standing at my bedside, staring at me gauntly. The hunger I had known before this had been no grim, hostile stranger; it had been a normal hunger that had made me beg constantly for bread, and when I ate a crust or two I was satisfied. But this new hunger baffled me, scared me, made me angry and insistent. Whenever I begged for food now my mother would pour me a cup of tea which would still the clamor in my stomach for a moment or two; but a little later I would feel hunger nudging my ribs, twisting my empty guts until they ached. I would grow dizzy and my vision would dim. I became less active in my play, and for the first time in my life I had to pause and think of what was happening to me.

"Mama, I'm hungry," I complained one afternoon.

"Jump up and catch a kungry," she said, trying to make me laugh and forget.

"What's a *kungry?*"

"It's what little boys eat when they get hungry," she said.

"What does it taste like?"

"I don't know."

"Then why do you tell me to catch one?"

"Because you said that you were hungry," she said, smiling.

I sensed that she was teasing me and it made me angry.

"But I'm hungry. I want to eat."

"You'll have to wait."

"But I want to eat now."

"But there's nothing to eat," she told me.

"Why?"

"Just because there's none," she explained.

"But I want to eat," I said, beginning to cry.

"You'll just have to wait," she said again.

"But why?"

"For God to send some food."

"When is He going to send it?"

"I don't know."

"But I'm hungry!"

She was ironing and she paused and looked at me with tears in her eyes.

"Where's your father?" she asked me.

I stared in bewilderment. Yes, it was true that my father had not come home to sleep for many days now and I could make as much noise as I wanted. Though I had not known why he was absent, I had been glad that he was not there to shout his restrictions at me. But it had never occurred to me that his absence would mean that there would be no food.

"I don't know," I said.

"Who brings food into the house?" my mother asked me.

"Papa," I said. "He always brought food."

"Well, your father isn't here now," she said.

"Where is he?"

"I don't know," she said.

"But I'm hungry," I whimpered, stomping my feet.

"You'll have to wait until I get a job and buy food," she said.

As the days slid past the image of my father became associated with my pangs of hunger, and whenever I felt hunger I thought of him with a deep biological bitterness.

My mother finally went to work as a cook and left me and my brother alone in the flat each day with a loaf of bread and a pot of tea. When she returned at evening she would be tired and dispirited and would cry a lot. Sometimes, when she was in despair, she would call us to her and talk to us for hours, telling us that we now had no father, that our lives would be different from those of other children, that we must learn as soon as possible to take care of ourselves, to dress ourselves, to prepare our own food; that we must take upon ourselves the responsibility of the flat while she worked. Half frightened, we would promise solemnly. We did not understand what had happened between our father and our mother and the most that these long talks did to us was to make us feel a vague dread. Whenever we asked why father had left, she would tell us that we were too young to know.

# WILLIAM MAXWELL

※ ※

*This passage from* They Came Like Swallows *shows how a small boy's world can be transformed by just the right question from his mother.*

BUNNY did not waken all at once. A sound (what, he did not know) struck the surface of his sleep and sank like a stone. His dream subsided, leaving him awake, stranded, on his bed. He turned helplessly and confronted the ceiling. A pipe had burst during the winter before, and now there was the outline of a yellow lake. The lake became a bird with a plumed head and straggling tail feathers, while Bunny was looking at it. When there were no further changes, his eyes wandered down by way of the blue-and-white-wallpaper to the other bed, where Robert lay sleeping. They lingered for a moment upon Robert's parted lips, upon his face drained and empty with sleep.

It was raining.

Outside, branches of the linden rose and fell in the wind, rose and fell. And November leaves came down. Bunny turned over upon the small unyielding body of Araminta Culpepper. Because he was eight, and somewhat past the age when boys are supposed to play with dolls, Araminta hung from the bedpost by day—an Indian papoose with an unbreakable expression on her face. But at night she shared his bed with him. A dozen times he drew her to him lovingly in sleep. And if he woke too soon, the darkness was neither frightful nor bare so long as he could put out his hand and touch her.

Before him—before Peter Morison who was called Bunny—was the whole of the second Sunday in November, 1918. He moved slightly in order that Araminta Culpepper might have room for her head on the pillow. If it had been a clear day, if the sky were blue and full of sunlight, he would have to go off to Sunday school and sing hymns and perhaps hear the same old story about Daniel who was put in the lions' den, or about Elisha, or about Elijah who went to heaven in a chariot of fire. And what would become of his morning? As soon as he got home and spread the funny-paper out on the floor where he could look at it comfortably, some one would be sure to come along and exclaim over him: *For Heaven's sake, it's too nice a day to be in the house. Why don't you go outdoors and get some exercise?* And if he pretended that he was going to but didn't, they would come again in a little while. He would have to put on his cap and his woolly coat and mittens, whether he wanted to or not. He would be driven out of the house to roll disconsolately in a bed of leaves or to wander through the garden where nothing bloomed; where there were only sticks and crisp grass and the stalks of summer flowers.

But not now, Bunny said to himself, hearing the sound of water dripping, dropping from the roof. Not this morning. And somewhere in the front part of the house a door opened so that his mother's voice came up the stairs. A spring inside him, a coiled spring, was set free. He sat up and threw his covers to the foot of the bed. When he was washed and dressed he went downstairs. His mother was sitting at the breakfast table before the fire in the library.

"How do you do?" He threw his arms about her and planted a kiss somewhat wildly on her mouth. "How do you do and how do you do again?"

"I do very well, thank you."

She held him off in front of her to see whether he had washed thoroughly, and Bunny noticed with relief the crumbs at his father's place, the carelessly folded napkin.

"Did you have a good night? Is Robert up?"

Bunny shook his head.

"Stirring?"

"No."

"I thought that would happen."

While Bunny settled himself at the table she buttered a piece of toast for him. He was old enough to butter his own but she liked doing it for him. She was that way. When she had finished she lifted the platter of bacon from the hearth.

"Robert stayed up until ten o'clock, trying to finish *The Boy Allies in Bulgaria*. I told him they wouldn't assassinate anybody without him, but he wanted to finish it just the same." She helped herself to another cup of coffee. "You know how he is."

Robert was thirteen and very trying. More so, it seemed to Bunny, than most people. He wouldn't go to bed and he wouldn't get up. He hated to bathe or be kissed or practise his music lesson. He left the light burning in the basement. He refused to eat oysters or squash. He wouldn't get up on cold mornings and close the window. He spread his soldiers all over the carpet in the living-room and when it came time to pick them up he was never there; he had gone off to help somebody dig a cave. And likely as not he would come home late for dinner, his clothes covered with mud, his knuckles skinned, his hair full of leaves and sticks, and a hole in his brand-new sweater.

There was no time (no time that Bunny could remember) when Robert had not made him cry at least once between morning and night. Robert hid Bunny's thrift stamps and his ball of lead foil. Or he danced through the house swinging Araminta Culpepper by the braids. Or he twisted Bunny's arm and showed him a fine new trick, the point of which was that he got his thumbs bent out of shape. Or he might do no more than sit across the room saying, *Creepy-creepy-creepy* . . . pointing his finger at Bunny and describing smaller and smaller circles until the tears would not stay back any longer.

Before this day was over, it too would be spoiled like all the others. But while Robert was still upstairs in bed there was nothing for Bunny to worry about, no reason on earth why he should not enjoy his breakfast.

"It's raining," he said, and helped himself to bacon.

"I see it is." His mother took the plate from him and put it back on the hearth to keep warm for Robert. "It's been raining since five o'clock."

Bunny looked out of the window hopefully.

"Hard?"

Sometimes when it rained heavily for a considerable time he was not expected to go outside even though it cleared up afterward. The ground was too wet, they said. He might catch his death.

"Hard, Muv?"

"Like this."

Bunny tried to persuade himself that it was a heavy rain, but there was too much wind and not enough water. All the whirling and criss-crossing, the beating against the window and sliding in sudden rivulets down the glass—there was very little to it. The wind rose higher and the rain turned itself about and about. The room became intensely still, so that the logs crackling and singing in the fireplace seemed loud and impressive. And because the lights were on in the daytime, the walls seemed immensely substantial, the way they did at night with curtains drawn across the windows and the room closed in upon itself.

"Do you think, Muv—"

Bunny hesitated, fearing at the last moment to expose himself. "Rain before seven—"

His mother got up from the table, having read his thought, and answered it, severely:

*Rain before seven*
*Clear by eleven.*

Bunny was obliged to unwind the proverb in his own mind. There was nothing else for him to do. The words she had left unspoken remained cruelly before his eyes even when he looked down at his plate. With great concentration he began to eat his cereal. It would have taken a very little thing at that moment to spill his sorrow. Let the clock catch its breath, let one log fall with a sudden shower of sparks up the chimney and he would have wept.

His mother sat down in the window seat and hunted through her sewing-kit impatiently. Bunny could hear her saying to herself that he was a grown man, or nearly so. Eight last August and not yet able to depend on his own strength, but coming to her again and again to be reassured.

Another time, he promised; another time he would try and not give in to weakness. If only she would not be severe with him now. He could not bear to have her that way. Not this morning. . . . Feeling altogether sorry for himself, he began to imagine what it would be like if she were not there. If his mother were not there to protect him from whatever was unpleasant—from the weather and from Robert and from his father—what would he do? Whatever would become of him in a world where there was neither warmth nor comfort nor love?

Rain washed against the window.

When his mother found the needle she had been looking for, she threaded it. Then she took up a square of white cloth. Her hand flew this way and that, over her sewing. Quite suddenly she spoke to him:

"Bunny, come here."

He got down from his chair at once. But while he stood waiting before her and while she considered him with eyes that were perplexed and brown, the weight grew. The weight grew and became like a stone. He had to lift it each time that he took a breath.

"Whose angel child are you?"

By these words and by the wholly unexpected kiss that accompanied them he was made sound and strong. His eyes met hers safely. With wings beating above him and a great noise as of trumpets and drums he returned to his breakfast.

# Mothers and Daughters

Mothers and Daughters

# G. W. COX

### ✿ ✿

*A mother's grief for a kidnapped daughter brought
winter to the world, according to the ancient Greek
legend of Demeter and Persephone, as retold in* Tales
of the Gods and Heroes.

## "The Sorrow of Demeter"

IN THE FIELDS of Enna, in the happy island of Sicily, the
beautiful Persephone was playing with the girls who lived there
with her. She was the daughter of the lady Demeter, and every
one loved them both; for Demeter was good and kind to all,
and no one could be more gentle and merry than Persephone.
She and her companions were gathering flowers from the
field, to make crowns for their long flowing hair. They had
picked many roses and lilies and hyacinths which grew in clusters
around them, when Persephone thought she saw a splendid
flower far off, and away she ran, as fast as she could, to get it.
It was a beautiful narcissus, with a hundred heads springing
from one stem; and the perfume which came from its flowers
gladdened the broad heaven above, and the earth and sea around
it. Eagerly Persephone stretched out her hand to take this
splendid prize, when the earth opened, and a chariot stood before her drawn by four coal-black horses; and in the chariot
there was a man with a dark and solemn face, which looked
as though he could never smile, and as though he had never been
happy. In a moment he got out of his chariot, seized Persephone
round the waist, and put her on the seat by his side. Then he
touched the horses with his whip, and they drew the chariot
down into the great gulf, and the earth closed over them again.

Presently the girls who had been playing with Persephone came
up to the place where the beautiful narcissus was growing; but
they could not see her anywhere. And they said, "Here is the very
flower which she ran to pick, and there is no place here where she

can be hiding." Still for a long time they searched for her through
the fields of Enna; and when the evening was come, they went
home to tell the lady Demeter that they could not tell what had
become of Persephone.

Very terrible was the sorrow of Demeter when she was told that
her child was lost. She put on a dark robe on her shoulders, and
took a flaming torch in her hand, and went over land and sea to
look for Persephone. But no one could tell her where she was
gone. When ten days were past she met Hekate, and asked her
about her child: but Hekate said, "I heard her voice, as she cried
out when some one seized her; but I did not see it with my eyes,
and so I know not where she has gone." Then she went to Helios,
and said to him, "O Helios, tell me about my child. Thou seest
everything on the earth, sitting in the bright sun." Then Helios
said, "O Demeter, I pity thee for thy great sorrow, and I will tell
thee the truth. It is Hades who has taken away Persephone to be
his wife in the dark and gloomy land which lies beneath in the
earth."

Then the rage of Demeter was more terrible than her sorrow
had been; and she would not stay in the palace of Zeus, on the
great Thessalian hill, because it was Zeus who had allowed Hades
to take away Persephone. So she went down from Olympus, and
wandered on a long way until she came to Eleusis, just as the sun
was going down into his golden cup behind the dark blue hills.
There Demeter sat down close to a fountain, where the water
bubbled out from the green turf, and fell into a clear bright basin,
over which some dark olive-trees spread their branches. Just then
the daughters of Keleüs, the king of Eleusis, came to the fountain
with pitchers on their heads to draw water; and when they saw
Demeter, they knew from her face that she must have some great
grief; and they spoke kindly to her, and asked if they could do
anything to help her. Then she told them how she had lost, and
was searching for, her child; and they said, "Come home and live
with us: and our father and mother will give you everything that
you can want, and do all that they can to soothe your sorrow." So
Demeter went down to the house of Keleüs, and she stayed there
for a whole year. And all this time, although the daughters of
Keleüs were very gentle and kind to her, she went on mourning

and weeping for Persephone. She never laughed or smiled, and scarcely ever did she speak to any one, because of her great grief. And even the earth, and the things which grow on the earth, mourned for the sorrow which had come upon Demeter. There was no fruit upon the trees, no corn came up in the fields, and no flowers blossomed in the gardens. And Zeus looked down from his high Thessalian hill, and saw that everything must die unless he could soothe the grief and anger of Demeter. So he sent Hermes down to Hades, the dark and stern king, to bid him send Persephone to see her mother Demeter. But before Hades let her go, he gave her a pomegranate to eat, because he did not wish her to stay away from him always, and he knew that she must come back if she tasted but one of the pomegranate seeds. Then the great chariot was brought before the door of the palace, and Hermes touched with his whip the coal-black horses, and away they went as swiftly as the wind, on and on, until they came close to Eleusis. Then Hermes left Persephone, and the coal-black horses drew the chariot away again to the dark home of King Hades.

The sun was sinking down in the sky when Hermes left Persephone, and as she came near to the fountain she saw some one sitting near it in a long black robe, and she knew that it must be her mother, who still wept and mourned for her child. And as Demeter heard the rustling of her dress, she lifted up her face, and Persephone stood before her.

Then the joy of Demeter was greater, as she clasped her daughter to her breast, than her grief and her sorrow had been. Again and again she held Persephone in her arms, and asked her about all that had happened to her. And she said, "Now that you are come back to me, I shall never let you go away again; Hades shall not have my child to live with him in his dreary kingdom." But Persephone said, "O mother, it may not be so; I cannot stay with you always; for before Hermes brought me away to see you Hades gave me a pomegranate, and I have eaten some of the seeds; and after tasting the seed I must go back to him again when six months have passed by. And indeed I am not afraid to go back; for although Hades never smiles or laughs, and everything in his palace is dark and gloomy, still he is very kind to me; and I think that he feels almost happy since I have been his wife. But do not be sorry, my mother, for he has promised to let me come up and stay with you for six months in every year, and the other six months I must spend with him in the land which lies beneath the earth."

So Demeter was comforted for her daughter Persephone, and the earth and all the things that grew in it felt that her anger and sorrow had passed away. Once more the trees bore their fruits, the flowers spread out their sweet blossoms in the garden, and the golden corn waved like the sea under the soft summer breeze. So the six months passed happily away, and then Hermes came with the coal-black horses to take Persephone to the dark land. And she said to her mother, "Do not weep much; the gloomy king whose wife I am is so kind to me that I cannot be really unhappy; and in six months more he will let me come to you again." But still, whenever the time came round for Persephone to go back to Hades, Demeter thought of the happy days when her child was a merry girl playing with her companions and gathering the bright flowers in the beautiful plains of Enna.

# THE HOLY BIBLE

## (Authorized King James Version)

⚔ ⚔

*As tender and strong as any blood tie can be the bond between a daughter-in-law and a mother-in-law. The story of Naomi and her daughter-in-law from the Book of Ruth is the classic example.*

## The Book of Ruth, Chapter I, Verses 1–17.

Now it came to pass in the days when the judges ruled, that there was a famine in the land. And a certain man of Bethlehem-judah went to sojourn in the country of Moab, he, and his wife, and his two sons.

And the name of the man *was* Elimelech, and the name of his wife Naomi, and the name of his two sons Mahlon and Chilion, Ephrathites of Bethlehem-judah. And they came into the country of Moab, and continued there.

And Elimelech Naomi's husband died; and she was left, and her two sons.

And they took them wives of the women of Moab; the name of the one *was* Orpah, and the name of the other Ruth: and they dwelled there about ten years.

And Mahlon and Chilion died also both of them; and the woman was left of her two sons and her husband.

Then she arose with her daughters in law, that she might return from the country of Moab: for she had heard in the country of Moab how that the LORD had visited his people in giving them bread.

Wherefore she went forth out of the place where she was, and her two daughters in law with her; and they went on the way to return unto the land of Judah.

And Naomi said unto her two daughters in law, Go, return each to her mother's house: the LORD deal kindly with you, as ye have dealt with the dead, and with me.

The LORD grant you that ye may find rest, each *of you* in the house of her husband. Then she kissed them; and they lifted up their voice, and wept.

And they said unto her, Surely we will return with thee unto thy people.

And Naomi said, Turn again, my daughters: why will ye go with me? *are* there yet *any more* sons in my womb, that they may be your husbands?

Turn again, my daughters, *go your way;* for I am too old to have an husband. If I should say, I have hope, *if* I should have an husband also tonight, and should also bear sons;

Would ye tarry for them till they were grown? would ye stay for them from having husbands? nay, my daughters; for it grieveth me much for your sakes that the hand of the LORD is gone out against me.

And they lifted up their voice, and wept again: and Orpah kissed her mother in law; but Ruth clave unto her.

And she said, Behold, thy sister in law is gone back unto her people, and unto her gods: return thou after thy sister in law.

And Ruth said, Entreat me not to leave thee, *or* to return from following after thee: for whither thou goest, I will go; and where thou lodgest, I will lodge: thy people *shall be* my people, and thy God my God:

Where thou diest, will I die, and there will I be buried: the LORD do so to me, and more also, *if aught* but death part thee and me.

# LEO TOLSTOY

*In* War and Peace *there is a timeless vignette of bed-time confidences between a mother and daughter.*

ONE EVENING the old countess in her bed-jacket, without her false curls, and with only one poor wisp of hair peeping out from under her white cotton nightcap, was bowing down on the carpet, sighing and moaning as she repeated her evening prayers. Her door creaked, and Natasha, also in a bed-jacket, ran in, bare-legged, with her feet in slippers, and her hair in curl papers. The countess looked round and frowned. She was repeating her last prayer. "Can it be this couch will be my bier?" Her devotional mood was dispelled. Natasha, flushed and eager, stopped suddenly short in her rapid movement as she saw her mother at her prayers. She half-sat down and unconsciously put out her tongue at herself. Seeing that her mother was still praying, she ran tiptoe to the bed; and rapidly slipping one little foot against the other, pushed off her slippers and sprang on to that couch which the countess in her prayer feared might become her bier. That couch was a high feather-bed, with five pillows, each smaller than the one below. Natasha skipped in, sank into the feather-bed, rolled over towards the side, and began snuggling up under the quilt, tucking herself up, bending her knees up to her chin, kicking out and giving a faintly audible giggle as she alternately hid her face under the quilt and peeped out at her mother. The countess had finished her prayers, and was approaching her bed with a stern face, but seeing that Natasha was playing bo-peep with her she smiled her good-natured, weak smile.

"Come, come, come!" said the mother.

"Mamma, may I speak, yes?" said Natasha. "Come, under the chin, one, and now another, and enough." And she clutched her mother's neck and kissed her favourite place on her chin. In Natasha's behaviour to her mother there was a superficial roughness of manner, but she had a natural tact and knack of doing things, so that, however she snatched her mother in her arms, she always managed so that she was not hurt, nor uncomfortable, nor displeased by it.

"Well, what is it to-night?" said her mother, settling herself in the pillows and waiting for Natasha, who had already rolled over twice, to lie down by her side under the bedclothes, to put out her arms and assume a serious expression.

These visits of Natasha to her mother at night before the count came home from the club were one of the greatest pleasures both of mother and daughter.

"What is it to-night? And I want to talk to you . . ." Natasha put her hand on her mother's lips.

"About Boris . . . I know," she said seriously; "that's what I have come about. Don't say it; I know. No, do say it!" She took her hand away. "Say it, mamma! He's nice, eh?"

"Natasha, you are sixteen! At your age I was married. You say Boris is nice. He is very nice, and I love him like a son! But what do you want? . . . What are you thinking about? You have quite turned his head, I can see that . . ."

As she said this, the countess looked round at her daughter. Natasha was lying, looking steadily straight before her at one of the mahogany sphinxes carved on a corner of the bedstead, so that the countess could only see her daughter's face in profile. Her face impressed the countess by its strikingly serious and concentrated expression.

Natasha was listening and considering.

"Well, so what then?" she said.

"You have completely turned his head, and what for? What do you want of him? You know you can't marry him."

"Why not?" said Natasha, with no change in her attitude.

"Because he is so young, because he's poor, because he's a relation . . . because you don't care for him yourself."

"How do you know that?"

"I know. It's not right, my darling."

"But if I want to . . ." said Natasha.

"Leave off talking nonsense," said the countess.

"But if I want to . . ."

"Natasha, I am serious . . ."

Natasha did not let her finish; she drew the countess's large hand to her, and kissed it on the upper side, and then on the palm, then turned it over again and began kissing it on the knuckle of the top joint of the finger, then on the space between the knuckle again, whispering: "January, February, March, April, May."

"Speak, mamma; why are you silent? Speak," she said, looking round at her mother, who was gazing tenderly at her daughter, and apparently in gazing at her had forgotten all she meant to say.

"This won't do, my dear. It's not every one who will understand your childish feelings for one another, and seeing him on such intimate terms with you may prejudice you in the eyes of other young men who visit us, and what is of more consequence, it's making him wretched for nothing. He had very likely found a match that would suit him, some wealthy girl, and now he's half-crazy."

"Half-crazy?" repeated Natasha.

"I'll tell you what happened in my own case. I had a cousin . . ."

"I know—Kirilla Matveitch; but he's old."

"He was not always old. But I tell you what, Natasha, I'll speak to Boris. He musn't come so often . . ."

"Why musn't he, if he wants to?"

"Because I know it can't come to anything."

"How do you know? No, mamma, don't speak to him. What

nonsense!" said Natasha, in the tone of a man being robbed of his property. "Well, I won't marry him, so let him come, if he enjoys it and I enjoy it." Natasha looked at her mother, smiling. "Not to be married, but—just so," she repeated.

"How so, my dear?"

"Oh, just *so*. I see it's very necessary I shouldn't marry him, but . . . just *so*."

"Just so, just so," repeated the countess, and shaking all over, she went off into a good-natured, unexpectedly elderly laugh.

"Don't laugh, stop," cried Natasha; "you're shaking all the bed. You're awfully like me, just another giggler . . . Stop . . ." She snatched both the countess's hands, kissed one knuckle of the little finger, for June, and went on kissing—July, August—on the other hand. "Mamma, is he very much in love? What do you think? Were men as much in love with you? And he's very, very, very nice! Only not quite to my liking—he's so narrow, somehow, like a clock on the wall. . . . Don't you understand? . . . Narrow, you know, grey, light-coloured . . ."

"What nonsense you talk!" said the countess.

Natasha went on:

"Don't you really understand? Nikolenka would understand . . . Bezuhov now—he's blue, dark blue and red, and he's quadrangular."

"You're flirting with him, too," said the countess laughing.

"No, he's a freemason, I have heard. He's jolly, dark blue and red; how am I to explain to you . . ."

"Little countess," they heard the count's voice through the door, "You're not asleep?" Natasha skipped up, snatched up her slippers, and ran barefoot to her own room. For a long while she could not go to sleep. She kept musing on no one's being able to understand all she understood and all that was in her.

# LAFCADIO HEARN

芝 芝

*A poignant Japanese legend from* Out of the East *tells
of a daughter's remembrance of her mother.*

LONG AGO, at a place called Matsuyama, in the province of
Echigo, there lived a young samurai husband and wife whose
names have been quite forgotten. They had a little daughter.

Once the husband went to Yedo,—probably as a retainer in the
train of the Lord of Echigo. On his return he brought presents
from the capital,—sweet cakes and a doll for the little girl (at least
so the artist tells us), and for his wife a mirror of silvered bronze.
To the young mother that mirror seemed a very wonderful thing;
for it was the first mirror ever brought to Matsuyama. She did not
understand the use of it, and innocently asked whose was the
pretty smiling face she saw inside it. When her husband answered
her, laughing, "Why, it is your own face! How foolish you are!"
she was ashamed to ask any more questions, but hastened to put
her present away, still thinking it to be a very mysterious thing.
And she kept it hidden many years,—the original story does not
say why. Perhaps for the simple reason that in all countries love
makes even the most trifling gift too sacred to be shown.

But in the time of her last sickness she gave the mirror to her
daughter, saying, "After I am dead you must look into this mirror
every morning and evening, and you will see me. Do not grieve."
Then she died.

And the girl thereafter looked into the mirror every morning
and evening, and did not know that the face in the mirror was her
own shadow,—but thought it to be that of her dead mother,
whom she much resembled. So she would talk to the shadow,
having the sensation, or, as the Japanese original more tenderly

says, "*having the heart of meeting her mother*" day by day; and she prized the mirror above all things.

At last her father noticed this conduct, and thought it strange, and asked her the reason of it, whereupon she told him all. "Then," says the old Japanese narrator, "he thinking it to be a very piteous thing, his eyes grew dark with tears."

# JOHN ERSKINE

*A mother finds that her own dramatic past makes her daughter heedless of her practical advice about love in* The Private Life of Helen of Troy.

"IF YOU INSIST on knowing my reasons," said Hermione, "they are three, as nearly as I can take an inventory at short notice. In the first place, I don't love him. In the second place, I do love Orestes. In the third place, Pyrrhus is a good deal of a brute, from all I have heard, and the strong-handed sort of husband doesn't appeal to me. I wonder that you continue the discussion. Let Pyrrhus come; I will look at him, as you wish, and then he can go home. All this talk makes me care less for him every day."

"If my object were merely to arrange a marriage between you and Pyrrhus," said Helen, "I certainly would not talk so much about it; I realize that the effect may be as you say. You may come to hate the sound of his name, and you may develop a strong dislike for me. When you see him, perhaps you will like him in spite of all that I have said in his favor. But however that may be, I wish you to become acquainted with a few plain truths about marriage, which most girls learn too late. It is your education I have set my heart on, even more than your marriage. If there were another way to bring the ideas to your mind, I wouldn't put them into words. Forgive me if I weary you, Hermione. Perhaps you could understand my point of view, if you made the effort; we of the elder generation have a point of view, you know. It comes from having brought children into the world. We wish to give them a better life than we had. The only way is to put our experience at their disposal. But nothing annoys the young so much. Now I don't pretend to know everything about love, but I know a great deal more than you do, and your three reasons for not considering Pyrrhus seem to me absurd. Don't be angry! Some day they will seem so to you, even though you continue to love Orestes."

"They don't seem absurd to me now," said Hermione, "and I'm the one who has to decide."

"You are," said Helen, "and I want you to decide with your eyes open, without deceiving yourself. You don't love Pyrrhus, you say. Why should you? You haven't met him. But he is coming here in a few weeks. I'm not asking you to lose your heart to him; I'm giving you fair warning that though you haven't seen him, and though you are now, as you think, in love with another man, you may wish you belonged to Pyrrhus, body and soul, twenty-four hours after you have met him. Don't think you are the one woman in history to whom that could not happen."

"If you mean that Orestes isn't so remarkable a person as Pyrrhus," said Hermione, "I am willing to accept your opinion. That is, I don't agree with it, but I don't mind your thinking so. You may be quite right. But that is no reason why I should hesitate a moment where my heart is committed once for all. Some men and some women are made for each other. I believe there is a destined mate for each one of us, if we are only lucky enough to find each other. Orestes and I are mates, that's all there is to it. Pyrrhus may be as wonderful as you say, but he is not my fate. It's no use arguing; I feel it."

"You feel that Orestes and you," said Helen, "were fashioned and preserved for each other, the product and climax of happy stars? I know the feeling well. I've had it several times, for different men. It's nature's fine way of saying that at the moment we want him very much. Haven't you ever seen a child, at first sight of a doll, clasp it to her arms and cry, 'That's my doll?' What we want very much always seems destined."

"You don't believe in people being spiritual mates?"

"They may become so in time," said Helen, "but it takes a great deal of adjustment, so much so that rather than be pessimistic about the accuracy of heavenly patterns, I'd rather say there are no predestined couples, no separated parts which brought together make a harmonious whole. You can't believe that spiritual mate nonsense, my daughter, after the experience of having two or more sincere men in love with you at once. Both think you are their fate, and when you choose one, the other will never be convinced that you knew what your fate was. Very probably you didn't. And certainly you can't believe the theory after you find yourself in love a second time—the same passion, the same heart-ache, the same sense of destiny—but another man. When we are young we are all inclined to believe in the one person intended for us, and when we learn that our devoted hearts can break a second time, or even a third, we despise ourselves. Then gradually we come to accept the order of nature, that love can strike again and again, as our personalities develop and change, and our destinies are not so final as we supposed them to be."

"Mother, you talk as though nothing were stable in this world," said Hermione. "I can't agree; it seems impious. I prefer to be loyal."

"Nothing is stable in this world, Hermione, unless we ourselves are so," said Helen. "Loyalty is an achievement in our character—you don't find it growing around you like a plant, or hitting you like lightning. There's a world of difference between loyalty and love. Lovers are often loyal, from youth to old age, and their constancy is all the more admired for not being natural. When once you marry, love may leave you, but the problem of loyalty never will. I want you to choose the man to whom it will be easiest in the long run for you to be loyal, and I insist it's more a matter of choice than you think. You say you are in love with Orestes now, and you can't resist this fatal passion. I warn you, though of course you won't believe me, that you may be quite as much in love later with some one else. You would tell me, I'm sure, that the second love can be resisted and should be. I agree that it can be—and so can the first."

"If you are drawing on your experience to advise me," said Hermione, "I'd like to ask you more about your life than seems quite proper; I doubt if a girl ought to ask such things of her mother."

"I'll tell you anything I know," said Helen, "and you are welcome to ask anything you can think of."

"Well, if you feel this way about love," said Hermione, "I can't see why you didn't stay with my father. You could very well have resisted your love for Paris; you could have set me an example of loyalty. I am confused, I must confess, between what you have done and what you advise."

"Dear child," said Helen, "there's no connection between them!"

"That's what I thought," said Hermione.

"No, indeed," said Helen. "I should never in the world advise you to do what I've done. It would be useless. You couldn't do it. And even if you could, you haven't my reasons for it."

"I agree that I couldn't imitate your life," said Hermione, "but I don't think you ought to say it as though it were a gift which I didn't inherit. We shall never think the same way as to what kind of life is desirable. I fear I can't imagine any reason which would justify your going off with Paris."

"I had no intention of justifying my life, Hermione—neither to you nor to anybody else. But your question made me think of the reasons for my actions, whether they are justified or not. Let me advise you not to justify your life after it is lived; at that stage it will speak for itself. And don't judge the past actions of other people—it's too late to change them. You seem to me a little censorious as you pronounce upon my career. I object not because it's my career, but because any final verdicts on others seem presumptuous for a human being to make. I discuss your life so much because it is still in the future; what you have once done, however, I shall say nothing about."

"I meant no discourtesy," said Hermione, "and I do see why you are different from other people. You are so beautiful that ordinary rules seem not to apply."

"They didn't apply," said Helen, "but they ought to have done so, and I wanted them to. That is the whole trouble. I never wanted to be different from my fellows, and yet I've never felt that I was living in the same world with them. Can't you see how the situation would arise, and how fatal it would be? No one has the right to shut us out from any part of life, not even from hard things, from the sorrows and sufferings. They always said I was beautiful, but the only effect I could notice was that they treated me as if I weren't a human being. My whole life has been an attempt to put myself back among other people, to make sure I wasn't missing anything. I resented being excused from the ordinary rules of life. If I did wrong when I was a child, I wasn't punished. When I asked why they didn't punish me, they thought I was abnormally good, or very conscientious, but the fact was I wanted everything that was supposed to go with my conduct. As a young girl, foolish and inexperienced, my mistakes never brought me to harm. In marriage at least I expected to find reality; living with a man, I thought, would bring home to me the mortal drama in which we are supposed to be playing our parts; surely I should feel it if the marriage turned out unhappy. But I was more sheltered than ever—practically immune to life. It wearied me to be complimented still on my good looks, for the phrase was always a reason why they should cheat me of what I wanted most. I understood what is meant when men say beauty is a curse. Without sharp edges, life is a smooth habit, and meaningless. I gave myself to Paris because I loved him, but somewhere in my thoughts was the hope that our love would actually be the great tragedy it seemed to promise, and that in the end I should suffer and feel. But my days in Troy might have been so many seconds in a dream; no one took me seriously; no one, not even Priam, upbraided me for ruining the city—not even Hector, who on general principles disapproved of Paris and me. When the end came, I said to myself, I shall live at last, for Menelaos will surely kill me. Your father will never know what was in my mind as I saw the anger go out of his face, and that sheltering look come back into it. It isn't exactly that he has forgiven me, but I am not counted in the same world with other people—I'm a sort of wraith. When he thinks of Paris and me, and I'm not in his presence, he feels murderous, I believe; but if I'm there when he remembers, he is, as you might say, merely annoyed. Hermione, the reason I have such a desire for life, the reason I want you to love life early, is that I have never lived. But in my search for the real things, I've learned to grasp at strict honesty with myself and complete frankness about myself with other people; it's my only hope. When you wished to save my reputation by saying I was in Egypt, never in Troy, don't you see what you robbed me of? For all of us, I'm sure, insincerity becomes a screen between life and our souls, but it would be particularly dangerous for me. I am as far away as I can get from the so-called respectable whose respectability means only that they are afraid to live."

"I doubt if I am so beautiful," said Hermione, "that I need follow your methods in order to make the acquaintance of sorrow. That's what you intimate, I suppose. But what has this to do with my choice of a husband?"

"You observed quite correctly," said Helen, "that my advice differed from my conduct. I have been explaining my conduct. Now let's come back to the advice. Or rather, to your reasons for not liking Pyrrhus. You said Orestes is your fate. I've expressed my opinion of that theory, applied to Orestes or any one else. You also said, if I remember, that Pyrrhus is a brute. Just what did you mean?"

"He has bloody hands, I think. I don't care to marry a murderer."

"He was a terrible fighter, if that's what you mean," said Helen. "Do you prefer Orestes because he wasn't at the war?"

"Oh, no," said Hermione. "I mean that Pyrrhus killed Polyxena afterward. I know there was some story about his being obliged to offer her up on his father's tomb, for some good reason, but that sort of thing belongs to another age, as far as Orestes and I are concerned. It was plain murder, no matter how you explain it; it was no better than the sacrifice of Iphigeneia, when the fleet was sailing. When I think of your hero, that big strong man you praise to me, seizing a frail girl, dragging her to his distinguished father's tomb, bending back her head, and cutting her throat, as we do the animals at a sacrifice—I hate him and everything about him. Do you think I could love him, and give myself up to his arms? I'd always think of that other girl, and wonder whether he'd like to make a pious offering of me. He killed Priam, too, they say—at the last moment, when the desperate old man tried to fight. A feeble dotard, who couldn't have harmed a child. Pyrrhus is a brute, and I rather think his father was too. Achilles liked to brain people, or cut them to pieces. Didn't he kill a girl once—the Amazon? Ran his spear right through her!"

"I've often thought of these killings," said Helen, "and with much the same horror as you express, but though there's evidently a good deal of wrong in it all, it's hard to know what is right. You say you can't bear to think of sacrificing a girl as we slay animals on the altars?"

"I certainly can't."

"But you don't object to sacrificing the animals?"

"Why should I? It's a ceremony—that's what they're for!"

"I dare say there are people," said Helen, "who shudder at the thought of drawing the knife across the throat of the poor sheep. Our religion is rather bloody, anyway, don't you think?"

"I see your argument," said Hermione; "you want me to say that the sacrifices aren't bloody, and then you'll say that Pyrrhus acted from a religious motive, and therefore he isn't brutal. Well, I really think our altars are barbarous—we should have outgrown them long ago, as we have outgrown human sacrifices."

"Many people feel that way," said Helen. "But if we kill the sheep for food, you have no prejudice against eating them, I know. If you consider meat for dinner a cannibalistic custom, you manage to hide your opinion."

"How foolish, mother! Of course we eat meat. Why shouldn't we?"

"The sheep might have an argument against it," said Helen, "but I have none. I merely wondered at what point you are at ease in the presence of what you call murder. I see. The animal slaughtered for religious purposes has your pity, but the one served up on your table fulfills its destiny as something for you to eat."

"I can't follow you when you are facetious. What am I to understand? Do you approve of human sacrifices? Do you think it was right to kill those two girls?"

"I wouldn't have killed them myself," said Helen, "yet in war men and women are sacrificed, in quite a religious sense, to the divine ends people think the war is serving. Whether it is good or bad for them to be sacrificed, I don't know. Nobody knows. But few object. If it is right to sacrifice people in war, I don't know what argument you could make against the altars. If you regret the sacrifice of those girls, you are regretting merely that they didn't exist for a few more years. You don't know what those extra years would have been like. If they were to be uneventful—I mean, inwardly so—if they were to be an unreal, unimportant number of breaths drawn, and meals eaten, and nights slept away, without any sense of living, then perhaps it was better for them to crowd many deep and strong emotions into a few hours. Don't think I'm against your humane tendencies, Hermione; I'm merely comparing the two girls you spoke of, sacrificed barbarously as they were, with myself, who have missed the excitements and enthusiasms of life, as I just told you."

"You don't mean," said Hermione, "you wish Menelaos had killed you?"

"I was disappointed," said Helen. "No, I didn't want to die, but I did hope to know at least the terrors of life—and then your father became humane, as you perhaps think, and I knew there was nothing for it but years even less eventful than before, old age creeping up on our dull hearts—unless I could find a vital happiness in guiding you to a real life. I've said enough, and there's no use repeating it, but if you had my passion for living, all the greater because it has been thwarted, you'd take Pyrrhus, reckless and brutal as he seems, instead of that cautious and safe cousin of yours."

"You would, but I wouldn't, and I won't," said Hermione. "It isn't simply the killing. He has taken women home as slaves, and he has the old-fashioned idea of a hero's rights over the women he captures. They say Agamemnon brought Cassandra home, and you told me yourself you feared Clytemnestra would be jealous. Of course she would, though I'm sure Cassandra means nothing to my uncle. Orestes is sure she doesn't. But Pyrrhus is living with Andromache, Hector's widow, and probably with the other women he acquired at Troy. That's the kind of hero he is, and I say he's a brute and out of date. Orestes sees these things as I do; I fancy most people of our age feel the same way. I didn't realize how antiquated some of your notions are, mother, nor how conventional until you began to urge Pyrrhus on me. I can just fancy myself as a further addition to his large herd—and my children playing cheerfully some day with Andromache's!"

"You are right again," said Helen—"partly right. The part you don't see, however, is the essence of the matter. I hesitate to answer you now, Hermione, for though I'm frank enough on any subject, there are things I'd rather not speak of unless to do so would be of service to you. This may well be the last time we discuss these questions; I've said all I could and told you all I know. Or almost all. I'll tell you the rest now. You'd like to have your man all to yourself. So would any woman who is in love— and men feel the same way about women. Love is very proprietary. But you go a step further, as I've noticed in others of your generation, and you want your man never to have cared for any one else. I dare say Orestes wouldn't feel sure of a wife who had previously lost her heart to another man. Now, that's all nonsense. If the world is to act on that philosophy, there's misery in store for lovers—all sorts of hypocrisy, and dark secrets, and skeletons in the closet. It's your notion of destined mates again, but in a sillier form. Of course, when two people love each other—it's safer to say, while they love—the rest of the race, for them, will not exist; in that sense you ought to have your lover quite to yourself. I should hate to see you married to Pyrrhus unless you loved him passionately, and he you. But let me tell you this, Hermione—the man who can make a woman most happy is the one who could love many women, who even has lived with several of them, perhaps as Pyrrhus has done, and who at last devotes all his love to her alone. By your theory, the best husband ought to be the man who couldn't possibly have loved before. Your theory is wrong. That kind of man, you'll find, quite frequently is incapable of loving anybody very much. . . . I suppose you think this wisdom of mine immoral."

"I do," said Hermione.

# ENID BAGNOLD

### ✖ ✖

*National Velvet shows a sturdy mother's concern for
the future of a sensitive, high-strung girl.*

THE CANDLE in the scarlet-painted candlestick was burnt low
and had a shroud. The bottle-candle was high and gave a good
light.

Spring and evening sky showed between undrawn cotton curtains.

Mrs. Brown sat on a stout mahogany chair before her dressing
table, and Velvet knelt behind her unhooking her dress from neck
to waist at the back. The dress was dark blue rep, built firm. It
was like unhooking the strain on a shrunk sofa-covering. Hook
after hook Velvet travelled down till at last she reached far below
the waist. Then Mrs. Brown stood up and the dark blue dress
dropped to the floor, leaving her in a princess petticoat like a great
cotton lily. The strings of this, untied at neck and waist by Velvet,
disclosed her in bust-bodice, stays and dark-blue cloth knickers.

"The iodine's in the wall cupboard," said mother.

Velvet went to the wall cupboard and extracted the iodine from
an army of bottles and jars.

" 'N' the cotton wool," said mother.

Velvet, behind her, undid the strings of the bust-bodice. Got
down to bedrock, she knelt and examined the wound.

"Mus' take your stays off, mother."

Mrs. Brown rose and drew breath. Working from the bottom up
she unhooked the metal fencework within which she lived, and
sat down again. "Star out," she said, staring through the window.
The star was like a slip of silver tinfoil plumb between the hang
of the curtains.

"M'm," said Velvet, and she glanced at the star over her

mother's shoulder. "Metal's worked right through the top of the stays and cut you," said Velvet.

"Ought to get whalebone," said Mrs. Brown, sniffing at her own economy.

"Yes," said Velvet, "you ought. S'made a nasty place." She dabbed the iodine on the abrasion caused by the jutting shaft of the stays. "Hurt?"

"Stings," said Mrs. Brown. The star winked and stuttered.

"Stick on a band-aid piece," said Mrs. Brown. "Thur's a tin'n the cupboard."

Velvet stuck the plaster on to the wide hard back.

Mrs. Brown glared at the star.

"Pray to God y'don't get fat, child," she said.

Velvet sat back on her heels aghast.

"You can't *be*," said Mrs. Brown, "what you don't *look*."

"You can, you can!" said Velvet. "You *are*, mother!"

"Maybe," said Mrs. Brown. . . . "But you gotter dig. You gotter know. You gotter believe."

Velvet put her thin arms on her mother's shoulders and kissed her on the enemy fat. She winced at a sign of regret or weakness in the beloved mountain.

"There's nothing, *nothing* you can't do, mother. You've got us all beat. Mi thinks you're Godalmighty. N'we all do."

Mrs. Brown smiled in the glass. "Chut, child! Don't mount up in a torment. M'not grumbling. M'out of condition, but it came on me. I'm only saying . . . you poor, thin hairpin . . . KEEP thin! There's no song an' dance . . ." Mrs. Brown was bolting herself back into the fence. She stood upright.

"S'awful to grow up," said Velvet.

"Nope," said Mrs. Brown.

"Why isn't it?"

"Things come suitable to the time," said Mrs. Brown.

The thin slip, the quivering twig looked back at her mother.

"Lot o' nonsense," said Mrs. Brown, "talked about growing up." She stepped into her princess petticoat and drew it up. "Tie me," she said. The candle in the red candlestick drowned itself in fat and went out. "Childbirth," said the voice, gruff and soothing, talking to the star and to the child (and the child knelt at the strings of the petticoat), "an' being in love. An' death. You can't know 'em till you come to 'em. No use guessing and dreading. You kin call it pain. . . . But what's pain? Depends on who you are an' how you take it. Tie that bottom string looser. Don't you dread nothing, Velvet."

"But you're so mighty. Like a tree," said Velvet.

"Shivery to be your age. You don't know nuthin'. Later on you get coated over." (Silence, and the hypnotic night.) "S'a good thing to be coated over. You don't change nothin' underneath."

"All the same it's awful to grow up," said Velvet. "All this changing and changing, an' got to be ready for something. I don't ever want children. Only horses."

"Who can tell?" said Mrs. Brown.

"I've got Me," said Velvet, putting her thin hand across her breast. "I can't ever be anything else but Me."

"You're all safe," said Mrs. Brown carelessly, stooping with grunts to pull up her dress. "You got both of us, you *an'* me. Say your prayers now an' get along."

"Not yet, not yet."

"Say your prayers, I say. Down on your knees an' say your prayers. You go plunging off this time o' night, don't you? Getting into your bed all of a daze an' a worry. Say your prayers, I say!"

Velvet went on her knees in the middle of the floor. Mrs. Brown sat down, the dress in wreaths around her, and took a knife to her nails.

"Ah . . .v'Farver . . . ch . . . art'n'eaven," mumbled the voice from the floor. The blue in the window had gone and the star had companions.

". . . powern'a GloryamEN. Mother . . ."

"Yes."

"You're all right, aren't you?"

"M'as good as living forever. Get on off to bed. N'I'm not comin' to say good-night. Father is."

Velvet kissed her. "Come an' say good-night . . ."

"No, I'm not. Hook me up before you go." Velvet nicked up the great line of steely hooks to the top.

"Now go." Velvet went.

"Child gets all alight at night," said Mrs. Brown to herself.

Velvet's head came back round the door.

"Good-night, mother—where you going?"

"Down the village."

"What for?"

"Will you GO!"

Mrs. Brown went down the village with the key of the empty shop in her pocket. She had accounts to finish. The Hullocks rose above her in hoops into the sky. The stars floated in the olive glaze of the weedy pond. The boys and the girls were hushed, black and still, against the doorways. Edwina stood like a statue at the cobbler's doorway as her mother passed, but her mother knew her.

"Growing," muttered Mrs. Brown as she went on. "Poor lass has to hide it."

The beautiful boy beside Edwina breathed again. He was golden-haired, and trying for the police. He felt he had no real chance for Mr. Brown's Edwina, and he had no idea he was her first, her breath-taking first man.

"What'll Velvet . . .?" murmured Mrs. Brown, looking a moment at the sky, and seeing Velvet's bony, fairy face. "What'll men say about my Velvet?"

# JOHN STEINBECK

⚥ ⚥

*In* The Grapes of Wrath, *an Okie mother manages to contrive some hope and comfort for her pregnant daughter.*

ROSE OF SHARON moved sluggishly about her work. Ma inspected her cautiously. "You feelin' pretty good? Your cheeks is kinda saggy."

"I ain't had milk like they said I ought."

"I know. We jus' didn' have no milk."

Rose of Sharon said dully, "Ef Connie hadn' went away, we'd a had a little house by now, with him studyin' an' all. Would a got milk like I need. Would a had a nice baby. This here baby ain't gonna be no good. I ought a had milk." She reached in her apron pocket and put something into her mouth.

Ma said, "I seen you nibblin' on somepin. What you eatin'?"

"Nothin'."

"Come on, what you nibblin' on?"

"Jus' a piece a slack lime. Foun' a big hunk."

"Why, tha's jus' like eatin' dirt."

"I kinda feel like I wan' it."

Ma was silent. She spread her knees and tightened her skirt. "I know," she said at last. "I et coal oncet when I was in a fambly way. Et a big piece a coal. Granma says I shouldn'. Don' you say that about the baby. You got no right even to think it."

"Got no husban'! Got no milk!"

Ma said, "If you was a well girl, I'd take a whang at you. Right in the face." She got up and went inside the tent. She came out and stood in front of Rose of Sharon, and she held out her hand. "Look!" The small gold earrings were in her hand. "These is for you."

The girl's eyes brightened for a moment, and then she looked aside. "I ain't pierced."

"Well, I'm a-gonna pierce ya." Ma hurried back into the tent. She came back with a cardboard box. Hurriedly she threaded a needle, doubled the thread and tied a series of knots in it. She threaded a second needle and knotted the thread. In the box she found a piece of cork.

"It'll hurt. It'll hurt."

Ma stepped to her, put the cork in back of the ear lobe and pushed the needle through the ear, into the cork.

The girl twitched. "It sticks. It'll hurt."

"No more'n that."

"Yes, it will."

"Well, then. Le's see the other ear first." She placed the cork and pierced the other ear.

"It'll hurt."

"Hush!" said Ma. "It's all done."

Rose of Sharon looked at her in wonder. Ma clipped the

needles off and pulled one knot of each thread through the lobes.

"Now," she said. "Ever' day we'll pull one knot, and in a couple weeks it'll be all well an' you can wear 'em. Here—they're your'n now. You can keep 'em."

Rose of Sharon touched her ears tenderly and looked at the tiny spots of blood on her fingers. "It didn't hurt. Jus' stuck a little."

"You oughta been pierced long ago," said Ma. She looked at the girl's face, and she smiled in triumph. "Now get them dishes all done up. Your baby gonna be a good baby. Very near let you have a baby without your ears was pierced. But you're safe now."

"Does it mean somepin?"

"Why, 'course it does," said Ma. "Course it does."

# KATHRYN FORBES

🌾 🌾

*The ingenuity of a mother can triumph over almost any obstacle when a little girl is sick, as witness this episode from* Mama's Bank Account.

## "Mama and the Hospital"

MAMA had tried everything she knew of to stop poor little Dagmar's earache. She'd warmed sweet oil and garlic, used the medicine Mr. Shultz had sent from the drugstore, but nothing had helped.

When Dr. Johnson came, he told Mama that Dagmar must be taken to the hospital.

"At once," he said. "We will have to operate."

I watched Mama's eyes grow dark with fright.

"Can wait?" she asked. "Until my husband comes home from work?"

"No time," the doctor said. "You must decide this morning. An immediate operation is her best chance."

Operation! Mama took a deep breath.

"We go," she said, and took down the Little Bank and emptied its contents onto the kitchen table. Then she looked up at the doctor. "Is enough?" she asked hopefully.

The doctor looked uncomfortable. "I was thinking of the County Hospital," he explained.

"No," Mama said. "No. We pay."

"Well, then, take her to the Clinic Hospital."

"Clinic?"

"Yes. There you pay what you can afford," Dr. Johnson explained. "Your child will have the same care as the other patients."

Mama looked worried. "I—I do not understand so well."

"Just leave it to me, then. Dagmar will be well taken care of, I promise you. I myself will do the operation."

"Is so good of you," Mama said gratefully, and sent Nels for a blanket to wrap around Dagmar. And because Papa was at work, Nels and I went to the hospital with Mama.

When we got there, two nurses put Dagmar on a high table and started to wheel her down the hall. Mama tried to go along too.

"She is my little girl," Mama explained.

"Hospital rules," the nurse said firmly. "You must wait here."

Mama obediently let go of Dagmar's hand then, and walked with slow steps to the desk. They gave her papers to sign, but she didn't even try to read them. Her eyes kept looking down the hall.

Nels and I had never been in a hospital before. With great interest we watched ladies in blue-and-white uniforms and important-looking men with little black bags hurry in and out of doors; watched the cleaning women as they took mops and buckets and long-handled brooms out of the closet by the elevator.

"Dr. Johnson is *fine* doctor," Mama said suddenly. "Surely Dagmar will be all right."

I started to cry then, and Mama patted my shoulder, and told stories of the old country. But somehow, Mama didn't tell the stories as well as usual; she kept forgetting parts of them.

When Dr. Johnson came hurrying down the hall, Mama stood up quickly.

"Dagmar came through it fine," he told us. "She is sleeping now, from the anesthetic."

Mama smiled tremulously and shook hands twice with the doctor.

"I go to her now," she said happily.

Dr. Johnson coughed. "Sorry. Against clinic rules. See her tomorrow."

"But she is so *little*," Mama said. "When she wakes she will be frightened."

"The nurses will take excellent care of her. Don't worry. You see, for the first twenty-four hours, clinic patients are not allowed visitors. The wards must be kept quiet. No interruption of routine."

Mama didn't seem to understand. "I will not make a *sound*," she said.

Dr. Johnson looked at his watch, lifted his hat politely, and hurried out of the hospital.

Mama looked bewildered. "Come," she said to Nels and to me. "Come. We go find Dagmar."

The nurse at the desk had quite a time explaining hospital rules to Mama.

"Your child is getting the best of care, Madam," the lady kept repeating.

"Is *fine* hospital," Mama agreed. "I see her now?"

"*No* visitors for the first twenty-four hours, madam."

"Am *not* visitor," Mama explained patiently, "I am her Mama."

"*Against-the-rules!*" The nurse spoke loudly and slowly and with great finality.

Mama stood looking down the hall for such a long time that I had to touch her arm to remind her that Nels and I were still there.

She held my hand tightly as we walked to the streetcar and never said a word all the way home.

Christine had kept lunch hot for us, but Mama just drank two cups of coffee. She did not take off her hat.

"We must think of some way," she worried, and we children sat very still.

"They'll let you see Dagmar tomorrow," Nels reminded her. "They said so."

"But unless I see her today," Mama asked, "how will I know that all is well with her? What can I tell Papa when he comes home from work?"

She shook her head. "No. *Today* I see Dagmar."

She stood up suddenly and took paper and string out of the kitchen drawer. Carefully, she wrapped Dagmar's little doll in one neat package and our big picture book in another. We watched uneasily.

"It will be like this," Mama explained. "I will go past the hospital desk very quickly. If anyone asks where I go, I will just say, 'Delivering packages to Dagmar.'"

When Mama came back—still carrying the packages—we knew she'd been unsuccessful. We knew, too, that she was upset, because she answered us in Norwegian.

"Almost," she said wearily, "almost did I get down the hall."

Then she tied the big apron around her waist, filled the bucket with hot, soapy water, and started to scrub the kitchen floor.

"You scrubbed yesterday," Christine reminded her.

"And the floor isn't a speck dirty," I said.

"It's almost time to get dinner," Nels protested.

"Comes a time," Mama answered strangely, "when you must get down on your knees."

And the whiteness of her face made me want to cry again.

Mama had scrubbed all but the part near the back door when she stood up suddenly and handed the scrub brush to Christine.

"You finish the floor. Katrin, you come with me." And she sent me for my coat.

"Come where, Mama?"

"To the hospital." Her face was serene. "I have thought of way to see Dagmar sure."

We walked in so quietly that the nurse at the desk didn't even look up. Mama motioned for me to sit in the big chair by the door. While I watched—mouth open in surprise—Mama took off her hat and coat and gave them to me to hold. Only then did I notice that she'd kept her apron on. She tiptoed over to the big closet by the elevator and took out a damp mop. She pushed the mop past the desk and as the nurse looked up, Mama nodded brightly.

"Very dirty floors," Mama said.

"Yes. I'm glad they've finally decided to clean them," the nurse answered. She looked at Mama curiously. "Aren't you working late?"

Mama just pushed more vigorously, each swipe of the mop taking her farther and farther down the hall. I watched until she was out of sight and the nurse had turned back to writing in the big book. Then I saw that I had held Mama's hat so tightly, one side was all out of shape.

After a long time, Mama came back. Her eyes were shining.

While the nurse stared with amazement, Mama placed the mop neatly back in the closet, put on her hat and coat, and took my hand. As we turned to go out the door, Mama bowed politely to the nurse and said, "Thank you."

Outside, Mama told me: "Dagmar is fine. No fever. I felt her forehead."

"You *saw* her, Mama?"

"Of course. She wakened while I was with her. I told her about clinic rules, she will not expect us until tomorrow."

"You won't try to see her again," I asked, "before then?"

"Why," Mama said, "that would be against the rules. Besides, I have seen for myself that all goes well with her. Papa will not worry, now."

I swallowed hard.

"Is a *fine* hospital," Mama said happily.

Then she clicked her tongue disapprovingly. "But such floors! A mop is never good. Floors should be scrubbed with a brush."

# ROSEMARY TAYLOR

🐞 🐞

*As it happens, mother's modesty is one of the facts*
*of life revealed to her daughter in* Chicken Every
Sunday.

## "A Little Sin at Midnight"

THE FIRST BOARDERS I can remember are Miss Gilley and
Mr. Robinson. Mr. Robinson was sleeping with Miss Gilley, and
that was why Mother told me the facts of life. She hadn't intended telling me so soon, but there was Mr. Robinson tiptoeing
into Miss Gilley's room at night—it *was* footsteps Mother heard
and not creaks as Father said—and there was that business of the
Indian jumping at Miss Gilley from the bushes, which was
really the reason for Mr. Robinson's going into her room. Naturally all this was pretty puzzling to a child of seven, and I was
pestering Mother with questions.

"All this" happened in Tucson where Mother and Father had
come after Father bought the laundry.

With part of the money they got from their property in
Phoenix they bought two lots in Tucson and built the "big
house." We call it the big house, for after a while Mother built a
little house in back of it.

But when they built there wasn't a house between us and the
Catalinas to the north. About a mile away to the east was the
university. (Father loved to tell how Tucson happened to get the
university instead of the insane asylum, which was what it really
wanted.) A half mile to the west was the Indian school and the
Roskruge Grade School, where I went, and which was the reason
we got Miss Gilley and so many other teachers as boarders.

Uncle Harry, Father's brother, said, "I think you two are crazy to build so far out; the town will never catch up with you." (And now we're zoned for business.)

A streetcar drawn by two little horses linked us to town and went on through open country to the university. Father was the manager of the streetcar company—yes, he'd got into that shortly after coming to Tucson. This was convenient for Mother when she forgot to order the meat in time for the morning delivery. She could telephone Pusch and Zellweger to put her chops on the streetcar. Then when the car got in front of our house, the driver yelled, "Whoa!" wound his reins around the whip, and delivered the meat to Mother. Yes, sometimes the passengers complained.

Mother had had boarders in Phoenix—I remember some of them vaguely—but now Father said why did she have any more. After all, Mother had three children now—me, the oldest; Phillip; and Oliver, the baby. Besides, in spite of Mother's predictions that the laundry would go broke because Father had put his barber in charge of it, it was really doing awfully well.

"Take in boarders if you like," Father said, "but you don't have to. I think it would be nice to have our home to ourselves for a while."

So Mother was a little surprised when shortly after that Father asked her if she wouldn't take in Mr. Robinson for a month or two.

Mr. Robinson was a mining man, from a company back east that had a lot of money, and he was looking for prospects.

"Robinson hates living in a hotel," Father said, "and you know how it is—he'll be sitting around that lobby and someone will sell him a mine."

"And why," Mother wanted to know, "do you care if someone sells him a mine?"

"Because," explained Father, "then he probably won't buy the Oro Blanco."

"Oro Blanco?" puzzled Mother.

"It means white gold. Pretty name, isn't it?"

Mother put her hand to her head. "Don't tell me you've bought a mine!"

Bought the Oro Blanco! Not at all. He just had an option on it. And if Mr. Robinson's company took it over, Father's commission might easily be $25,000." "And," gloated Father, "You can't sneeze at $25,000."

"No, you can't," Mother agreed, "not until you have it."

So Mr. Robinson moved in with us, but Mother didn't put him in the big front room. She put him in the room next to it, the middle room. She put a schoolteacher, Miss Gilley, in the front room.

"Well," reasoned Mother, "if we're going to have one boarder, we might as well have two. Miss Gilley will be here all the year and will pay me $40 a month. And," said Mother firmly, "I don't sneeze at $40."

Miss Gilley taught history and girls' athletics and was a great big blond woman who didn't wear corsets. She was always telling Mother not to lace so much, and Mother said she didn't lace at all. But Miss Gilley said no one could have as small a waist as Mother and not lace, and that she'd pushed herself all up and down.

"Am I all up and down?" I heard Mother ask Father once. And Father said of course she was and wasn't she glad she had an up and down and wasn't all level like Miss Gilley.

Mr. Robinson didn't seem to mind Miss Gilley's being level, for he liked her very much. "Your food is wonderful," he told Mother, "but what I like best is the kind of people you take in." And he would smile at Miss Gilley.

"Do you think those two are sweet on each other?" Father asked Mother.

"I shouldn't be surprised," Mother said.

Mr. Robinson always brought Miss Gilley a box of candy when he came back from his trips. He brought us children a box, too. And he used to give us specimens. He'd open up his bags and give each one of us two or three pretty stones and tell us, "Now that's molybdenite. And that's porphyry. And that's malachite." Then he'd tie up the bags very carefully and put them in the hall closet and say to us, "Now you children wouldn't salt them on me, would you?"

Father had specimens, too, and he was always trying to show them to Mr. Robinson. "That's from the Oro Blanco's new crosscut, and here's something from Level No. 6." And Mr. Robinson would nod his head and say, "Yes, yes. Very nice." Then he'd look around and ask, "Where's Miss Gilley? When is she coming out?"

Miss Gilley was very peculiar in one way. She was scared to death of Indians. Even though Father told her there hadn't been any bad Indians around Tucson for years, Miss Gilley still felt the only good Indian was a dead Indian. Of course in those days there were lots of Indians about. There was old Meta who came to wash for us every Monday—except the Mondays she had a baby and then she came Tuesdays—and the Indians who used to sell us wood, and the boys and girls from the Indian school. Sometimes we had Indian girls as cooks, but when Miss Gilley was there we had Ruth, a darky from Georgia.

Miss Gilley's room had an outside entrance, and she didn't like the latch on the French doors. She said anyone could push those doors open with one good push, and even if she screamed we were so far away no one would hear her. Mr. Robinson said he'd surely hear her and would come right in to rescue her. But lots of times Mr. Robinson wasn't there, and then Miss Gilley was far away from anybody, for we slept on a big screen porch at the rear of the house—all five of us, in five beds, lined up like a dormitory. Mother thought fresh air was good for us, and if it was good for us in the daytime it was good for us at night. And besides, that way we had more rooms to rent.

So Mother put a big bolt on the French doors to keep out the Indians, and Miss Gilley felt happier. But Mother didn't put any bolt on the door into the little hall that led into Mr. Robinson's room.

However, the Indian didn't try to push in the French doors. He jumped at Miss Gilley from the bushes.

I remember it was just at dinnertime when it happened. Mother had put Oliver to bed and was helping Ruth bring on the ham and vegetables when we heard screams and footsteps running on the porch, and in burst Miss Gilley in a dreadful state. She fell into a chair, and kept swallowing and swallowing, and trying to tell us something. You could hear her heart, it was beating so hard.

"Indian . . . he . . . he . . ." and she'd stop and wave toward the street with a long purse she was carrying.

"Was someone trying to get your purse?" Mother asked.

"Not my purse—not my *purse!*" And she let out another shriek.

"What *was* he trying to get, Miss Gilley?" asked my brother Phillip. Phillip was always the one who asked the questions.

"You children go on out," Mother ordered, and, "Ruth, put the dinner back on the stove."

Father came from his room where he'd been having a before-dinner snooze, and we children listened at the swinging door that led into the pantry. Little by little we pushed the door open until we were back in the dining room again.

Finally Miss Gilley got out what had happened, how she'd been walking home from town, not wanting to wait for the horsecar, and across the street, right in front of our house, where the bushes were thick because of the little arroyo, an Indian—a great big Indian—had leaped out at her. And she said again, "He wasn't after my purse, but I hit him with it." She started to scream again.

"Now, now," soothed Mother, "you've got to get hold of yourself."

"We must call the police!" cried Miss Gilley. "Maybe he's left footprints. Maybe they can track him down with bloodhounds."

Father said he didn't think the town had any bloodhounds. But he called Ed Peters, the chief of police, and then he went outside to look for footprints.

"Did you find any?" Miss Gilley asked when he came back in.

"No," said Father, "not a footprint. But I found the Indian. He's lying out there in the street. You said you hit him, didn't you?"

"As hard as I could."

"Hard enough. He's out cold. Smells to high heaven of booze, too. He's just a little fellow, looks about seventeen. Probably one of those boys from the Indian school."

"But it was a great big Indian," protested Miss Gilley.

"No, he's little. I dragged him into the yard."

"Into the yard?" gasped Miss Gilley and Mother at the same time.

"He was on the streetcar tracks. Did you want him run over? Do you want," asked Father severely, "to destroy the evidence?"

"I want to see the Indian," cried Phillip and dashed out with me after him. He was a little one, too, in blue overalls and a purple shirt. Phillip leaned down and smelled him. "Nasty," he said.

But Father came out and dragged us back into the house, and Miss Gilley was now saying that if only Mr. Robinson were there.

Mother said what could Mr. Robinson do more than they were doing, and for her to go to bed and have her dinner on a tray.

Miss Gilley said, oh, dear, she couldn't sleep in that room away off by herself and Mother said for her to go into Mr. Robinson's room, that the sheets were clean on the bed, and she'd be nearer us.

So Miss Gilley went into Mr. Robinson's room, and Mother asked Father if there was any danger of the Indian coming to and getting away.

"I don't think so," said Father, "but maybe I ought to bring him in here where we can watch him." So father lugged him in and dumped him on the parlor floor. Then Ed Peters drove up and Mother took him in to talk to Miss Gilley. After a while they came out and Ed Peters said they'd have to get hold of the people who were selling liquor to Indians.

"She's crazy scared of Indians," Father told Ed Peters. "I don't believe that little fellow tried to do anything to her. I think he just stepped into the bushes to . . . well, you know what . . . and then came staggering out and fell against her."

"Sure," agreed Ed Peters, "probably held on to her to keep himself from falling."

"After all," Father went on, "if a man had that in mind, why would he pick on a woman twice his size?"

And Mother sniffed and said when men had that in mind they didn't ask how much a woman weighed.

Ruth brought in the dinner and Ed Peters took one look and one smell at the ham and said, my, wasn't that a good ham, and how he was simply crazy about ham.

Mother said for him to sit down and have some dinner with us, but Ed Peters said he'd better take the Indian over to the school and talk to the superintendent, and anyway he had to go home to his own dinner. But then he took another smell and said yes, he would have just one little bite.

So Ed Peters sat down and ate three slices of ham and some candied sweet potatoes and some baby Lima beans, and then he said he must get along to his own meal, and for Father to give him a hand.

"Mother," I asked, when they'd carried the Indian out, "if the Indian wasn't after Miss Gilley's purse, what *was* he after?"

"My dear," said Mother, "there are bad men in the world . . ." Then she stopped. "Probably," she began again, "he was after her beads, those pretty beads she wears."

Miss Gilley's beads were pretty. They were of turquoise and Mr. Robinson had brought them to her from New Mexico. Once or twice she had let me wear them.

Phillip said if he wanted the beads he wouldn't jump at her from the bushes; he'd wait until she took them off to wash her neck and then he'd get them.

"But you live here," I told him. "You know when she's in the bathroom."

"Now you children stop talking and eat your dinner," Mother ordered, "and put all this out of your mind entirely."

But I couldn't help thinking about it and somehow Mother's bead story didn't satisfy me.

One day just before lunch Mr. Robinson came back from Mexico. Of course we told him about the Indian, and he said if he'd been there he'd have torn the Indian limb from limb.

Mr. Robinson had a whole lot more specimens with him and some queer Mexican candy made of peanuts and brown sugar. Mother told us not to eat it before lunch. But we played with the specimens and Father brought out some of the Oro Blanco specimens which he said were from Level No. 7, and he said some people went chasing all over the country trying to find something when all the time it was in their own backyard.

That afternoon after school Mr. Robinson came up in a buggy and took Miss Gilley for a ride. They were gone so long they were late for dinner. Mother said it was all right with her if they wanted to eat burned-up roast.

Mr. Robinson said the roast wasn't burned; it was wonderful. Then he turned to Father and said, "I ran that Oro Blanco ore this afternoon and it's wonderful. Everything is wonderful." And he looked at Miss Gilley and laughed.

And that was the night I woke up and heard Mother and Father arguing about the footsteps.

"It's creaks," I heard Father say, "you know this house creaks."

"No," insisted Mother, "it's footsteps. I know a footstep from a creak."

"Well," demanded Father, "do we wait for her to scream, or do we go running in now and make damned fools of ourselves waking her out of a sound sleep?"

"She won't scream," said Mother. "I'm positive she's not going to scream."

Said Father, "You women! Nice charitable minds you have!"

"There . . . listen! Those are footsteps."

"Creaks," repeated Father. "Go to sleep."

"There . . . he's opened her door."

By this time I was wide awake. "Mother," I cried, sitting straight up in bed, "is Mr. Robinson after Miss Gilley's beads?"

Mother reached over and caught my arm. After a minute she said, "What's the matter, dear? Did you have a nightmare?"

"But I heard you and Father talking. . . ."

"You must have been dreaming. Lie down and go to sleep."

So I lay very still and took deep breaths pretending I was asleep.

Pretty soon they began to talk again, but this time they whispered.

From Mother, "The first thing tomorrow I tell them to go."

"W-h-a-t!" hissed Father, "just when he's going to buy the Oro Blanco, just when we're going to be on Easy Street."

Mother said Easy Street was Easy Street, and she'd like to have a look at that street, but there was also such a thing as easy virtue, and she wasn't going to have it in her house.

"There's such a thing as minding your own business, too. Just because a floor creaks. Women have the most suspicious minds. You have no proof, absolutely no proof. . . ."

"Keep your voice down or you'll wake that child again."

So then they talked so low I couldn't hear them.

In the morning Mother talked to me about my dream. She said yes, it was a very queer dream, and people often had queer dreams, but I mustn't mention it to anyone.

The queerest change came over our house after that. Mother got polite and called Miss Gilley "Miss Gilley" instead of "dear" or "honey," and Mr. Robinson "Mr. Robinson" and not "Mr. Man" as she usually did. And at the table she didn't say, "Pass your plate this way," or "Here's a chop with your name on it," but merely, "May I serve anyone anything?" Father looked worried and talked a lot, mostly about the Oro Blanco, and I knew something was terribly wrong.

Two or three times at night I woke up and heard the noises and heard Mother and Father arguing in whispers about them. Sometimes I thought Father was right—that they were creaks—and sometimes I sided with Mother and was sure they were footsteps. And once I heard Mother say, "I'm not going to put up with this much longer."

Then Mr. Robinson got a very bad cold. But Mother didn't make him any hot lemonade or tell him he ought to go to bed or in fact pay any attention to it.

Mr. Robinson's cold got worse and worse, and one Sunday he coughed so hard he could scarcely eat. Mother didn't mention it, but Father said, "You sound like a lunger. Are you doing anything for that cough?"

And Miss Gilley said, "I certainly am. I got up three times last night and rubbed his chest, and I . . ."

Then all of a sudden she stopped talking, and there was the strangest silence. I looked up from my drumstick to see what was the matter. Miss Gilley was fiery red and Mr. Robinson had his handkerchief over his face as if he were trying to hide it. Father was patting his mashed potatoes into a neat little mountain, and Mother looked pleased as anything.

"You say you got up three times last night and rubbed his chest," Mother repeated very carefully as if she hadn't heard Miss Gilley the first time.

Then Mr. Robinson came out from behind his handkerchief and gave a great big laugh. He slapped Miss Gilley on the back. "Well, old girl, you'll have to tell them now."

Miss Gilley and Mr. Robinson were married! They'd got married the afternoon they were late for dinner. They were going to wait until school was out, but because of the Indian Miss Gilley was afraid to sleep in the front room by herself. They didn't want to tell anyone, for in Tucson a schoolteacher had to give up her job when she got a husband, and Miss Gilley wanted to teach until the end of the year.

" 'Fraid cat—that's why I got her," laughed Mr. Robinson.

"Well, for Heaven's sake," said Mother, "as if you couldn't trust us not to tell."

And she kissed Miss Gilley, and Father shook hands with Mr. Robinson, and Miss Gilley kissed me, and Father got out the bottle of brandy Mother kept to flavor desserts, and we were all very happy. The brandy did Mr. Robinson's cold a lot of good, for he stopped coughing and sat there with his arm around Miss Gilley.

"You sure spilled the beans, old girl," he teased her.

But Mother said she hadn't at all, that what really spilled the beans was Mr. Robinson's tiptoeing around like an elephant.

Then she turned to Father. "You and your creaks!" she scoffed.

That night when I was helping Mother with the dishes—Ruth didn't come back for Sunday suppers—I asked her what I'd been wanting to ask all afternoon.

"Why," I demanded, "is it all right for Miss Gilley to rub Mr. Robinson's chest now, when it wasn't before?"

Mother swished the dishrag around furiously for a minute, and then she said, "I didn't intend to tell you so soon, but perhaps I'd better."

And she turned her back on me and ran a lot of water and began a long story about men and women loving each other and having babies and how it was all very beautiful and wonderful, and please would I bring her that platter to wash. She said maybe I wouldn't understand it all now, but I would later on, and anyway that was how God had arranged matters, and I'd just have to accept it.

Poor Mother. I can remember how embarrassed she was, and that's about all I can remember. She must have been pretty confusing, because for years I thought you got babies by rubbing people's chests.

# HORTENSE CALISHER

꽃 꽃

*A daughter finds a new understanding of herself as
she seeks a truer understanding of her mother in this
story from* In the Absence of Angels.

## "The Middle Drawer"

THE DRAWER was always kept locked. In a household where
the tangled rubbish of existence had collected on surfaces like
a scurf, which was forever being cleared away by her mother and
the maid, then by her mother, and, finally, hardly at all, it had
been a permanent cell—rather like, Hester thought wryly, the
gene that is carried over from one generation to the other. Now,
holding the small, square, indelibly known key in her hand, she
shrank before it, reluctant to perform the blasphemy that the living must inevitably perpetrate on the possessions of the dead.
There were no revelations to be expected when she opend the
drawer, only the painful reiteration of her mother's personality
and the power it had held over her own, which would rise—an
emanation, a mist, that she herself had long since shredded away,
parted, and escaped.

She repeated to herself, like an incantation, "I am married. I
have a child of my own, a home of my own five hundred miles
away. I have not even lived in this house—my parents' house—for
over seven years." Stepping back, she sat on the bed where her
mother had died the week before, slowly, from cancer, where
Hester had held the large, long-fingered, competent hand for a
whole night, watching the asphyxiating action of the fluid mounting in the lungs until it had extinguished the breath. She sat
facing the drawer.

It had taken her all her own lifetime to get to know its full contents, starting from the first glimpses, when she was just able to lean her chin on the side and have her hand pushed away from the packets and japanned boxes, to the last weeks, when she had made a careful show of not noticing while she got out the necessary bankbooks and safe-deposit keys. Many times during her childhood, when she had lain blandly ill herself, elevated to the honor of the parental bed while she suffered from the "autointoxication" that must have been 1918's euphemism for plain piggishness, the drawer had been opened. Then she had been allowed to play with the two pairs of pearled opera glasses or the long string of graduated white china beads, each with its oval sides flushed like cheeks. Over these she had sometimes spent the whole afternoon, pencilling two eyes and a pursed mouth on each bead, until she had achieved an incredible string of minute, doll-like heads that made even her mother laugh.

Once while Hester was in college, the drawer had been opened for the replacement of her grandmother's great sunburst pin, which she had never before seen and which had been in pawn, and doggedly reclaimed over a long period by her mother. And for Hester's wedding her mother had taken out the delicate diamond chain—the "lavaliere" of the Gibson-girl era—that had been her father's wedding gift to her mother, and the ugly, expensive bar pin that had been his gift to his wife on the birth of her son. Hester had never before seen either of them, for the fashion of wearing diamonds indiscriminately had never been her mother's, who was contemptuous of other women's display, although she might spend minutes in front of the mirror debating a choice between two relatively gimcrack pieces of costume jewelry. Hester had never known why this was until recently, when the separation of the last few years had relaxed the tension between her mother and herself—not enough to prevent explosions when they met but enough for her to see obscurely the long motivations of her mother's life. In the European sense, family jewelry was Property, and with all her faultless English and New World poise, her mother had never exorcised her European core.

In the back of the middle drawer, there was a small square of brown-toned photograph that had never escaped into the large, ramshackle portfolio of family pictures kept in the drawer of the old break-front bookcase, open to any hand. Seated on a bench, Hedwig Licht, aged two, brows knitted under ragged hair, stared mournfully into the camera with the huge, heavy-lidded eyes that had continued to brood in her face as a woman, the eyes that she had transmitted to Hester, along with the high cheekbones that she had deplored. Fat, wrinkled stockings were bowed into arcs that almost met at the high-stretched boots, which did not touch the floor; to hold up the stocking, strips of calico matching the dumpy little dress were bound around the knees.

Long ago, Hester, in her teens, staring tenaciously into the drawer under her mother's impatient glance, had found the little square and exclaimed over it, and her mother, snatching it away from her, had muttered, "If that isn't Dutchy!" But she had looked at it long and ruefully before she had pushed it back into a corner. Hester had added the picture to the legend of her mother's childhood built up from the bitter little anecdotes that her mother had let drop casually over the years.

She saw the small Hedwig, as clearly as if it had been herself, haunting the stiff rooms of the house in the townlet of Oberelsbach, motherless since birth and almost immediately stepmothered by a woman who had been unloving, if not unkind, and had soon borne the stern, *Haustyrann* father a son. The small figure she saw had no connection with the all-powerful figure of her mother but, rather, seemed akin to the legion of lonely children who were a constant motif in the literature that had been her own drug—the Sara Crewes and Little Dorrits, all those children who inhabited the familiar terror-struck dark that crouched under the lash of the adult. She saw Hedwig receiving from her dead mother's mother —the Grandmother Rosenberg, warm and loving but, alas, too far away to be of help—the beautiful, satin-incrusted bisque doll, and she saw the bad stepmother taking it away from Hedwig and putting it in the drawing room, because "it is too beautiful for a child to play with." She saw all this as if it had happened to her and she had never forgotten.

Years later, when this woman, Hester's step-grandmother, had come to the United States in the long train of refugees from Hitler, her mother had urged the grown Hester to visit her, and she had refused, knowing her own childishness but feeling the resentment rise in her as if she were six, saying, "I won't go. She wouldn't let you have your doll." Her mother had smiled at her sadly and had shrugged her shoulders resignedly. "You wouldn't say that if you could see her. She's an old woman. She has no teeth." Looking at her mother, Hester had wondered what her feelings were after forty years, but her mother, private as always in her emotions, had given no sign.

There had been no sign for Hester—never an open demonstration of love or an appeal—until the telephone call of a few months before, when she had heard her mother say quietly, over the distance, "I think you'd better come," and she had turned away from the phone saying bitterly, almost in awe, "If she *asks me* to come, she must be dying!"

Turning the key over in her hand, Hester looked back at the composite figure of her mother—that far-off figure of the legendary child, the nearer object of her own dependence, love, and hate—looked at it from behind the safe, dry wall of her own "American" education. We are told, she thought, that people who do not experience love in their earliest years cannot open up; they cannot give it to others; but by the time we have learned this from books or dredged it out of reminiscence, they have long since left upon us their chill, irremediable stain.

If Hester searched in her memory for moments of animal maternal warmth, like those she self-consciously gave her own child (as if her own childhood prodded her from behind), she thought always of the blue-shot twilight of one New York evening, the winter she was eight, when she and her mother were returning from a shopping expedition, gay and united in the shared guilt of being late for supper. In her mind, now, their arrested figures stood like two silhouettes caught in the spotlight of time. They had paused under the brightly agitated bulbs of a movie-theatre marquee, behind them the broad, rose-red sign of a Happiness candy store. Her mother, suddenly leaning down to her, had encircled her with her arm and nuzzled her, saying almost anxiously, "We do have fun together, don't we?" Hester had stared back stolidly, almost suspiciously, into the looming, pleading eyes, but she had rested against the encircling arm, and warmth had trickled through her as from a closed wound reopening.

After this, her mother's part in the years that followed seemed

blurred with the recriminations from which Hester had retreated
ever farther, always seeking the remote corners of the household
—the sofa-fortressed alcoves, the store closet, the servants' bathroom—always bearing her amulet, a book. It seemed to her now,
wincing, that the barrier of her mother's dissatisfaction with her
had risen imperceptibly, like a coral cliff built inexorably from the
slow accretion of carelessly ejaculated criticisms that had grown
into solid being in the heavy fullness of time. Meanwhile, her
father's uncritical affection, his open caresses, had been steadiness
under her feet after the shifting waters of her mother's personality, but he had been away from home on business for long
periods, and when at home he, too, was increasingly a target for
her mother's deep-burning rage against life. Adored member of a
large family that was almost tribal in its affections and unity, he
could not cope with this smoldering force and never tried to understand it, but the shield of his adulthood gave him a protection that
Hester did not have. He stood on equal ground.

Hester's parents had met at Saratoga, at the races. So dissimilar
were their backgrounds that it was improbable that they would
ever have met elsewhere than in the somewhat easy social flux of a
spa, although their brownstone homes in New York were not
many blocks apart, his in the gentility of upper Madison Avenue,
hers in the solid, Germanic comfort of Yorkville. By this time,
Hedwig had been in America ten years.

All Hester knew of her mother's coming to America was that
she had arrived when she was sixteen. Now that she knew how
old her mother had been at death, knew the birth date so zealously
guarded during a lifetime of evasion and so quickly exposed by the
noncommittal nakedness of funeral routine, she realized that
her mother must have arrived in 1900. She had come to the home
of an aunt, a sister of her own dead mother. What family drama
had preceded her coming, whose decision it had been, Hester did
not know. Her mother's one reply to a direct question had been a
shrugging "There was nothing for me there."

Hester had a vivid picture of her mother's arrival and first years
in New York, although this was drawn from only two clues. Her
great-aunt, remarking once on Hester's looks in the dispassionate
way of near relations, had nodded over Hester's head to her

mother. "She is dark, like the father, no? Not like you were." And Hester, with a naïve glance of surprise at her mother's sedate pompadour, had eagerly interposed, "What was she like, Tante?"

"*Ach,* when she came off the boat, *war sie hübsch!*" Tante had said, lapsing into German with unusual warmth, "Such a color! Pink and cream!"

"Yes, a real Bavarian *Mädchen,*" said her mother with a trace of contempt. "Too pink for the fashion here. I guess they thought it wasn't real."

Another time, her mother had said, in one of her rare bursts of anecdote, "When I came, I brought enough linen and under-clothing to supply two brides. At the convent school where I was sent, the nuns didn't teach you much besides embroidery, so I had plenty to bring, plenty. They were nice, though. Good, simple women. Kind. I remember I brought four dozen handkerchiefs, beautiful heavy linen that you don't get in America. But they were large, bigger than the size of a man's handkerchief over here, and the first time I unfolded one, everybody laughed, so I threw them away." She had sighed, perhaps for the linen. "And under-drawers! Long red flannel, and I had spent months embroidering them with yards of white eyelet work on the ruffles. I remember Tante's maid came in from the back yard quite angry and refused to hang them on the line any more. She said the other maids, from the houses around, teased her for belonging to a family who would wear things like that."

Until Hester was in her teens, her mother had always employed young German or Czech girls fresh from "the other side"— Teenies and Josies of long braided hair, broad cotton ankles and queer, blunt shoes, who had clacked deferentially to her mother in German and had gone off to marry their waiter's and baker's apprentices at just about the time they learned to wear silk stockings and "just as soon as you've taught them how to serve a dinner," returning regularly to show off their square, acrid babies. "Greenhorns!" her mother had always called them, a veil of something indefinable about her lips. But in the middle drawer there was a long rope of blond hair, sacrificed, like the handkerchiefs, but not wholly discarded.

There was no passport in the drawer. Perhaps it had been

destroyed during the years of the first World War, when her mother, long since a citizen by virtue of her marriage, had felt the contemporary pressure to excise everything Teutonic. "If that nosy Mrs. Cahn asks you when I came over, just say I came over as a child," she had said to Hester. And how easy it had been to nettle her by pretending that one could discern a trace of accent in her speech! Once, when the family had teased her by affecting to hear an echo of "puplic" in her pronunciation of "public," Hester had come upon her, hours after, standing before a mirror, color and nose high, watching herself say, over and over again, "Public! Public!"

Was it this, thought Hester, her straining toward perfection, that made her so intolerant of me, almost as if she were castigating in her child the imperfections that were her own? "Big feet, big hands, like mine," her mother had grumbled. "Why? Why? When every woman in your father's family wears size one! But their nice, large ears—you must have *those!*" And dressing Hester for Sunday school she would withdraw a few feet to look at the finished product, saying slowly, with dreamy cruelty, "I don't know why I let you wear those white gloves. They make your hands look clumsy, just like a policeman's."

It was over books that the rift between Hester and her mother had become complete. To her mother, marrying into a family whose bookish traditions she had never ceased trying to undermine with the sneer of the practical, it was as if the stigmata of that tradition, appearing upon the girl, had forever made them alien to one another.

"Your eyes don't look like a girl's, they look like an old woman's! Reading! Forever reading!" she had stormed, chasing Hester from room to room, flushing her out of doors, and on one remote, terrible afternoon, whipping the book out of Hester's hand, she had leaned over her, glaring, and had torn the book in two.

Hester shivered now, remembering the cold sense of triumph that had welled up in her as she had faced her mother, rejoicing in the enormity of what her mother had done.

Her mother had faltered before her. "Do you want to be a dreamer all your life?" she had muttered.

Hester had been unable to think of anything to say for a

.moment. Then she had stuttered, "All you think of in life is money!" and had made her grand exit. But huddling miserably in her room afterward she had known even then that it was not as simple as that, that her mother, too, was whipped and driven by some ungovernable dream she could not express, which had left her, like the book, torn in two.

Was it this, perhaps, that had sent her across an ocean, that had impelled her to perfect her dress and manner, and to reject the humdrum suitors of her aunt's circle for a Virginia bachelor twenty-two years older than herself? Had she, perhaps, married him not only for his money and his seasoned male charm but also for his standards and traditions, against which her railings had been a confession of envy and defeat?

So Hester and her mother had continued to pit their implacable difference against each other in a struggle that was complicated out of all reason by their undeniable likeness—each pursuing in her own orbit the warmth that had been denied. Gauche and surly as Hester was in her mother's presence, away from it she had striven successfully for the very falsities of standard that she despised in her mother, and it was her misery that she was forever impelled to earn her mother's approval at the expense of her own. Always, she knew now, there had been the lurking, buried wish that someday she would find the final barb, the homing shaft, that would maim her mother once and for all, as she felt herself to have been maimed.

A few months before, the barb had been placed in her hand. In answer to the telephone call, she had come to visit the family a short time after her mother's sudden operation for cancer of the breast. She had found her father and brother in an anguish of helplessness, fear, and male distaste at the thought of the illness, and her mother a prima donna of fortitude, moving unbowed toward the unspoken idea of her death but with the signs on her face of a pitiful tension that went beyond the disease. She had taken to using separate utensils and to sleeping alone, although the medical opinion that cancer was not transferable by contact was well known to her. It was clear that she was suffering from a horror of what had been done to her and from a fear of the revulsion of others. It was clear to Hester, also, that her father and brother had such a revulsion and had not been wholly successful in concealing it.

One night she and her mother had been together in her mother's bedroom. Hester, in a shabby housegown, stretched out on the bed luxuriously, thinking of how there was always a certain equivocal ease, a letting down of pretense, an illusory return to the irresponsibility of childhood, in the house of one's birth. Her mother, back turned, had been standing unnecessarily long at the bureau, fumbling with the articles upon it. She turned slowly.

"They've been giving me X-ray twice a week," she said, not looking at Hester, "to stop any involvement of the glands."

"Oh," said Hester, carefully smoothing down a wrinkle on the bedspread. "It's very wise to have that done."

Suddenly, her mother had put out her hand in a gesture almost of appeal. Half in a whisper, she asked, "Would you like to see it? No one has seen it since I left the hospital."

"Yes," Hester said, keeping her tone cool, even, full only of polite interest. "I'd like very much to see it." Frozen there on the bed, she had reverted to childhood in reality, remembering, as if they had all been crammed into one slot in time, the thousands of incidents when she had been the one to stand before her mother, vulnerable and bare, helplessly awaiting the cruel exactitude of her displeasure. "I know how she feels as if I were standing there myself," thought Hester. "How well she taught me to know!"

Slowly her mother undid her housegown and bared her breast. She stood there for a long moment, on her face the looming, pleading look of twenty years before, the look it had once shown under the theatre marquee.

Hester half rose from the bed. There was a hurt in her own breast that she did not recognize. She spoke with difficulty.

"Why . . . it's a beautiful job, Mother," she said, distilling the carefully natural tone of her voice. "Neat as can be. I had no idea . . . I thought it would be ugly." With a step toward her mother, she looked, as if casually, at the dreadful neatness of the cicatrix, at the twisted, foreshortened tendon of the upper arm.

"I can't raise my arm yet," whispered her mother. "They had to cut deep. . . . Your father won't look at it."

In an eternity of slowness, Hester stretched out her hand. Trembling, she touched a tentative finger to her mother's chest, where the breast had been. Then, with rising sureness, with infinite delicacy, she drew her fingertips along the length of the scar in a light, affirmative caress, and they stood eye to eye for an immeasurable second, on equal ground at last.

In the cold, darkening room, Hester unclenched herself from remembrance. She was always vulnerable, Hester thought. As we all are. What she bequeathed me unwittingly, ironically, was fortitude—the fortitude of those who have had to live under the blow. But pity—that I found for myself.

She knew now that the tangents of her mother and herself would never have fully met, even if her mother had lived. Holding her mother's hand through the long night as she retreated over the border line of narcosis and coma into death, she had felt the giddy sense of conquering, the heady euphoria of being still alive, which comes to the watcher in the night. Nevertheless, she had known with sureness, even then, that she would go on all her life trying to "show" her mother, in an unsatisfied effort to earn her approval—and unconditional love.

As a child, she had slapped at her mother once in a frenzy of rebellion, and her mother, in reproof, had told her the tale of the peasant girl who had struck her mother and had later fallen ill and died and been buried in the village cemetery. When the mourners came to tend the mound, they found that the corpse's offending hand had grown out of the grave. They cut it off and reburied it, but when they came again in the morning, the hand had grown again. So, too, thought Hester, even though I might learn—have learned in some ways—to escape my mother's hand, all my life I will have to push it down; all my life my mother's hand will grow again out of the unquiet grave of the past.

It was her own life that was in the middle drawer. She was the person she was not only because of her mother but because, fifty-eight years before, in the little town of Oberelsbach, another woman, whose qualities she would never know, had died too soon. Death, she thought, absolves equally the bungler, the evildoer, the unloving, and the unloved—but never the living. In the end, the cicatrix that she had, in the smallest of ways, helped her mother to bear had eaten its way in and killed. The living carry, she thought, perhaps not one tangible wound but the burden of the innumerable small cicatrices imposed on us by our beginnings; we carry them with us always, and from these, from this agony, we are not absolved.

She turned the key and opened the drawer.

# COLETTE

*In* My Mother's House, *the French writer recalls her mother's pervasive influence.*

## "My Mother and the Books"

THROUGH THE OPEN TOP of its shade, the lamp cast its beams upon a wall entirely corrugated by the backs of books, all bound. The opposite wall was yellow, the dirty yellow of the paper-backed volumes, read, re-read and in tatters. A few "Translated from the English"—price, one franc twenty-five—gave a scarlet note to the lowest shelf.

Halfway up, Musset, Voltaire and the Gospels gleamed in their leaf-brown sheepskin. Littré, Larousse and Becquerel displayed bulging backs like black tortoises, while d'Orbigny, pulled to pieces by the irreverent adoration of four children, scattered its pages blazoned with dahlias, parrots, pink-fringed jellyfish and duck-billed platypi.

Camille Flammarion, in gold-starred blue, contained the yellow planets, the chalk-white frozen craters of the moon, and Saturn rolling within his orbit like an iridescent pearl.

Two solid earth-coloured partitions held together Elisée Reclus, Voltaire in marbled boards, Balzac in black, and Shakespeare in olive-green.

After all these years, I have only to shut my eyes to see once more those walls faced with books. In those days I could find them in the dark. I never took a lamp when I went at night to choose one, it was enough to feel my way, as though on the keyboard of a piano, along the shelves. Lost, stolen or strayed, I could catalogue them to-day. Almost every one of them had been there before my birth.

There was a time, before I learned to read, when I would curl up into a ball, like a dog in its kennel, between two volumes of Larousse. Labiche and Daudet wormed their way early into my happy childhood, condescending teachers who played with a familiar pupil. Mérimée came along with them, seductive and severe, dazzling my eight years at times with an incomprehensible light. *Les Misérables* also, yes, *Les Misérables*—in spite of Gavroche; but that was a case of a reasoned passion which lived to weather coldness and long infidelities. No love lost between me and Dumas, save that the *Collier de la Reine* glittered for a few nights in my dreams upon the doomed neck of Jeanne de la Motte. Neither the enthusiasm of my brothers nor the disapproving surprise of my parents could persuade me to take an interest in the Musketeers.

There was never any question of my taste in children's books. Enamoured of the Princess in her chariot, dreaming beneath an attenuated crescent moon, and of Beauty sleeping in the wood surrounded by her prostrate pages; in love with Lord Puss in his gigantic funnel boots, I searched vainly in Perrault's text for the velvet blacks, the flash of silver, the ruins, the knights, the elegant little hooves of the horses of Gustave Doré; after a couple of pages I returned, disappointed, to Doré himself. I read the story of the Hind and that of Beauty only in Walter Crane's pure, fresh illustrations. The large characters of his text linked up picture with picture like the plain pieces of net connecting the patterns in lace. But not a single word ever passed the barrier that I erected against them. What becomes in later life of that tremendous determination not to know, that quiet strength expended on avoidance and rejection?

Books, books, books. It was not that I read so many. I read and re-read the same ones. But all of them were necessary to me. Their presence, their smell, the letters of their titles and the texture of their leather bindings. Perhaps those most hermetically sealed were the dearest. I have long forgotten the name of the author of a scarlet-clad Encyclopedia, but the alphabetical references marked upon each volume have remained for me an indelible and magic word: *Aphbicécladiggalhymaroidphorebstevanzy.* And how I loved the Guizot whose ornate green and gold was never opened! And the inviolate *Voyage d'Anacharsis!* If the *Histoire du Consulat et de l'Empire* ever found its way to the Quais, I wager that a label would proudly proclaim its condition as "mint."

The twenty-odd volumes of Saint-Simon replaced each other nightly at my mother's bedside; their pages provided her with endlessly renewed pleasure, and she thought it strange that at eight years old I should sometimes fail to share in her enjoyment.

"Why don't you read Saint-Simon?" she would ask me. "I can't understand why children are so slow in learning to appreciate really interesting books!"

Beautiful books that I used to read, beautiful books that I left unread, warm covering of the walls of my home, variegated tapestry whose hidden design rejoiced my initiated eyes. It was from them I learned, long before the age for love, that love is complicated, tyrannical and even burdensome, since my mother grudged the prominence they gave it.

"It's a great bore—all the love in these books," she used to say. "In life, my poor Minet-Chéri, folk have other fish to fry. Did none of these lovesick people you read of have children to rear or a garden to care for? Judge for yourself, Minet-Chéri, have you or your brothers ever heard me harp on love as they do in books? And yet I think I ought to know something about it, having had two husbands and four children!"

If I bent over the fascinating abysses of terror that opened in many a romance, there swarmed there plenty of classically white ghosts, sorcerers, shadows and malevolent monsters, but the denizens of that world could never climb up my long plaits to get at me, because a few magic words kept them at bay.

"Have you been reading that ghost story, Minet-Chéri? It's a lovely story, isn't it? I can't imagine anything lovelier than the description of the ghost wandering by moonlight in the churchyard. The part, you know, where the author says that the moonlight shone right through the ghost and that it cast no shadow on the grass. A ghost must be a wonderful thing to see. I only wish I could see one; I should call you at once if I did. Unfortunately, they don't exist. But if I could become a ghost after my death, I certainly should, to please you and myself too. And have you read that idiotic story about a dead woman's revenge? I ask you, did you ever hear such rubbish! What would be the use of dying if one didn't gain more sense by it? No, my child, the dead are a peaceful company. I don't fall out with my living neighbours, and I'll undertake to keep on good terms with the dead ones!"

I hardly know what literary coldness, healthy on the whole, protected me from romantic delirium, and caused me—a little later, when I sampled certain books of time-honoured and supposedly infallible seductiveness—to be critical when I should by rights have fallen an intoxicated victim. There again I was perhaps influenced by my mother, whose innate innocence made her inclined to deny evil, even when her curiosity led her to seek it out, and to consider it, jumbled up with good, with wondering eyes.

"This one? Oh, this isn't a harmful book, Minet-Chéri," she would say. "Yes, I know there's one scene, one chapter . . . But it's only a novel. Nowadays writers sometimes run short of ideas, you know. You might have waited a year or two before reading it, perhaps. But after all, Minet-Chéri, you must learn to use your judgment. You've got enough sense to keep it to yourself if you understand too much, and perhaps there are no such things as harmful books."

Nevertheless, there were those that my father locked away in his thuya-wood desk. But chiefly it was the author's name that he locked away.

"I fail to see the use of these children reading Zola!"

Zola bored him, and rather than seek in his pages for reasons that would explain why he allowed or forbade us to read him, he placed upon the index a vast, complete Zola, periodically increased by further yellow deposits.

"Mother, why aren't I allowed to read Zola?"

Her grey eyes, so unskilled at dissimulation, revealed their perplexity.

"It's quite true there are certain Zola's that I would rather you didn't read."

"Then let me have the ones that aren't 'certain'."

She gave me *La Faute de l'Abbé Mouret, Le Docteur Pascal* and *Germinal*, but I, wounded at the mistrust that locked away from me a corner of that house where all doors were open, where cats came and went by night and the cellar and larder were mysteriously depleted, was determined to have the others. I got them. Although she may be ashamed of it later, a girl of fourteen has no difficulty, and no credit, in deceiving two trustful parents. I went out into the garden with my first pilfered book. Like several others by Zola it contained a rather insipid story of heredity, in which an amiable and healthy woman gives up her beloved cousin to a sickly friend, and all of it might well have been written by Ohnet, God knows, had the puny wife not known the joy of bringing a child into the world. She produced it suddenly, with a blunt, crude wealth of detail, an anatomical analysis, a dwelling on the colour, odour, contortions and cries, wherein I recognised nothing of my quiet country-bred experience. I felt credulous, terrified, threatened in my dawning femininity. The matings of browsing cattle, of tom-cats covering their females like jungle beasts, the simple, almost austere precision of the farmers' wives discussing their virgin heifer or their daughter in labour, I summoned them all to my rescue. But above all I invoked the exorcising voice.

"When you came into the world, my last born, Minet-Chéri, I suffered for three days and two nights. When I was carrying you I was as big as a house. Three days seems a long time. The beasts put us to shame, we women who can no longer bear our children joyfully. But I've never regretted my suffering. They do say that children like you, who have been carried so high in the womb and have taken so long to come down into the daylight, are always the children that are most loved, because they have lain so near their mother's heart and have been so unwilling to leave her."

Vainly I hoped that the gentle words of exorcism, hastily summoned, would sing in my ears, where a metallic reverberation was deafening me. Beneath my eyes other words painted the flesh split open, the excrement, the polluted blood. I managed to raise my head, and saw a bluish garden and smoke-coloured walls wavering strangely under a sky turned yellow. I collapsed on the grass, prostrate and limp like one of those little leverets that the poachers bring, fresh killed, into the kitchen.

When I regained consciousness, the sky was blue once more, and I lay at the feet of my mother, who was rubbing my nose with eau de Cologne.

"Are you better, Minet-Chéri?"

"Yes. I can't think what came over me."

The grey eyes, gradually reassured, dwelt on mine.

"I think I know what it was. A smart little rap on the knuckles from Above."

I remained pale and troubled and my mother misunderstood:

"There, there now. There's nothing so terrible as all that in the birth of a child, nothing terrible at all. It's much more beautiful in real life. The suffering is so quickly forgotten, you'll see! The proof that all women forget is that it is only men—and what business was it of Zola's, anyway?—who write stories about it."

# PHYLLIS McGINLEY

Times Three *records the one inescapable difficulty in the mother-daughter relationship.*

## "The Adversary"

A MOTHER's hardest to forgive.
Life is the fruit she longs to hand you,
Ripe on a plate. And while you live,
Relentlessly she understands you.

# Brothers and Sisters

# THE HOLY BIBLE

## (Authorized King James Version)

🙢 🙠

*In the Gospel According to St. Luke the differing tem-*
*peraments of two sisters are shown in illuminating*
*contrast.*

## The Gospel According to Saint Luke,
## Chapter 10, Verses 38–42

Now it came to pass, as they went, that he entered into a
certain village; and a certain woman named Martha received him
into her house.

And she had a sister called Mary, which also sat at Jesus' feet,
and heard his word.

But Martha was cumbered about much serving, and came to
him, and said, Lord, dost thou not care that my sister hath left me
to serve alone, bid her therefore that she help me.

And Jesus answered and said unto her, Martha, Martha, thou
art careful and troubled about many things:

But one thing is needful: and Mary hath chosen that good part,
which shall not be taken away from her.

# MOTHER GOOSE

*A rhyme offers further evidence that sisters are apt to disagree.*

### "Coffee and Tea"

MOLLY, my sister and I fell out,
And what do you think it was all about?
She loved coffee and I loved tea,
And that was the reason we couldn't agree.

# JANE AUSTEN

*A happy view of the relationship possible between sisters is given in* Pride and Prejudice. *Here Jane Bennet, who has been given every reason to think that Mr. Bingley, of nearby Netherfield, is in love with her, finds her sister Elizabeth, her chief comforter after a letter from Mr. Bingley's sister, Caroline, shatters her hopes.*

MISS BINGLEY'S LETTER arrived, and put an end to doubt. The very first sentence conveyed the assurance of their being all settled in London for the winter, and concluded with her brother's regret at not having had time to pay his respects to his friends in Hertfordshire before he left the country.

Hope was over, entirely over; and when Jane could attend to the rest of the letter, she found little, except the professed affection of the writer, that could give her any comfort. Miss Darcy's praise occupied the chief of it. Her many attractions were again dwelt on, and Caroline boasted joyfully of their increasing intimacy, and ventured to predict the accomplishment of the wishes which had been unfolded in her former letter. She wrote also with great pleasure of her brother's being an inmate of Mr. Darcy's house, and mentioned with raptures some plans of the latter with regard to new furniture.

Elizabeth, to whom Jane very soon communicated the chief of all this, heard it in silent indignation. Her heart was divided between concern for her sister, and resentment against all others. To Caroline's assertion of her brother's being partial to Miss Darcy she paid no credit. That he was really fond of Jane, she doubted no more than she had ever done; and much as she had always been disposed to like him, she could not think without anger, hardly without contempt, on that easiness of temper, that want of proper resolution, which now made him the slave of his designing friends, and led him to sacrifice his own happiness to the caprice of their inclinations. Had his own happiness, however, been the only sacrifice, he might have been allowed to sport with it in whatever manner he thought best, but her sister's was involved in it, as she thought he must be sensible himself. It was a subject, in short, on which reflection would be long indulged, and must be unavailing. She could think of nothing else; and yet whether Bingley's regard had really died away, or were suppressed by his friends' interference; whether he had been aware of Jane's attachment, or whether it had escaped his observation; whatever were the case, though her opinion of him must be materially affected by the difference, her sister's situation remained the same, her peace equally wounded.

A day or two passed before Jane had courage to speak of her feelings to Elizabeth; but at last, on Mrs. Bennet's leaving them together, after a longer irritation than usual about Netherfield and its master, she could not help saying:

"Oh, that my dear mother had more command over herself! She can have no idea of the pain she gives me by her continual reflections on him. But I will not repine. It cannot last long. He will be forgot, and we shall all be as we were before."

Elizabeth looked at her sister with incredulous solicitude, but said nothing.

"You doubt me," cried Jane, slightly colouring; "indeed you have no reason. He may live in my memory as the most amiable man of my acquaintance, but that is all. I have nothing either to hope or fear, and nothing to reproach him with. Thank God! I have not *that* pain. A little time therefore—I shall certainly try to get the better—"

With a stronger voice she soon added, "I have this comfort immediately, that it has not been more than an error of fancy on my side, and that it has done no harm to anyone but myself."

"My dear Jane!" exclaimed Elizabeth, "you are too good. Your sweetness and disinterestedness are really angelic; I do not know what to say to you. I feel as if I had never done you justice, or loved you as you deserve."

Miss Bennet eagerly disclaimed all extraordinary merit, and threw back the praise on her sister's warm affection.

"Nay," said Elizabeth, "this is not fair. *You* wish to think all the world respectable, and are hurt if I speak ill of anybody. *I* only want to think *you* perfect, and you set yourself against it. Do not be afraid of my running into any excess, of my encroaching on your privilege of universal good-will. You need not. There are few people whom I really love, and still fewer of whom I think well. The more I see of the world, the more am I dissatisfied with it; and every day confirms my belief of the inconsistency of all human characters, and of the little dependence that can be placed on the appearance of either merit or sense. I have met with two instances lately, one I will not mention; the other is Charlotte's marriage. It is unaccountable! In every view it is unaccountable!"

"My dear Lizzy, do not give way to such feelings as these. They will ruin your happiness. You do not make allowance enough for difference of situation and temper. Consider Mr. Collins's respectability, and Charlotte's prudent, steady character. Remember that she is one of a large family; that as to fortune, it is a most eligible match; and be ready to believe, for everybody's sake, that she may feel something like regard and esteem for our cousin."

"To oblige you, I would try to believe almost anything, but no one else could be benefited by such a belief as this; for were I persuaded that Charlotte had any regard for him, I should only think worse of her understanding than I now do of her heart. My dear Jane, Mr. Collins is a conceited, pompous, narrow-minded, silly man; you know he is, as well as I do; and you must feel, as well as I do, that the woman who marries him cannot have a proper way of thinking. You shall not defend her, though it is Charlotte Lucas. You shall not, for the sake of one individual, change the meaning of principle and integrity, nor endeavour to persuade yourself or me, that selfishness is prudence, and insensibility of danger security for happiness."

"I must think your language too strong in speaking of both," replied Jane; "and I hope you will be convinced of it, by seeing them happy together. But enough of this. You alluded to something else. You mentioned *two* instances. I cannot misunderstand you, but I entreat you, dear Lizzy, not to pain me by thinking *that person* to blame, and saying your opinion of him is sunk. We must not be so ready to fancy ourselves intentionally injured. We must not expect a lively young man to be always so guarded and circumspect. It is very often nothing but our own vanity that deceives us. Women fancy admiration means more than it does."

"And men take care that they should."

"If it is designedly done, they cannot be justified; but I have no idea of there being so much design in the world as some persons imagine."

"I am far from attributing any part of Mr. Bingley's conduct to design," said Elizabeth; "but without scheming to do wrong, or to make others unhappy, there may be error, and there may be misery. Thoughtlessness, want of attention to other people's feelings, and want of resolution, will do the business."

"And do you impute it to either of those?"

"Yes; to the last. But if I go on, I shall displease you by saying what I think of persons you esteem. Stop me whilst you can."

"You persist, then, in supposing his sisters influence him?"

"Yes, in conjunction with his friend."

"I cannot believe it. Why should they try to influence him? They can only wish his happiness; and if he is attached to me, no other woman can secure it."

"Your first position is false. They may wish many things besides his happiness; they may wish his increase of wealth and conse- quence; they may wish him to marry a girl who has all the im- portance of money, great connections, and pride."

"Beyond a doubt, they do wish him to choose Miss Darcy," replied Jane; "but this may be from better feelings than you are supposing. They have known her much longer than they have known me; no wonder if they love her better. But, whatever may be their own wishes, it is very unlikely they should have opposed their brother's. What sister would think herself at liberty to do it, unless there were something very objectionable? If they believed him attached to me, they would not try to part us; if he were so, they could not succeed. By supposing such an affection, you make everybody act unnaturally and wrong, and me most unhappy. Do not distress me by the idea. I am not ashamed of having been mistaken—or, at least, it is light, it is nothing in comparison of what I should feel in thinking ill of him or his sisters. Let me take it in the best light, in the light in which it may be understood."

Elizabeth could not oppose such a wish; and from this time Mr. Bingley's name was scarcely ever mentioned between them.

# LOUISA MAY ALCOTT

*Four sisters, Meg, Jo, Beth, and Amy, achieved immor-
tality in the pages of* Little Women. *But for all the
sunshiny wholesomeness of their relationship in general, they had their clashes.*

"GIRLS, where are you going?" asked Amy, coming into their room one Saturday afternoon, and finding them getting ready to go out, with an air of secrecy which excited her curiosity.

"Never mind; little girls shouldn't ask questions," returned Jo sharply.

Now if there *is* anything mortifying to our feelings, when we are young, it is to be told that; and to be bidden to "run away, dear," is still more trying to us. Amy bridled up at this insult, and determined to find out the secret, if she teased for an hour. Turning to Meg, who never refused her anything very long, she said coaxingly, "Do tell me! I should think you might let me go, too; for Beth is fussing over her piano, and I haven't got anything to do, and am *so* lonely."

"I can't dear, because you aren't invited," began Meg; but Jo broke in impatiently, "Now, Meg, be quiet, or you will spoil it all. You can't go, Amy; so don't be a baby, and whine about it."

"You are going somewhere with Laurie, I know you are; you were whispering and laughing together, on the sofa, last night, and you stopped when I came in. Aren't you going with him?"

"Yes, we are; now do be still, and stop bothering."

Amy held her tongue, but used her eyes, and saw Meg slip a fan into her pocket.

"I know! I know! you're going to the theatre to see the 'Seven Castles!'" she cried; adding resolutely, "and I *shall* go, for mother said I might see it; and I've got my rag-money, and it was mean not to tell me in time."

"Just listen to me a minute, and be a good child," said Meg soothingly. "Mother doesn't wish you to go this week, because your eyes are not well enough yet to bear the light of this fairy piece. Next week you can go with Beth and Hannah, and have a nice time."

"I don't like that half as well as going with you and Laurie. Please let me; I've been sick with this cold so long, and shut up, I'm dying for some fun. Do, Meg! I'll be ever so good," pleaded Amy, looking as pathetic as she could.

"Suppose we take her. I don't believe mother would mind, if we bundle her up well," began Meg.

"If *she* goes, *I* sha'n't; and if I don't, Laurie won't like it; and it will be very rude, after he invited only us, to go and drag in Amy. I should think she'd hate to poke herself where she isn't wanted," said Jo crossly, for she disliked the trouble of overseeing a fidgety child, when she wanted to enjoy herself.

Her tone and manner angered Amy, who began to put her boots on, saying, in her most aggravating way, "I *shall* go; Meg says I may; and if I pay for myself, Laurie hasn't anything to do with it."

"You can't sit with us, for our seats are reserved, and you mustn't sit alone; so Laurie will give you his place, and that will spoil our pleasure; or he'll get another seat for you, and that isn't proper, when you weren't asked. You sha'n't stir a step; so you may just stay where you are," scolded Jo, crosser than ever, having just pricked her finger in her hurry.

Sitting on the floor, with one boot on, Amy began to cry, and Meg to reason with her, when Laurie called from below, and the two girls hurried down, leaving their sister wailing; for now and then she forgot her grown-up ways, and acted like a spoilt child. Just as the party was setting out, Amy called over the banisters, in a threatening tone, "You'll be sorry for this, Jo March; see if you ain't."

"Fiddlesticks!" returned Jo, slamming the door.

They had a charming time, for "The Seven Castles of the Diamond Lake" were as brilliant and wonderful as heart could wish. But, in spite of the comical red imps, sparkling elves, and gorgeous princes and princesses, Jo's pleasure had a drop of bitterness in it; the fairy queen's yellow curls reminded her of Amy; and between the acts she amused herself with wondering what her sister would do to make her "sorry for it." She and Amy had had many lively skirmishes in the course of their lives, for both had quick tempers, and were apt to be violent when fairly roused. Amy teased Jo, and Jo irritated Amy, and semi-occasional explosions occurred, of which both were much ashamed afterward. Although the oldest, Jo had the least self-control, and had hard times trying to curb the fiery spirit which was continually getting her into trouble; her anger never lasted long, and, having humbly confessed her fault, she sincerely repented, and tried to do better. Her sisters used to say that they rather liked to get Jo into a fury, because she was such an angel afterward. Poor Jo tried desperately to be good, but her bosom enemy was always ready to flame up and defeat her; and it took years of patient effort to subdue it.

When they got home, they found Amy reading in the parlor.

She assumed an injured air as they came in; never lifted her eyes from her book, or asked a single question. Perhaps curiosity might have conquered resentment, if Beth had not been there to inquire, and receive a glowing description of the play. On going up to put away her best hat, Jo's first look was toward the bureau; for, in their last quarrel, Amy had soothed her feelings by turning Jo's top drawer upside down on the floor. Everything was in its place, however; and after a hasty glance into her various closets, bags, and boxes, Jo decided that Amy had forgiven and forgotten her wrongs.

There Jo was mistaken; for next day she made a discovery which produced a tempest. Meg, Beth, and Amy were sitting together, late in the afternoon, when Jo burst into the room, looking excited, and demanding breathlessly, "Has any one taken my book?"

Meg and Beth said "No," at once, and looked surprised; Amy poked the fire, and said nothing. Jo saw her color rise, and was down upon her in a minute.

"Amy, you've got it!"

"No, I haven't."

"You know where it is, then!"

"No, I don't."

"That's a fib!" cried Jo, taking her by the shoulders, and looking fierce enough to frighten a much braver child than Amy.

"It isn't. I haven't got it, don't know where it is now, and don't care."

"You know something about it, and you'd better tell at once, or I'll make you," and Jo gave her a slight shake.

"Scold as much as you like, you'll never see your silly old book again," cried Amy, getting excited in her turn.

"Why not?"

"I burnt it up."

"What! my little book I was so fond of, and worked over, and meant to finish before father got home? Have you really burnt it?" said Jo, turning very pale, while her eyes kindled and her hands clutched Amy nervously.

"Yes, I did! I told you I'd make you pay for being so cross yesterday, and I have, so—"

Amy got no farther, for Jo's hot temper mastered her, and she shook Amy till her teeth chattered in her head; crying, in a passion of grief and anger,—

"You wicked, wicked girl! I never can write it again, and I'll never forgive you as long as I live."

Meg flew to rescue Amy, and Beth to pacify Jo, but Jo was quite beside herself; and, with a parting box on her sister's ear, she rushed out of the room up to the old sofa in the garret, and finished her fight alone.

The storm cleared up below, for Mrs. March came home, and, having heard the story, soon brought Amy to a sense of the wound she had done her sister. Jo's book was the pride of her heart, and was regarded by her family as a literary sprout of great promise. It was only half a dozen little fairy tales, but Jo had worked over them patiently, putting her whole heart into her work, hoping to make something good enough to print. She had just copied them with great care, and had destroyed the old manuscript, so that Amy's bonfire had consumed the loving work of several years. It seemed a small loss to others, but to Jo it was a dreadful calamity, and she felt that it never could be made up to her. Beth mourned as for a departed kitten, and Meg refused to defend her pet; Mrs. March looked grave and grieved, and Amy felt that no one would love her till she had asked pardon for the act which she now regretted more than any of them.

When the tea-bell rung, Jo appeared, looking so grim and unapproachable that it took all Amy's courage to say meekly,—

"Please forgive me, Jo; I'm very, very sorry."

"I never shall forgive you," was Jo's stern answer; and, from that moment, she ignored Amy entirely.

No one spoke of the great trouble,—not even Mrs. March,—for all had learned by experience that when Jo was in that mood words were wasted; and the wisest course was to wait till some little accident, or her own generous nature, softened Jo's resentment, and healed the breach. It was not a happy evening; for, though they sewed as usual, while their mother read aloud from Bremer, Scott, or Edgeworth, something was wanting, and the sweet home peace was disturbed. They felt this most when singing-time came; for Beth could only play, Jo stood dumb as a stone, and

Amy broke down, so Meg and mother sung alone. But, in spite of their efforts to be as cheery as larks, the flute-like voices did not seem to chord as well as usual, and all felt out of tune.

As Jo received her good-night kiss, Mrs. March whispered gently,—

"My dear, don't let the sun go down upon your anger; forgive each other, help each other, and begin again tomorrow."

Jo wanted to lay her head down on that motherly bosom and cry her grief and anger all away; but tears were an unmanly weakness, and she felt so deeply injured that she really *couldn't* quite forgive yet. So she winked hard, shook her head, and said, gruffly because Amy was listening,—

"It was an abominable thing, and she don't deserve to be forgiven."

With that she marched off to bed, and there was no merry or confidential gossip that night.

Amy was much offended that her overtures of peace had been repulsed, and began to wish she had not humbled herself, to feel more injured than ever, and to plume herself on her superior virtue in a way which was particularly exasperating. Jo still looked like a thunder-cloud, and nothing went well all day. It was bitter cold in the morning; she dropped her precious turn-over in the gutter, Aunt March had an attack of fidgets, Meg was pensive, Beth *would* look grieved and wistful when she got home, and Amy kept making remarks about people who were always talking about being good, and yet wouldn't try, when other people set them a virtuous example.

"Everybody is so hateful, I'll ask Laurie to go skating. He is always kind and jolly, and will put me to rights, I know," said Jo to herself, and off she went.

Amy heard the clash of skates, and looked out with an impatient exclamation,—

"There! she promised I should go next time, for this is the last ice we shall have. But it's no use to ask such a cross-patch to take me."

"Don't say that; you *were* very naughty, and it *is* hard to forgive the loss of her precious little book; but I think she might do it now, and I guess she will, if you try her at the right minute," said

Meg. "Go after them; don't say anything till Jo has got good-natured with Laurie, then take a quiet minute, and just kiss her, or do some kind thing, and I'm sure she'll be friends again, with all her heart."

"I'll try," said Amy, for the advice suited her; and, after a flurry to get ready, she ran after the friends, who were just disappearing over the hill.

It was not far to the river, but both were ready before Amy reached them. Jo saw her coming, and turned her back; Laurie did not see, for he was carefully skating along the shore, sounding the ice, for a warm spell had preceded the cold snap.

"I'll go on to the first bend, and see if it's all right, before we begin to race," Amy heard him say, as he shot away, looking like a young Russian, in his fur-trimmed coat and cap.

Jo heard Amy panting after her run, stamping her feet and blowing her fingers, as she tried to put her skates on; but Jo never turned, and went slowly zigzagging down the river, taking a bitter, unhappy sort of satisfaction in her sister's troubles. She had cherished her anger till it grew strong, and took possession of her, as evil thoughts and feelings always do, unless cast out at once. As Laurie turned the bend, he shouted back,—

"Keep near the shore; it isn't safe in the middle."

Jo heard, but Amy was just struggling to her feet, and did not catch a word. Jo glanced over her shoulder, and the little demon she was harboring said in her ear,—

"No matter whether she heard or not, let her take care of herself."

Laurie had vanished round the bend; Jo was just at the turn, and Amy, far behind, striking out toward the smoother ice in the middle of the river. For a minute Jo stood still, with a strange feeling at her heart; then she resolved to go on, but something held and turned her round, just in time to see Amy throw up her hands and go down, with the sudden crash of rotten ice, the splash of water, and a cry that made Jo's heart stand still with fear. She tried to call Laurie, but her voice was gone; she tried to rush forward, but her feet seemed to have no strength in them; and, for a second, she could only stand motionless, staring, with a terror-stricken face, at the little blue hood above the black water.

Something rushed swiftly by her, and Laurie's voice cried out,—
"Bring a rail; quick, quick!"

How she did it, she never knew; but for the next few minutes
she worked as if possessed, blindly obeying Laurie, who was quite
self-possessed, and, lying flat, held Amy up by his arm and hockey
stick till Jo dragged a rail from the fence, and together they got
the child out, more frightened than hurt.

"Now then, we must walk her home as fast as we can; pile our
things on her, while I get off these confounded skates," cried
Laurie, wrapping his coat round Amy, and tugging at the straps,
which never seemed so intricate before.

Shivering, dripping, and crying, they got Amy home; and, after
an exciting time of it, she fell asleep, rolled in blankets, before a
hot fire. During the bustle Jo had scarcely spoken; but flown
about, looking pale and wild, with her things half off, her dress
torn, and her hands cut and bruised by ice and rails and refractory
buckles. When Amy was comfortably asleep, the house quiet, and
Mrs. March sitting by the bed, she called Jo to her, and began to
bind up the hurt hands.

"Are you sure she is safe" whispered Jo, looking remorsefully at
the golden head, which might have been swept away from her
sight forever under the treacherous ice.

"Quite safe, dear; she is not hurt, and won't even take cold, I
think, you were so sensible in covering and getting her home
quickly," replied her mother cheerfully.

"Laurie did it all; I only let her go. Mother, if she *should* die, it
would be my fault;" and Jo dropped down beside the bed, in a
passion of penitent tears, telling all that had happened, bitterly
condemning her hardness of heart, and sobbing out her gratitude
for being spared the heavy punishment which might have come
upon her.

# GEORGE ELIOT

♋ ♋

*Financial considerations often play a large role in
family relationships. In* Middlemarch *a sister has her
own reasons for concern about an ailing brother.*

"WHAT ARE YOU driving at there?" said Mr. Featherstone,
holding his stick between his knees and settling his wig, while
he gave her a momentary sharp glance, which seemed to react on
him like a draught of cold air and set him coughing.

Mrs. Waule had to defer her answer till he was quiet again, till
Mary Garth had supplied him with fresh syrup, and he had begun
to rub the gold knob of his stick, looking bitterly at the fire. It was
a bright fire, but it made no difference to the chill-looking
purplish tint of Mrs. Waule's face, which was as neutral as her
voice, having mere chinks for eyes, and lips that hardly moved in
speaking.

"The doctors can't master that cough, brother. It's just like what
I have; for I'm your own sister, constitution and everything. But,
as I was saying, it's a pity Mrs. Vincy's family can't be better
conducted."

"Tchah! You said nothing o' the sort. You said somebody had
made free with my name."

"And no more than can be proved, if what everybody says is
true. My brother Solomon tells me it's the talk up and down in
Middlemarch how unsteady young Vincy is, and has been forever
gambling at billiards since home he came."

"Nonsense! What's a game of billiards? It's a good gentlemanly
game; and young Vincy is not a clodhopper. If your son John took
to billiards, now, he'd make a fool of himself."

"Your nephew John never took to billiards or any other game,
brother, and is far from losing hundreds of pounds, which, if what
everybody says is true, must be found somewhere else than out of

Mr. Vincy, the father's, pocket. For they say he's been losing money for years, though nobody would think so to see him go coursing and keeping open house, as they do. And I've heard say Mr. Bulstrode condemns Mrs. Vincy beyond anything for her flightiness, and spoiling her children so."

"What's Bulstrode to me? I don't bank with him."

"Well, Mrs. Bulstrode is Mr. Vincy's own sister, and they do say that Mr. Vincy mostly trades on the bank money; and you may see yourself, brother, when a woman past forty has pink strings always flying, and that light way of laughing at everything, it's very unbecoming. But indulging your children is one thing, and finding money to pay their debts is another. And it's openly said that young Vincy has raised money on his expectations. I don't say what expectations. Miss Garth hears me, and is welcome to tell again. I know young people hang together."

"No, thank you, Mrs. Waule," said Mary Garth. "I dislike hearing scandal too much to wish to repeat it."

Mr. Featherstone rubbed the knob of his stick and made a brief convulsive show of laughter, which had much the same genuineness as an old whist-player's chuckle over a bad hand. Still looking at the fire, he said:

"And who pretends to say Fred Vincy hasn't got expectations? Such a fine, spirited fellow is like enough to have 'em."

There was a slight pause before Mrs. Waule replied; and when she did so, her voice seemed to be slightly moistened with tears, though her face was still dry.

"Whether or no, brother, it is naturally painful to me and my brother Solomon to hear your name made free with, and your complaint being such as may carry you off sudden, and people who are no more Featherstones than the Merry-Andrew at the fair, openly reckoning on your property coming to *them*. And me, your own sister, and Solomon, your own brother! And if that's to be it, what has it pleased the Almighty to make families for?" Here Mrs. Waule's tears fell, but with moderation.

"Come, out with it, Jane!" said Mr. Featherstone, looking at her. "You mean to say Fred Vincy has been getting somebody to advance him money on what he says he knows about my will, eh?"

"I never said so, brother," (Mrs. Waule's voice had again

become dry and unshaken). "It was told me by my brother Solomon last night when he called coming from market to give me advice about the old wheat, me being a widow and my son John only three-and-twenty, though steady beyond anything. And he had it from most undeniable authority, and not one, but many."

"Stuff and nonsense! I don't believe a word of it. It's all a got-up story. Go to the window, missy; I thought I heard a horse. See if the doctor's coming."

"Not got up by me, brother, nor yet by Solomon, who, whatever else he may be—and I don't deny he has oddities—has made his will and parted his property equal between such kin as he's friends with; though, for my part, I think there are times when some should be considered more than others. But Solomon makes it no secret what he means to do."

"The more fool he!" said Mr. Featherstone, with some difficulty; breaking into a severe fit of coughing that required Mary Garth to stand near him, so that she did not find out whose horses they were which presently paused, stamping on the gravel before the door.

Before Mr. Featherstone's cough was quiet, Rosamond entered, bearing up her riding-habit with much grace. She bowed ceremoniously to Mrs. Waule, who said stiffly, "How do you do, miss?" smiled and nodded silently to Mary, and remained standing till the coughing should cease, and allow her uncle to notice her.

"Heyday, miss!" he said at last, "you have a fine color. Where's Fred?"

"Seeing about the horses. He will be in presently."

"Sit down, sit down. Mrs. Waule, you'd better go."

Even those neighbors who had called Peter Featherstone an old fox, had never accused him of being insincerely polite, and his sister was quite used to the peculiar absence of ceremony with which he marked his sense of blood-relationship. Indeed, she herself was accustomed to think that entire freedom from the necessity of behaving agreeably was included in the Almighty's intentions about families. She rose slowly without any sign of resentment and said in her usual muffled monotone, "Brother, I hope the new doctor will be able to do something for you. Solomon says there's great talk of his cleverness. I'm sure it's my wish you should be spared. And there's none more ready to nurse you than your own sister and your own nieces, if you'd only say the word. There's Rebecca, and Joanna, and Elizabeth, you know."

"Ay, ay, I remember—you'll see I've remembered 'em all—all dark and ugly. They'd need have some money, eh? There never was any beauty in the women of our family; but the Featherstones have always had some money, and the Waules too. Waule had money too. A warm man was Waule. Ay, ay; money's a good egg; and if you've got money to leave behind you, lay it in a warm nest. Good-bye, Mrs. Waule."

Here Mr. Featherstone pulled at both sides of his wig as if he wanted to deafen himself, and his sister went away ruminating on this oracular speech of his. Notwithstanding her jealousy of the Vincys and of Mary Garth, there remained as the nethermost sediment in her mental shallows a persuasion that her brother Peter Featherstone could never leave his chief property away from his blood-relations:—else why had the Almighty carried off his two wives, both childless, after he had gained so much by manganese and things, turning up when nobody expected it?— and why was there a Lowick parish church, and the Waules and Powderells all sitting in the same pew for generations, and the Featherstone pew next to them, if, the Sunday after her brother Peter's death, everybody was to know that the property was gone out of the family?

# ROGER MARTIN DU GARD

*A young man is baffled by an older brother's newly protective attitude in the panoramic novel-cycle of French family life,* The Thibaults.

"You know, I think we'll do very well here, you and I. Nice little flat, isn't it?"

"Yes."

"Well, sit down, Jacques, and make yourself at home. Try that chair over there, it's very comfortable, and tell me what you think of it. Now I'll make some tea. I suppose you're hungry? Go and choose us some cakes at the pastrycook's."

"Thanks. I'm not hungry."

"But *I* am!" Nothing could repress Antoine's geniality. After a laborious, solitary youth, Antoine was now experiencing for the first time the pleasure of loving and protecting someone, sharing his life with another. And for the sheer joy of it he was laughing, carried away by an exhilaration that was making him expansive as he had never been before.

"Have a cigarette then. No? You keep on looking at me. . . . Don't you smoke? You keep on looking at me, I was going to say, as if I was laying a trap for you. Look here, Jacques, let yourself go a bit. Have a little confidence, damn it! You're not in the reformatory now. Can't you trust me even now?"

"Of course I trust you."

"Well, then, what is it? Are you afraid I've let you down, that I've got you back on false pretences and you're not as free as you expected?"

"N-no."

"Then what is it? What's going on behind that stubborn-looking forehead of yours? Out with it!" He went up to the boy, on the point of bending over him, giving him a brotherly kiss, but he refrained. Jacques looked up at his brother with forlorn, hopeless eyes; he realized an answer was expected of him.

"Why do you ask me all those questions?" He shuddered slightly, then added in a very low voice: "What difference can it make?"

There was a short silence. Antoine was gazing at his brother, and there was such affectionate compassion in his eyes that once more Jacques felt inclined to cry.

"Yes, Jacques, just now you're like a sick man." All the gaiety had left Antoine's voice. "But, never fear, you'll get over it. Only let yourself be looked after—and loved!" he added shyly, without looking at the boy. "We don't yet know one another well. Just think, nine years between us—it was a regular abyss as long as you were a child. You were eleven when I was twenty; we couldn't have anything in common. But now it's very different. . . . No, I couldn't say if I had any affection for you in those days. I didn't ever think about it. You see I'm being quite frank with you. But now—well, all that, too, is changed. I'm delighted—yes, damn it—I'm thrilled to have you here with me. Life will be more pleasant, better in many ways, now that there are two of us. Don't you think so? For instance, when I'm coming back from the hospital, I'm sure to hurry now, so as to get home quickly. And I'll find you here, sitting at your desk, after a strenuous day's work. Shan't I? And in the evening we'll come down from dinner early, and each will settle down in his own study, under a lamp; but we'll leave the doors open so as to see each other and feel we are together. Or else, some nights, we'll have a good talk, like two old friends, and it'll be an effort to drag ourselves to bed. What's up? Why are you crying?"

He went up to Jacques, sat on the arm of his chair, and after a brief hesitation took his hand. Jacques turned away his tearful face, but returned the pressure of Antoine's hand, and for some moments clung to it feverishly with all his might.

"Oh, Antoine!" The cry seemed choking in his throat. "If you only knew all that's happened inside me, in the last year!"

He was sobbing so violently that Antoine did not dream of putting any further questions. Placing his arm round Jacques's shoulders, he pressed the boy tenderly to him. Once before, on that evening when in the darkness of the cab the barriers between them had fallen, he had experienced that thrill of vast compassion, that sensation of a sudden access of strength and will-power—the feeling that he alone must supply the vital force for both of them. And very often since, an idea had hovered in the background of his mind, an idea which now was taking clear and definite form. Rising, he began to pace the room.

"Listen!" he began. His voice had an unusual intensity of feeling. "I don't know why I'm speaking to you of this so soon, on our first day. Anyhow, we've plenty of time to return to it. Well, this is what I've been thinking—you and I are brothers. That doesn't sound much of a discovery, does it? And yet the idea is a new one, for me, and one that deeply moves me. We're brothers!

Not merely of the same blood, but springing from the same origins since the beginning of time, from the same germ-cells, the same vital impulse. We're not just any two young men, named Antoine and Jacques; we're two Thibaults, we *are* the Thibaults. Do you see what I mean? And what's so alarming in a way is that we both have in us that same vital impulse, that special Thibault temperament. Do you see? For we Thibaults are somehow different from the rest of mankind. I rather suspect we have something in us that others haven't got; just because we *are* Thibaults. Personally, wherever I've been, in college, medical school, or hospital, I've felt myself a man apart; I hardly like to say 'superior to the others'— though, after all, why shouldn't I? Yes, we are superior, we're equipped with an energy others don't possess. What's your opinion? Don't you agree? I know that you passed for a bit of a duffer at school, but didn't you feel it there, too, that 'urge' as they call it, which somehow gave you more—more driving force than the other boys?"

"Yes!" Jacques had stopped crying and was staring at his brother with passionate interest. His face had suddenly an expression of intelligence and maturity that made him seem ten years older.

"It's a long while now since I first noticed it," Antoine went on. "There must be some particular combination in our make-up, of pride and violence and obstinacy—I don't know how to put it. Take Father, for instance. But, of course, you don't know him very well. And it takes a different form with him. Now listen!" He drew up his chair in front of Jacques and leaned forward, his hands resting on his knees: one of M. Thibault's favourite attitudes. "What I wanted to say to you today was that this secret force is always making itself felt in my life; I don't know how to describe it, it's like a wave—one of those sudden swelling waves that buoy you up when you're swimming, and carry you in one tremendous rush a great way forward. But you must know how to turn it to good account. Nothing's impossible, nothing's even difficult, when one has that vital force; and we have it, you and I. Do you understand? In my own case, for example—but I'm not telling you all this just to talk about myself. I want to talk about you. It's up to you now to take stock of this driving force you have in you, to analyse it and apply it rightly. If you make up your mind, you can in one stride catch up on all the time you've wasted. It's a matter of will-power. Some people simply haven't any—as I've discovered only quite recently. I've got it, and you can have it, too. All the Thibaults can have it. And that's why they can make good at anything they turn their hand to. Think of what it means, to forge ahead of others, to make one's value recognized. I tell you, it's our duty to bring this vital energy, which is our heritage, to full fruition. It's in us—in you and in me—that the Thibault stock must come to flower—the full flower of a lineage. Do you see what I mean?" Jacques's eyes had been riveted on Antoine with all but painful fixity. Antoine repeated: "Do you understand all this?"

"Yes, yes, I understand!" he all but shouted. His pale eyes were sparkling, there was an almost vicious edge to his voice, and his lips were curiously twisted. It looked as if he were furious with his brother for shattering his peace of mind by this so unexpected outburst of enthusiasm. A tremor passed through his body, then his features relaxed, and a look of profound weariness settled on his face.

"Oh, let me be!" he suddenly exclaimed, letting his forehead sink between his hands.

Antoine said nothing; he was observing his brother. How much thinner and paler he had grown, in a fortnight! The close-cropped reddish hair made still more apparent the abnormal size of his skull, the scragginess of his neck, and his protruding ears.

"By the way," he suddenly asked, point-blank, "have you turned over a new leaf?"

"In what way?" Jacques murmured, and a mist crept over the brightness of his eyes. He flushed, and, though he managed to keep up an expression of surprise, it was obviously feigned.

Antoine made no reply.

It was getting late. He looked at his watch and rose; he had his second round to make, at five. He pondered if he should tell his brother he was going to leave him alone till dinner; but much to his surprise, Jacques seemed almost glad to see him go.

And indeed, when he was alone, he felt as if a weight had been lifted from him. He had the idea of making an inspection of the flat, but in the hall in front of the closed doors a vague anxiety came over him and he went back to his own room and shut himself in. At last he noticed the bunch of violets, and the paper streamer. All the events of the day merged together in his memory: his father's welcome, Antoine's conversation. He lay down on the sofa and began crying again, but not with despair; he was weeping above all from exhaustion, but also because of the room, and the violets, and the hand his father had laid on his head, and Antoine's solicitude, and the new life which was beginning for him. He wept because on all sides they seemed to want to love him, because henceforth people were going to take notice of him, and speak to him, and smile towards him, and he would have to respond; because his days of tranquillity were over.

# MAZO DE LA ROCHE

*The Canadian novelist wrote of the tempestous White-oaks family in a series of popular books. From the first and most famous,* Jalna, *here is a scene that takes Piers from the raptures of love to the satisfactions of teasing a younger brother.*

IT WAS ALMOST DARK when Piers crossed the lawn, passed through a low wicket gate in the hedge, and pressed eagerly along a winding path that led across a paddock where three horses were still cropping the new grass. The path wandered then down into the ravine; became a path again, still narrower, that wound up the opposite steep, curved through a noble wood; and at last, by a stile, was wedded to another path that had been shaped for no other purpose but to meet it on the boundary between Jalna and the land belonging to the Vaughans.

Down in the ravine it was almost night, so darkly the stream glimmered amid the thick undergrowth and so close above him hung the sky, not yet pricked by a star. Climbing up the steep beyond, it was darker still, except for the luminous shine of the silver birches that seemed to be lighted by some secret beam within. A whippoorwill darted among the trees, catching insects, uttering, each time it struck, a little throaty cluck, and showing a gleam of white on its wings. Then suddenly, right over his head, another whippoorwill burst into its loud lilting song.

When he reached the open wood above, Piers could see that there was still a deep red glow in the west, and the young leaves of the oaks had taken a burnished look. The trees were lively with the twittering of birds seeking their nests, their lovemaking over for the day—his just to begin.

His head was hot and he took off his cap to let the cool air fan it. He wished that his love for Pheasant were a calmer love. He would have liked to stroll out with her in the evenings, just pleasantly elated, taking it as a natural thing, as natural as the life of these birds, to love a girl and be loved by her. But it had come upon him suddenly, after knowing her all his life, like a storm that shook and possessed him. As he hurried on through the soft night air, each step drawing him nearer to the stile where Pheasant was to meet him, he tormented himself by picturing his disappointment if she were not there. He saw, in his fancy, the stile, bare as a waiting gallows, mocking the sweet urge that pressed him. He saw himself waiting till dark night and then stumbling back to Jalna filled with despair because he had not held her in his arms. What was it that had overtaken them both that day, when, meeting down in the ravine, she had been startled by a water snake and had caught his sleeve and had pointed down into the stream where it had disappeared? Bending over the water, they had suddenly seen their two faces reflected in a still pool, looking up at them not at all like the faces of Piers and Pheasant who had known each other all their days. The faces reflected had had strange, timid eyes and parted lips. They had turned to look at each other. Their own lips had met.

Remembering that kiss, he began to run across the open field toward the stile.

She was sitting on it, waiting for him, her drooping figure silhouetted against the blur of red in the west. He slackened his pace as soon as he saw her, and greeted her laconically as he came up.

"Hullo, Pheasant!"

"Hullo, Piers! I've been waiting quite a while."

"I couldn't get away. I had to stop and admire a beastly cow Renny bought at Hobbs's sale to-day." He climbed to the stile and sat down beside her. "It's the first warm evening, isn't it?" he observed, not looking at her. "I got as hot as blazes coming over. I wasn't letting the grass grow under my feet, I can tell you." He took her hand and drew it against his side. "Feel that."

"Your heart is beating rather hard," she said, in a low voice. "Is it because you hurried or because—" She leaned against his shoulder and looked into his face.

It was what Piers had been waiting for, this moment when she should lean toward him. Not without a sign from her would he let the fountain of his love leap forth. Now he put his arms about her and pressed her to him. He found her lips and held them with his own. The warm fragrance of her body made him dizzy. He was no longer strong and practical. He wished in that moment that they two might die thus happily clasped in each other's arms in the tranquil spring night.

"I can't go on like this," he murmured. "We simply must get married."

"Remember what Renny has said. Are you going to defy him? He'd be in a rage if he knew we were together here now."

"Renny be damned! He's got to be taught a lesson. It's time he was taught that he can't lord it over everyone. He's spoiled, that's the trouble with him. I call him the Rajah of Jalna."

"After all, you have the right to say who you will marry, even if the girl is beneath you, haven't you?"

He felt a sob beneath her breast; her sudden tears wet his cheek.

"Oh, Pheasant, you little fool," he exclaimed. "You beneath me? What rot!"

"Well, Renny thinks so. All your family think so. Your family despise me."

"My family may go to the devil. Why, after all, you're a Vaughan. Everybody knows that. You're called by the name."

"Even Maurice looks down on me. He's never let me call him Father."

"He deserves to be shot. If I had ever done what he did, I'd stand by the child. I'd brave the whole thing out, by God!"

"Well, he has—in a way. He's kept me. Given me his name."

"His parents did that. He's never liked you or been really kind to you."

"He thinks I've spoiled his life."

"With Meggie, you mean. Picture Meg and Maurice married!" He laughed and kissed her temple, and, feeling her silky brow touch his cheek, he kissed that, too.

She said: "I can picture that more easily than I can our own marriage. I feel as though we should go on and on, meeting and parting like this forever. In a way I think I'd like it better, too."

"Better than being married to me? Look here, Pheasant, you're just trying to hurt me."

"No, really. It's so beautiful, meeting like this. All day I'm in a kind of dream, waiting for it; then after it comes the night, and you're in the very heart of me all night—"

"What if I were beside you?"

"It couldn't be so lovely. It couldn't. Then in the morning, the moment I waken, I am counting the hours till we meet again. Maurice might not exist. I scarcely see or hear him."

"Dreams don't satisfy me, Pheasant. This way of living is torture to me. Every day as the spring goes on it's a greater torture. I want you—not dreams of you."

"Don't you love our meeting like this?"

"Don't be silly! You know what I mean." He moved away from her on the stile and lighted a cigarette. "Now," he went on, in a hard, businesslike tone, "let us take it for granted that we're going to be married."

"Yes . . . You might offer me a cigarette."

He gave her one and lighted it for her.

"Very well. Can you tell me any reason for hanging back? I'm twenty, you're seventeen. Marriageable ages, eh?"

"Too young, they say."

"Rot. They would like us to wait till we're too decrepit to creep to this stile. I'm valuable to Renny. He's paying me decent wages. I know Renny. He's good-natured at bottom, for all his temper. He'd never dream of putting me out. There's lots of room at Jalna. One more would never be noticed."

"Meg doesn't like me. I'm rather afraid of her."

"Afraid of Meggie! Oh, you little coward! She's gentle as a lamb. And Gran always liked you. I'll tell you what, Pheasant, we'll stand in with Gran. She has a lot of influence with the family. If we make ourselves pleasant to her, there's no knowing what she may do for us. She's often said that I am more like my grandfather than any of the others, and she thinks he was the finest man that ever lived."

"What about Renny? She's always talking about his being a perfect Court. Anyhow, I expect her will was made before we were born."

"Yes, but she's always changing it or pretending that she does. Only last week she had her lawyer out for hours, and the whole family was upset. Wake peeked in at the keyhole and he said all she did was feed the old fellow peppermints. Still, you can never tell." He shook his head sagaciously and then heaved a gusty sigh. "One thing is absolutely certain: I can't go on like this. I've either got to get married or go away. It's affecting my nerves. I scarcely knew what I was eating at dinner to-day, and such a hullabaloo there was over this book of Eden's. Good Lord! Poetry! Think of it! And at tea time Finch had come home with a bad report from one of his masters and there was another row. It raged for an hour."

But Pheasant had heard nothing but the calculated cruelty of the words "go away." She turned toward him a frightened, wide-eyed face.

"Go away! How can you say such a thing? You know I'd die in this place without you."

"How pale you've got," he observed, peering into her face. "Why are you turning pale? Surely it wouldn't matter to you if I went away. You could go right on dreaming about me, you know."

Pheasant burst into tears and began to scramble down from the stile. "If you think I'll stop here to be tortured!" she cried, and began to run from him.

"Yet you expect me to stay and be tortured!" he shouted.

She ran into the dusk across the wet meadow, and he sat obstinately staring after her, wondering if her will would hold out till she reached the other side. Already her steps seemed to be slackening. Still her figure became less clear. What if she should run on and on till she reached home, leaving him alone on the stile with all his love turbulent within him? The mere thought of that was enough to make him jump down and begin to run after her, but even as he did so he saw her coming slowly back, and he clambered again to his seat just in time to save his dignity. He was thankful for that.

She stopped within ten paces of him.

"Very well," she said, in a husky voice, "I'll do it."

He was acutely aware of her nearness in every sensitive nerve, but he puffed stolidly at his cigarette a moment before he asked gruffly: "When?"

"Whenever you say." Her head drooped and she gave a childish sob.

"Come here, you little baggage," he ordered peremptorily. But when he had her on the stile again a most delicious tenderness took possession of him and withal a thrilling sense of power. He uttered endearments and commands with his face against her hair.

All the way home he was full of lightness and strength, though he had worked hard that day. Halfway down the steep into the ravine a branch of an oak projected across the path above him. He leaped up and caught it with his hands and so hung aloof from the earth that seemed too prosaic for his light feet. He swung himself gently a moment, looking up at the stars that winked at him through the young leaves. A rabbit ran along the path beneath, quite unaware of him. His mind was no longer disturbed by anxiety, but free and exultant. He felt himself one with the wild things of the wood. It was spring, and he had chosen his mate.

When he crossed the lawn he saw that the drawingroom was lighted. Playing cards as usual, he supposed. He went to one of the French windows and looked in. By the fire he could see a table drawn up, at which sat his grandmother and his uncle Ernest, playing at draughts. She was wrapped in a bright green-and-red plaid shawl, and wearing a much beribboned cap. Evidently she was beating him, for her teeth were showing in a broad grin and a burst of loud laughter made the bridge players at the other table turn in their chairs with looks of annoyance. The long aquiline face of Uncle Ernest drooped wistfully above the board. On the blackened walnut mantelpiece Sasha lay curled beside a china shepherdess, her gaze fixed on her master with a kind of ecstatic contempt.

At the bridge table sat Renny, Meg, Nicholas, and Mr. Fennel, the rector. The faces of all were illumined by firelight, their expressions intensified: Nicholas, sardonic, watchful; Renny, frowning, puzzled; Meg, sweet, complacent; Mr. Fennel, pulling his beard and glowering. Poor creatures all, thought Piers, as he let himself in at the side door and softly ascended the stair, playing their little games, their paltry pastimes, whilst he played the great game of life.

A light showed underneath Eden's door. More poetry, more paltry pastime! Had Eden ever loved? If he had, he'd kept it well to himself. Probably he only loved his Muse. His Muse—ha, ha! He heard Eden groan. So it hurt, did it, loving the pretty Muse? Poetry had its pain, then. He gave a passing thump to the door.

"Want any help in there?"

"You go to hell," rejoined the young poet, "unless you happen to have a rag about you. I've upset the ink."

Piers poked his head in at the door. "My shirt isn't much better than a rag," he said. "I can let you have that."

Eden was mopping the stained baize top of the desk with blotting paper. On a sheet of a writing pad was neatly written what looked like the beginning of a poem.

"I suppose you get fun out of it," remarked Piers.

"More than you get from chasing a girl about the wood at night."

"Look here, you'd better be careful!" Piers raised his voice threateningly, but Eden smiled and sat down at his desk once more.

It was uncanny, Piers thought, as he went on to his room. How ever had Eden guessed? Was it because he was a poet? He had always felt, though he had given the matter but little thought, that a poet would be an uncommonly unpleasant person to have in the house, and now, by God, they had a full-fledged one at Jalna. He didn't like it at all. The first bloom of his happy mood was gone as he opened the door into his bedroom.

He shared it with sixteen-year-old Finch. Finch was now

humped over his Euclid, an expression of extreme melancholy lengthening his already long sallow face. He had been the centre of a whirlpool of discussion and criticism all tea time, and the effect was to make his brain, never quite under his control, completely unmanageable. He had gone over the same problem six or seven times and now it meant nothing to him, no more than a senseless nursery rhyme. He had stolen one of Piers's cigarettes to see if it would help him out. He had made the most of it, inhaling slowly, savoring each puff, retaining the stub between his bony fingers till they and even his lips were burned, but it had done no good. When he heard Piers at the door he had dropped the stub, a mere crumb, to the floor and set his foot on it.

Now he glanced sullenly at Piers out of the corners of his long light eyes.

Piers sniffed. "H-m. Smoking, eh? One of my fags, too, I bet. I'll just thank you to leave them alone, young man. Do you think I can supply you with smokes? Besides, you're not allowed."

Finch returned to his Euclid with increased melancholy. If he could not master it when he was alone, certainly he should never learn it with Piers in the room. That robust, domineering presence would crush the last spark of intelligence from his brain. He had always been afraid of Piers. All his life he had been kept in a state of subjection by him. He resented it, but he saw no way out of it. Piers was strong, handsome, a favorite. He was none of these things. And yet he loved all his family, in a secret, sullen way, even Piers who was so rough with him. Now, if Piers had been some brothers one might ask him to give one a helping hand with the Euclid; Piers had been good at the rotten stuff. But it would never do to ask Piers for help. He was too impatient, too intolerant of a fellow who got mixed up for nothing.

"I'd thank you," continued Piers, "to let my fags, likewise my handkerchiefs, socks, and ties alone. If you want to pinch other people's property, pinch Eden's. He's a poet and probably doesn't know what he has." He grinned at his reflection in the glass as he took off his collar and tie.

Finch made no answer. Desperately he sought to clamp his attention to the problem before him. Angles and triangles tangled themselves into strange patterns. He drew a grotesque face on the

margin of the book. Then horribly the face he had created began
to leer at him. With a shaking hand he tried to rub it out, but he
could not. It was not his to erase. It possessed the page. It
possessed the book. It was Euclid personified, sneering at him!

Piers had divested himself of all his clothes and had thrown
open the window. A chill night wind rushed in. Finch shivered as
it embraced him. He wondered how Piers stood it on his bare skin.
It fluttered the pages of a French exercise all about the room.
There was no use in trying; he could not do the problem.

Piers, in his pyjamas now, jumped into bed. He lay staring at
Finch with bright blue eyes, whistling softly. Finch began to
gather up his books.

"All finished?" asked Piers, politely. "You got through in a
hurry, didn't you?"

"I'm not through," bawled Finch. "Do you imagine I can work
with a cold blast like that on my back and you staring at me in
front? It just means I'll have to get up early and finish before
breakfast."

Piers became sarcastic. "You're very temperamental, aren't you?
You'll be writing poetry next. I dare say you've tried it already. Do
you know, I think it would be a good thing for you to go down to
New York in the Easter holidays and see if you can find a
publisher."

"Shut up," growled Finch, "and let me alone."

Piers was very happy. He was too happy for sleep. It would ease
his high spirits to bait young Finch. He lay watching him
speculatively while he undressed his long, lanky body. Finch
might develop into a distinguished-looking man. There was something arresting even now in his face; but he had a hungry,
haunted look, and he was uncomfortably aware of his long wrists
and legs. He always sat in some ungainly posture and, when
spoken to suddenly, would glare up, half defensively, half timidly,
as though expecting a blow. Truth to tell, he had had a good
many, some quite undeserved.

Piers regarded his thin frame with contemptuous amusement.
He offered pungent criticisms of Finch's prominent shoulder
blades, ribs, and various other portions of his anatomy. At last the
boy, trembling with anger and humiliation, got into his nightshirt,

turned out the light, and scrambled over Piers to his place next the wall. He curled himself up with a sigh of relief. It had been a nervous business scrambling over Piers. He had half expected to be grabbed by the ankle and put to some new torture. But he had gained his corner in safety. The day with its miseries was over. He stretched out his long limbs.

They lay still, side by side, in the peaceful dark. At length Piers spoke in a low, accusing tone.

"You didn't say your prayers. What do you mean by getting into bed without saying your prayers?"

Finch was staggered. This was something new. Piers, of all people, after him about prayers! There was something ominous about it.

"I forgot," he returned, heavily.

"Well, you've no right to forget. It's an important thing at your time of life to pray long and earnestly. If you prayed more and sulked less, you'd be healthier and happier."

"Rot. What are you givin' us?"

"I'm in dead earnest. Out you get and say your prayers."

"You don't pray yourself," complained Finch, bitterly. "You haven't said prayers for years."

"That's nothing to you. I've a special compact with the Devil, and he looks after his own. But you, my little lamb, must be separated from the goats."

"Oh, let me alone," growled Finch. "I'm sleepy. Let me alone."

"Get up and say your prayers."

"Oh, Piers, don't be a—"

"Be careful what you call me. Get out."

"Shan't." He clutched the blankets desperately, for he feared what was coming.

"You won't get up, eh? You won't say your prayers, eh? I've got to force you, eh?"

With each question Piers's strong fingers sought a tenderer spot in Finch's anatomy.

"Oh—oh—oh! Piers! Please let me up! Ow-eee-ee!" With a last terrible squeak Finch was out on the floor. He stood rubbing his side cautiously. Then he almost blubbered: "What the hell do you want me to do, anyway?"

"I want you to say your prayers properly. I'm not going to have you start being lax at your age. Down on your knees."

Finch dropped to his knees on the cold floor. Kneeling by the bedside in the pale moonlight, he was a pathetic young figure. But the sight held no pathos for Piers.

"Now, then," he said. "Fire away." Finch pressed his face against his clenched hands.

"Why don't you begin?" asked Piers, rising on his elbow and speaking testily.

"I—I have begun," came in a muffled voice.

"I can't hear you. How do you expect the Almighty to hear you if I can't? Speak up."

"I c-can't. I won't!"

"You *shall*. Or you'll be sorry."

In the stress of the moment, all Finch's prayers left him, as earlier all his Euclid had done. In the dim chaos of his soul only two words of supplication remained. "Oh, God," he muttered, hoarsely, and because he could think of nothing else, and must pray or be abused by that devil Piers, he repeated the words again and again in a hollow, shaking voice.

Piers lay listening blandly. He thought Finch the most ridiculous duffer he had ever known. He was a mystery Piers would never fathom. Suddenly he thought: "I'm fed up with this," and said: "Enough, enough. It's not much of a prayer you've made, but still you've a nice intimate way with the Almighty. You'd make a good Methodist of the Holy Roller variety." He added, not unkindly, "Hop into bed now."

But Finch would not hop. He clutched the counterpane and went on sobbing, "Oh, God!" The room was full of the presence of the Deity to him, now wearing the face of the terrible, austere Old Testament God, now, miraculously, the handsome, sneering face of Piers. Only a rap on the head brought him to his senses. He somehow got his long body back into bed, shivering all over.

Eden threw the door open. "One might as well," he complained in a high voice, "live next door to a circus. You're the most disgusting young—" and he delivered himself of some atrocious language. He interrupted himself to ask, cocking his head, "Is he crying? What's he crying for?"

"Just low-spirited, I expect," replied Piers, in a sleepy voice.

"What are you crying for, Finch?"

"Let me alone, can't you?" screamed Finch, in a sudden fury. "You let me alone!"

"I think he's sniveling over his report. Renny was up in the air about it," said Piers.

"Oh, is that it? Well, study will do more than sniveling to help that." And Eden disappeared as he had come.

The two brothers lay in the moonlight. Finch was quiet save for an occasional gulp. Piers's feelings toward him were magnanimous now. He was such a helpless young fool. Piers thought it rather hard that he had been born between Eden and Finch. Wedged in between a poet and a fool. What a sandwich! Of a certainty, he was the meaty part.

His thoughts turned to Pheasant. She was of never-failing interest to him: her pretty gestures, her reckless way of throwing her heart open to him, her sudden withdrawals, the remoteness of her profile. He could see her face in the moonlight as though she were in the room with him. Soon she would be, instead of snuffling young Finch! He loved her with every inch of his body. He alone of all the people in Jalna knew what real love was. Strange that, being absorbed by love as he was, he should have time to play with young Finch and make him miserable. No denying that there lurked a mischievous devil in him. Then, too, he had suffered so much anxiety lately that to have everything settled, to be certain of having his own way, made him feel like a young horse suddenly turned out into the spring pastures, ready to run and kick and bite his best friend from sheer high spirits.

Poor old Finch! Piers gave the bedclothes a jerk over Finch's protruding shoulder and put an arm around him.

# WILLIAM SAROYAN

𝍑 𝍑

*An adolescent comes to understand his love for his
brother and his fellow man as well, in this story of an
Armenian family in California, from* Inhale and Exhale.

## "The Broken Wheel"

WE HAD A SMALL HOUSE on Santa Clara Avenue, in the
foreign district where everyone moved about freely and where
conversations were carried on across yards and alleys and streets.
This house had been the home of a man who had been in the
business of roasting and marketing all kinds of nuts. We found
small and large pieces of his machinery in the two barns, and in
the cracks of the floors we sometimes found nut-shells and bits of
nut-meats. The house had a clean wholesome smell. There were
a number of crickets somewhere near the kitchen sink and quite
a few house spiders, the kind that are called daddy-long-legs.
There was also a cat. The cat was there when we moved into the
house, so we took it for granted. It was a big black tom with a
proud demeanor, an aristocratic air of superiority and indiffer-
ence. At first it lived under the house in the dark, but later on
when it got cold it moved into the house. We never bothered to
give it a name, but referred to it simply as the *Gadou*, which is
cat in Armenian.

Our trees were two sycamores at the side of the house, by the
alley; an English walnut tree in the back yard that was perhaps
twenty years old; a small olive tree; and three lilac trees that were
growing close to the front porch. The porch was shaded by a thick
honeysuckle plant. There were also geraniums and Bermuda grass
and other weeds. After a while we planted two peach trees, a

cactus tree, and a castor plant. The peach trees happened accidentally; we hadn't meant to plant them, we had only thrown peach-pits in the back yard and the trees had come up by themselves and we hadn't transplanted them. They were growing much too close to one another but they were either very lucky or very stubborn and after three years the leaves that fell from them in the fall were enough to rake into a pile and burn. They were growing just outside our yard but since we had no fence and no close neighbors, except for the family immediately across the alley, we considered the peach trees our trees. It wasn't a question of fruit; we could buy peaches cheaper than they could be grown; it was rather a question of being responsible for the growth of something fine or perhaps a question of blossoms in the spring. Once a year my sister Naomi would bring some of the pink blossoms into the house and place them in a black vase.

We used to see the blossoms in the black vase and suddenly we used to feel that it was all splendid. It seemed to mean that we were alive and we used to laugh about it. In the winter we laughed a great deal. We would be sullen and sorrowful for weeks at a time and then suddenly all of us would begin to laugh. We would laugh fifteen or twenty minutes and then we would be sullen and sorrowful again. It was all splendid and at the same time we felt that it must be pretty sad because it was in us to feel bewildered and futile.

My brother Krikor was responsible for the cactus tree. He came home one afternoon with a piece of thorny-cactus in his hand. He said to me, Did you know that all of this country was desert once and that cactus was growing everywhere?

Do you mean, I asked, no one was living here?

Yes, said Krikor. No one but the lizards, I guess, and the snakes and the horny-toads and the chicken-hawks and things like that. No people.

I thought of our valley without people and streets and houses and I thought it was very strange, very irregular.

Do you mean, I said, all the way to Selma and all the way to Clovis and away over to Kerman, past Skaggs Bridge?

I mean the whole valley, Krikor replied. I mean all this level land between the Coast Ranges and the Sierra Nevadas. All this country where the vineyards are growing now. It was dry here in those days, so they began to bring in the water in canals and irrigation ditches.

Krikor planted the cactus that afternoon and by the time I was ten it was producing splendid red blossoms and a fruit no one knew how to eat; and it was taller than a tall man.

The castor tree happened accidentally too. An old castor tree was growing in the yard of our neighbors across the alley and one summer some of its seeds got into our yard and the following summer we had a small castor tree of our own. It was a spurious sort of a tree, growing much too rapidly and being much too delicate for a tree. A small boy couldn't climb it and the least little storm that came along would tear some of its branches away. But it had a nice leaf and a clean growing-odor and it made a lot of shade. We hadn't planted it, but as long as it started to grow we were glad about it. Everyone hated castor-oil but we thought the tree itself was innocent enough.

In the summertime it would be very hot and we would have to get up early in the morning to feel a cool breeze. Every summer the city sent out a long tractor to plow into the tar of Santa Clara Avenue and improve the condition of the street. This tractor made a monotonous noise, pounding steadily and hollowly, approaching and going away from our house. In the morning we would begin to hear its far-away *boom-boom-boom* and as it came closer to our house we would hear the noise louder and louder and we used to think that this coming and going was like something in life but we couldn't tell just what. We used to say in Armenian, *Yegav noren,* Here it is again. We had no definite basis for our objection, but we sometimes asked what difference it made if the street was a little uneven. No one uses it, anyway, we said. Casparian, the man who sold watermelons each summer, passed over the street every afternoon with his old horse and his wobbly wagon, crying watermelon in Armenian, but there wasn't much other traffic. Those who wanted to get around in a hurry rode bicycles.

One year my uncle Vahan, then a young man, drove down from San Francisco in a brand new Apperson roadster and stopped in front of our house.

How do you like it? he asked. There are only eleven Appersons

in America and only one red one. His was the red one. We felt
splendid and we all laughed and my uncle Vahan smoked cigarettes. He took his sister, my mother, for a ride to Roeding Park. It
was her first ride in an automobile and she felt very proud of her
brother. We all thought he was splendid. It wasn't only the
Apperson, it was also his nervousness and his energy and the way
he laughed and talked. When he came back with my mother he
took my sisters, Lucy and Naomi, for a ride to town. My brother
Krikor sat on the front porch with a book, waiting nervously for
his turn to ride. Krikor said the automobile could go fifty miles an
hour. Rouben, our neighbor, was sitting on the porch with us and
he said his uncle Levon had a Cadillac which was a more expensive car than an Apperson and could go sixty miles an hour.

Yes, I said, but is it red? He admitted sadly that it was black.
There is only one red Apperson in America, I said. It was like
saying that one's great-grandfather had seen Lincoln or that one's
ancestors came over on the *Mayflower*; only it was more impressive. You knew that a great big piece of red junk on wheels would
come around the corner, thundering, and stop before your house,
and you felt that it was a big thing. This is the machine age, and
*Over in Europe they are using machine-guns in the War*, and,
*They are inventing all sorts of things that turn swiftly, saving
time*.

My uncle Vahan came home with Lucy and Naomi and went
inside for a cup of Turkish coffee. We could hear him telling his
sister how splendidly he had been getting along in San Francisco.
He had passed his Bar examination and was now an attorney-at-
law, but he had made most of his money selling watermelons
wholesale. Eventually he hoped to open an office in the Rowell
Building right here at home. My mother was very happy about
her young brother and we could hear her laughing with him and
asking him questions.

Krikor was very ill at ease because his uncle Vahan had not
offered to take him for a ride and because he was too proud or too
polite to ask for a ride, but I felt, There is a lawyer in our family
and he has a red Apperson. We are an enterprising people. I was
so happy about this that I couldn't sit still and kept walking on the
porch-railing and jumping down.

When my uncle Vahan came out of the house Krikor was

standing a few feet from the automobile, admiring it. He was admiring it so humbly, with so much youthful adoration, that my uncle understood what it was that was eating him and said, Come on, you fellows. I'll give you a ride.

Our neighbor Rouben and Krikor got into the car first, and I sat on Krikor's lap. My uncle Vahan started the motor and we went off, making much smoke and a terrific noise. I remember that my mother and Lucy and Naomi stood on the front porch and waved to us. We had an exciting ride through town and felt very elated. When we returned, my mother had cut two cold watermelons and we all sat in the parlor, eating watermelon and talking. It was very hot and we were all perspiring but it was a clear moment in our lives.

My uncle Vahan said, We do not know how fortunate we are to be in such a country as this. Opportunities are unlimited here. Every man is free and he can go as far as he is able. He spoke in Armenian because it was easier for him. He had been thirteen when he came to America and now he was twenty-two. He asked Krikor if he had yet decided on a career for himself and Krikor became embarrassed and began to eat watermelon very rapidly. I hope, my uncle Vahan said, you will decide to study law. And my mother replied, Of course. I thought, Krikor wants to be a musician because he told me, but I didn't say anything. In a day or two my uncle Vahan drove away in his red Apperson and we began to remember all the little details of his visit that we hadn't paid much attention to at first.

Everything was solid and permanent at our house and we didn't notice the time that was passing. One afternoon Krikor came home with a small black satchel. He placed the satchel on the table in our dining-room and we all gathered around to see what was in it. We never knew what Krikor was likely to do and we were always prepared for anything. Krikor was very excited and silent. He placed a small key into the key-hole of the satchel and turned it and opened the satchel, and we saw that it contained a cornet. My mother asked in Armenian, What is that, Krikor? and Krikor replied in Armenian that it was called a cornet.

As far back as I could remember we had always had a piano wherever we had lived. There would be times when no one would go near the piano for months and then suddenly all of us would be playing it. My sister Lucy had taken lessons and could play by note. She played serious music like the works of Chopin and Liszt and Mozart. Naomi played by ear and she played the songs that seemed to be without printed music and that seemed to be the songs of the people, *Keep the Home Fires Burning, I Love You, California, There's a Long Long Trail, Smiles, Dardanella, Oh, What a Pal Was Mary*, and songs like that. I couldn't play by note and I couldn't play by ear but I had managed to invent a few melodies from which it seemed I could never escape and to which I seemed always to be returning, a bit sullenly, as it were. In my despair I used to beat the keys of the piano, employing all the variations of tempo and volume I could devise, and I was always being driven away from the piano by one of my sisters. They said I played as if I were half-crazy. I didn't know why I had to try to play the piano but it seemed to me that I had to. We were all living and it seemed to me that something should happen. I believed this fiercely and when it always turned out that everything remained the same and we kept on doing things over and over again I would be frantic and I wouldn't know what to do with myself. And then once again we would all be laughing.

And now we were to have another musical instrument in our house. Krikor's cornet was a blunt and tangled affair, more a piece of plumbing than a musical instrument. He brought home a music stand and a book on how to play the cornet. By Christmas, he said, I'll be playing *Barcarole*. He blew into the horn and his lips became swollen and sore. Somehow he taught himself to play a very mediocre version of *America* and an even worse version of *My Old Kentucky Home*, and he always insisted that I stand up when he tried to play *America*.

He practiced a long time and we began to accept the horn as something permanent around the house, like the cat or the crickets or the English walnut tree; but he never learned to play *Barcarole*. Krikor had a very bad time of it from the beginning and gradually his ardor cooled and he began to be suspicious. He would fidget with his music and make a valiant effort to play only the printed notes and then suddenly he would go off and make all sorts of noises, and we knew that he could be heard as far south as the brewery and as far north as the Court House Park because we had been told. After a while he would be too tired to blow any more and he would sit down and look very miserable. He would say, I don't know what's the matter. I have done everything the book says to do and I have practiced regularly. He would look at the horn bitterly and ask, Do you think it's because this horn is so old or is it just that I haven't any talent for cornet-playing? I wouldn't know what to think but I would understand how he felt because I felt the same way. There was something to be done, something perfect and precise and graceful, but we hadn't found out what it was.

Everyone for blocks around knew that Krikor had a cornet and when he passed people in the street they would whisper to one another, There he goes. The boy who is making all that noise. He has a cornet and he is trying to learn to play. We thought it was those street cats, but cats don't make that noise in the daytime.

Each summer the long tractor came back and filled the days with its dismal hollow pounding, the nuts from the English walnut tree fell to earth and we gathered them into boxes. Imperceptibly the change was always going on and each spring my sister Naomi placed peach blossoms in the black vase.

One day Krikor said, I have decided to give up the cornet. I can't play it. He spoke deliberately and, I thought, bravely. Less than a week later he came home on a bicycle, riding under the cross-bar because he couldn't reach the pedals from the seat. He was almost twelve but he was small for his age. When my mother saw him coming up our street, pumping under the cross-bar, his body all out of shape, she ran down the front porch steps to the sidewalk. What is this you've brought home? she said. Get out of that crazy thing. Do you want to cripple yourself for life?

Krikor took the bicycle to the back yard and began trying to lower the seat. He worked hard and after a while he got the seat down as far as it would go, but even at that the bicycle was too big for him and he had to go on riding it from under the bar. My mother carried the bicycle into the house one evening and locked it in a closet. Your father, she told Krikor, was an erect man and your mother is an erect woman and I am sure I am not going to let you make a cripple of yourself. If you must ride a bicycle you had better get one you can ride from the top.

Krikor had been selling the *Evening Herald* after school almost two years and he had been saving money. My mother encouraged him to save his earnings but she did not object to his spending as much as he felt he ought to spend. On his twelfth birthday he came home with a cake which had cost him seven dollars and fifty cents. When we asked why he had gone to such an unreasonable expense and why he had brought home such a large cake when there were only five of us to eat it, he said, This was the first cake the baker showed me and I hadn't ever bought a birthday cake before. I thought it was about the right size. Is it too big?

Lucy said, Why, we couldn't eat this cake in a month.

We had cake at every meal for a whole week and we never stopped laughing about it.

So Krikor took the big bicycle back to the shop and traded it in for a smaller one. He had very little talent for making bargains and the only reason he had bought the big bicycle in the first place was that Kebo, the bicycle man, had insisted on selling it to him. He came home on a smaller bicycle, sitting on the seat where he belonged and my mother said, That's more like it. You look like something now.

It wasn't long before I was riding the bicycle more than Krikor was, and finally we got into a fight over it. We had had fights before, but this was our biggest fight because we had grown bigger. Krikor chased me around the house and then suddenly I turned and chased him around the other way. We were wrestling and doing everything we could to be properly angry and at the same time not really to hurt one another when my mother separated us and said that we could not have the bicycle at all if we could not keep from fighting over it. I knew, and I think Krikor knew, it wasn't the bicycle. We would have fought over something else. The bicycle just happened to be there. It was because we were brothers and because we loved one another and because we had been together through so many different things. One day when Krikor and I were fighting silently in the back yard old man Andreas, who was passing through the empty lot next to our house, ran up to our front door and cried in Armenian, Ester, Ester, your sons are killing one another.

Somehow we began to use the bicycle together, hiking one another. Sometimes I hiked Krikor but most of the time he hiked me. There were lots of brothers in the town who were doing this. We had made a path across the lot and at the end of the lot there was a steep bank of three or four feet. We used to start from our back yard and after picking up some speed we used to go down this bank.

One Sunday afternoon in November we decided to ride out to the County Fair Grounds. There was no Fair and no baseball game but we wanted to go out there and get on the dirt track with our bicycle. We had done this before and we had enjoyed being in the deserted Fair Grounds because it was different from being out there when all the people were there. It was finer and more private and we had lots more fun being alone. We liked the quiet and the enormity of the place, the strangeness of the empty grandstands. We used to take turns riding the bicycle around the mile track. Krikor had a watch and he would time me and then I would time him and we had a small book in which we kept a written record of our speed.

The castor plant had grown a lot and the peach trees had spread out. Easter and Christmas and Raisin Day had come around, we had thinned the honeysuckle plant to give it new life, we had bought new shoes and new clothes, we had got ill with the flu, but we hadn't noticed and we hadn't remembered. There were a few photographs of us in the family album, but to look at them it didn't seem as if we had changed. We had gone on quietly, sitting through the winter evenings, doing our school lessons, playing the piano, talking with one another, and laughing loudly for no reason. It had all happened and it was all there, but we hadn't remembered about it and now we wanted to get on our bicycle and go out to the County Fair Grounds again.

I sat on the cross-bar and Krikor got on the seat and we went across the lot. Now for the big dip, Krikor said. We came to the bank and went down it but while we were going down it something happened. The fork of our bicycle cracked and broke and the front wheel sank on its side. It happened almost too slowly to be real and while it was happening, while the fork was cracking and the wheel was sinking, we seemed to be coming out of an endless dream and we seemed to feel that this trivial occurrence was a vast and vital thing. It ought to have been amusing and we ought to have laughed about it, but it wasn't at all amusing and we didn't laugh. We walked back to the house without saying a word.

My mother had seen what had happened from the window of Naomi's room and when we went into the house, bewildered and frantically awake, she said, Don't you boys realize you've grown? You're much too big for one bicycle now.

We didn't speak of the matter all afternoon. We sat around the house trying to read, trying to feel that everything was the same and that only the fork of our bicycle had broken but we knew that everything was not the same. It seemed to me that we had forgotten our lives and that now because of this little incident we were remembering all the little details that marked the stages of our growth. I remembered the time Krikor and I made a canoe of plaster laths and burlap and tar, because we wanted to go down a stream, and walked with it six miles to Thompson Ditch through a burning sun and saw it sink.

I remembered the time I nearly drowned in Kings River and Krikor swam after me shouting frantically in Armenian. The time Lucy lost her job at Woolworth's and cried for a week. The time Naomi was ill with pneumonia and we all prayed she wouldn't die. The time Krikor came home with a small phonograph and two records: *Barcarole* and *O Sole Mio*.

And I remembered with a sickening sensation the day my uncle Vahan came to our house in a soldier's uniform and played *Johnny Get Your Gun* on his violin; my mother's cheerfulness when he sat at our table and her sobbing when he went away in a train. I remembered all the days she sat in the parlor reading the *Asbarez* and telling us about the misery and the pain and the dying in the old country.

And I remembered the day we learned that my uncle Vahan had been killed in France and we all sat at the supper table and couldn't eat and went to bed and couldn't sleep because we were all crying and talking about him.

I remembered that I had run down to the *Herald* office each noon for the extra edition about the War and had run through the streets shouting. I remembered the day it ended and the *Herald* printed a front-page etching of our Lord and the words *Peace on*

*Earth, Good Will Toward Men.* How I came home, hoarse from shouting and sick in my soul because it was all over and my uncle Vahan was out there dead. I remembered the times I had walked alone, seeing things and being alive and thinking of my uncle Vahan, and suddenly burst into tears because life was so bright and clean and fierce.

All afternoon and almost all evening there was no talking in our house. My sister Lucy played the piano for a few minutes and my sister Naomi hummed *Smiles* until she remembered that my mother had asked her never to hum that song because her brother Vahan had sung it. We all felt sullen and bewildered. We were getting ready to go to bed when Krikor said, Wasn't it funny the way the bicycle broke under us?

My mother and my sisters said it was the funniest sight they had ever seen and they began to laugh about it. They laughed softly at first. They would stop laughing for a moment and then remember how funny it had been and then they would start laughing again, only louder. Krikor began to laugh with them and it almost seemed as if everything in our world was all right and that we had nothing to feel sad about. I couldn't decide what to do and I didn't think the incident had been funny at all, but after a while I began to laugh, too. All those things had happened and yet we were still living together in our house and we still had our trees and in the summer the city would send out the long tractor again and we would hear it and old Casparian would pass before our house in his wagon, crying watermelon in Armenian. I didn't feel at all happy but I laughed until tears came from my eyes.

Then suddenly something strange happened, it happened inside of me, and at the same time it seemed to be happening all over the world, in the cities, on the surface of the earth everywhere, wherever there were men. I felt that at last I was a part of life, that at last I knew how all things ended. A strange, desolating sadness swept through the earth and for the first time in my life I was feeling it definitely, personally. It seemed as if I had just been born, that I had at that moment become aware of the earth, of man on it, of life, of the beauty and the pain, the joy and the fear and the ugliness. It was all very clear to me and I knew why I had always sat at the piano pounding the keys, why I had fought with my brother Krikor, and why we had laughed together. And because I had been laughing, and because tears had come from my eyes, I sat on my bed and began to cry.

Without saying a word, Krikor began to cry, and after him my sisters began to cry.

My mother said in Armenian, It is no use to cry. We have always had our disappointments and hardships and we have always come out of them and always shall.

When we were all supposed to be asleep, I got up from my bed and went to the door that opened on our parlor and opened it an inch or two. I saw that my mother had taken her brother's photograph from the piano. She had placed it before her on the table and I could hear her weeping softly, and I could see her swaying her head from side to side the way people from the old country do.

# PHYLLIS McGINLEY

Times Three *presents a younger sister's views.*

## "Triolet Against Sisters"

SISTERS are always drying their hair.
   Locked into rooms, alone,
They pose at the mirror, shoulders bare,
Trying this way and that their hair,
Or fly importunate down the stair
   To answer a telephone.
Sisters are always drying their hair,
   Locked into rooms, alone.

# Aunts, Uncles, Nieces, Nephews, and Cousins

# CHARLES DICKENS

*A cheerfully eccentric aunt, Betsey Trotwood, protects, defends, and offers a new life to a young nephew in* David Copperfield.

ON GOING DOWN in the morning, I found my aunt musing so profoundly over the breakfast-table, with her elbow on the tray, that the contents of the urn had overflowed the teapot and were laying the whole table-cloth under water, when my entrance put her meditations to flight. I felt sure that I had been the subject of her reflections, and was more than ever anxious to know her intentions towards me. Yet I dared not express my anxiety, lest it should give her offence.

My eyes, however, not being so much under control as my tongue, were attracted towards my aunt very often during breakfast. I never could look at her for a few moments together but I found her looking at me—in an odd thoughtful manner, as if I were an immense way off, instead of being on the other side of the small round table. When she had finished her breakfast, my aunt very deliberately leaned back in her chair, knitted her brows, folded her arms, and contemplated me at her leisure, with such a fixedness of attention that I was quite overpowered by embarrassment. Not having as yet finished my own breakfast, I attempted to hide my confusion by proceeding with it; but my knife tumbled over my fork, my fork tripped up my knife. I chipped bits of bacon a surprising height into the air instead of cutting them for my own eating, and choked myself with my tea, which persisted in going the wrong way instead of the right one, until I gave in altogether, and sat blushing under my aunt's close scrutiny.

"Hallo!" said my aunt, after a long time.

I looked up, and met her sharp bright glance respectfully.

"I have written to him," said my aunt.

"To—?"

"To your father-in-law," said my aunt. "I have sent him a letter that I'll trouble him to attend to, or he and I will fall out, I can tell him!"

"Does he know where I am, aunt?" I inquired, alarmed.

"I have told him," said my aunt, with a nod.

"Shall I—be—given up to him?" I faltered.

"I don't know," said my aunt. "We shall see."

"Oh! I can't think what I shall do," I exclaimed, "if I have to go back to Mr. Murdstone!"

"I don't know anything about it," said my aunt, shaking her head. "I can't say, I am sure. We shall see."

My spirits sank under these words, and I became very downcast and heavy of heart. My aunt, without appearing to take much heed of me, put on a coarse apron with a bib, which she took out of the press; washed up the teacups with her own hands; and, when everything was washed and set in the tray again, and the cloth folded and put on the top of the whole, rang for Janet to remove it. She next swept up the crumbs with a little broom (putting on a pair of gloves first), until there did not appear to be one microscopic speck left on the carpet; next dusted and arranged the room, which was dusted and arranged to a hair's-breadth already. When all these tasks were performed to her satisfaction, she took off the gloves and apron, folded them up, put them in the particular corner of the press from which they had been taken, brought out her work-box to her own table in the open window, and sat down, with the green fan between her and the light, to work.

"I wish you'd go up-stairs," said my aunt, as she threaded her needle, "and give my compliments to Mr. Dick, and I'll be glad to know how he gets on with his Memorial."

I rose with all alacrity, to acquit myself of this commission.

"I suppose," said my aunt, eyeing me as narrowly as she had eyed the needle in threading it, "you think Mr. Dick a short name, eh?"

"I thought it was rather a short name, yesterday," I confessed.

"You are not to suppose that he hasn't got a longer name, if he chose to use it," said my aunt, with a loftier air. "Babley—Mr. Richard Babley—that's the gentleman's true name."

I was going to suggest, with a modest sense of my youth and the familiarity I had been already guilty of, that I had better give him the full benefit of that name, when my aunt went on to say:

"But don't you call him by it, whatever you do. He can't bear his name. That's a peculiarity of his. Though I don't know that it's much of a peculiarity, either; for he has been ill-used enough, by some that bear it, to have a mortal antipathy for it, Heaven knows. Mr. Dick is his name here, and everywhere else, now—if he ever went anywhere else, which he don't. So take care, child, you don't call him anything *but* Mr. Dick."

I promised to obey, and went upstairs with my message; thinking as I went, that if Mr. Dick had been working at his Memorial long, at the same rate as I had seen him working at it, through the open door, when I came down, he was probably getting on very well indeed. I found him still driving at it with a long pen, and his head almost laid upon the paper. He was so intent upon it, that I had ample leisure to observe the large paper kite in a corner, the confusion of bundles of manuscript, the number of pens, and, above all, the quantity of ink (which he seemed to have in, in half-gallon jars by the dozen), before he observed my being present.

"Ha! Phoebus!" said Mr. Dick, laying down his pen. "How does the world go? I'll tell you what," he added, in a lower tone, "I shouldn't wish it to be mentioned, but it's a"—here he beckoned to me, and put his lips close to my ear—"it's a mad world. Mad as Bedlam, boy!" said Mr. Dick, taking snuff from a round box on the table, and laughing heartily.

Without presuming to give my opinion on this question, I delivered my message.

"Well," said Mr. Dick, in answer, "my compliments to her, and I—I believe I have made a start. I think I have made a start," said Mr. Dick, passing his hand among his grey hair, and casting anything but a confident look at his manuscript. "You have been to school?"

"Yes, sir," I answered; "for a short time."

"Do you recollect the date," said Mr. Dick, looking earnestly at me, and taking up his pen to note it down, "when King Charles the First had his head cut off?"

I said I believed it happened in the year sixteen hundred and forty-nine.

"Well," returned Mr. Dick, scratching his ear with his pen, and looking dubiously at me. "So the books say; but I don't see how that can be. Because, if it was so long ago, how could the people about him have made that mistake of putting some of the trouble out of *his head,* after it was taken off, into *mine?*"

I was very much surprised by the inquiry; but could give no information on this point.

"It's very strange," said Mr. Dick, with a despondent look upon his papers, and with his hand among his hair again, "that I never can get that quite right. I never can make that perfectly clear. But no matter, no matter!" he said cheerfully, and rousing himself, "there's time enough! My compliments to Miss Trotwood, I am getting on very well indeed."

I was going away, when he directed my attention to the kite.

"What do you think of that for a kite?" he said.

I answered that it was a beautiful one. I should think it must have been as much as seven feet high.

"I made it. We'll go and fly it, you and I," said Mr. Dick. "Do you see this?"

He showed me that it was covered with manuscript, very closely and laboriously written; but so plainly, that as I looked along the lines, I thought I saw some allusion to King Charles the First's head again, in one or two places.

"There's plenty of string," said Mr. Dick, "and when it flies high, it takes the facts a long way. That's my manner of diffusing 'em. I don't know where they may come down. It's according to circumstances, and the wind, and so forth; but I take my chance of that."

His face was so very mild and pleasant, and had something so reverend in it, though it was hale and hearty, that I was not sure but that he was having a good-humoured jest with me. So I laughed, and he laughed, and we parted the best friends possible.

"Well, child," said my aunt, when I went down-stairs. "And what of Mr. Dick, this morning?"

I informed her that he sent his compliments, and was getting on very well indeed.

"What do you think of him?" said my aunt.

I had some shadowy idea of endeavouring to evade the question by replying that I thought him a very nice gentleman; but my aunt was not to be so put off, for she laid her work down in her lap, and said, folding her hands upon it:

"Come! Your sister Betsey Trotwood would have told me what she thought of any one, directly. Be as like your sister as you can, and speak out!"

"Is he—is Mr. Dick—I ask because I don't know, aunt—is he at all out of his mind, then?" I stammered; for I felt I was on dangerous ground.

"Not a morsel!" said my aunt.

"Oh, indeed!" I observed faintly.

"If there is anything in the world," said my aunt, with great decision and force of manner, "that Mr. Dick is not, it's that."

I had nothing better to offer, than another timid "Oh, indeed!"

"He has been *called* mad," said my aunt. "I have a selfish pleasure in saying he has been called mad, or I should not have had the benefit of his society and advice for these last ten years and upwards—in fact, ever since your sister, Betsey Trotwood, disappointed me."

"So long as that?" I said.

"And nice people they were, who had the audacity to call him mad," pursued my aunt. "Mr. Dick is a sort of distant connexion of mine; it doesn't matter how; I needn't enter into that. If it hadn't been for me, his own brother would have shut him up for life. That's all."

I am afraid it was hypocritical in me, but seeing that my aunt felt strongly on the subject, I tried to look as if I felt strongly too.

"A proud fool!" said my aunt. "Because his brother was a little eccentric—though he is not half so eccentric as a good many people—he didn't like to have him visible about his house, and sent him away to some private asylum-place: though he had been left to his particular care by their deceased father, who thought him almost a natural. And a wise man *he* must have been to think him so! Mad himself, no doubt."

Again, as my aunt looked quite convinced, I endeavoured to look quite convinced also.

"So I stepped in," said my aunt, "and made him an offer. I said, 'Your brother's sane—a great deal more sane than you are, or ever will be, it is to be hoped. Let him have his little income, and come and live with me. *I* am not afraid of him, *I* am not proud. *I* am ready to take care of him, and shall not ill-treat him as some people (besides the asylum-folks) have done.' After a good deal of squabbling," said my aunt, "I got him; and he has been here ever since. He is the most friendly and amenable creature in existence; and as for advice!—But nobody knows what that man's mind is, except myself."

My aunt smoothed her dress and shook her head, as if she smoothed defiance of the whole world out of the one, and shook it out of the other.

"He had a favourite sister," said my aunt, " a good creature, and very kind to him. But she did what they all do—took a husband. And *he* did what they all do—made her wretched. It had such an effect upon the mind of Mr. Dick (*that's* not madness, I hope!) that, combined with his fear of his brother, and his sense of his unkindness, it threw him into a fever. That was before he came to me, but the recollection of it is oppressive to him even now. Did he say anything to you about King Charles the First, child?"

"Yes, aunt."

"Ah!" said my aunt, rubbing her nose as if she were a little vexed. "That's his allegorical way of expressing it. He connects his illness with great disturbance and agitation, naturally, and that's the figure, or the simile, or whatever it's called, which he chooses to use. And why shouldn't he, if he thinks proper?"

I said: "Certainly, aunt."

"It's not a business-like way of speaking," said my aunt, "nor a worldly way. I am aware of that; and that's the reason why I insist upon it, that there shan't be a word about it in his Memorial."

"Is it a Memorial about his own history that he is writing, aunt?"

"Yes, child," said my aunt, rubbing her nose again. "He is memorialising the Lord Chancellor, or the Lord Somebody or other—one of those people, at all events, who are paid to *be* memorialised—about his affairs. I suppose it will go in, one of these days. He hasn't been able to draw it up yet, without introducing that mode of expressing himself; but it don't signify; it keeps him employed."

In fact, I found out afterwards that Mr. Dick had been for upwards of ten years endeavouring to keep King Charles the First out of the Memorial; but he had been constantly getting into it, and was there now.

"I say again," said my aunt, "nobody knows what that man's mind is except myself; and he's the most amenable and friendly creature in existence. If he likes to fly a kite sometimes, what of that! Franklin used to fly a kite. He was a Quaker, or something of that sort, if I am not mistaken. And a Quaker flying a kite is a much more ridiculous object than anybody else."

If I could have supposed that my aunt had recounted these particulars for my especial behoof, and as a piece of confidence in me, I should have felt very much distinguished, and should have augured favorably from such a mark of her good opinion. But I could hardly help observing that she had launched into them, chiefly because the question was raised in her own mind, and with very little reference to me, though she had addressed herself to me in the absence of anybody else.

At the same time, I must say that the generosity of her championship of poor harmless Mr. Dick, not only inspired my young breast with some selfish hope for myself, but warmed it unselfishly towards her. I believe that I began to know that there was something about my aunt, notwithstanding her many eccentricities and odd humours, to be honoured and trusted in. Though she was just as sharp that day as on the day before, and was in and out about the donkeys just as often, and was thrown into a tremendous state of indignation, when a young man, going by, ogled Janet at a window (which was one of the gravest misdemeanours that could be committed against my aunt's dignity), she seemed to me to command more of my respect, if not less of my fear.

The anxiety I underwent, in the interval which necessarily elapsed before a reply could be received to her letter to Mr. Murdstone, was extreme; but I made an endeavour to suppress it, and to be as agreeable as I could in a quiet way, both to my aunt and Mr. Dick. The latter and I would have gone out to fly the great kite; but that I had still no other clothes than the anything but ornamental garments with which I had been decorated on the first day, and which confined me to the house, except for an hour after dark, when my aunt, for my health's sake paraded me up and down on the cliff outside before going to bed. At length the reply from Mr. Murdstone came, and my aunt informed me, to my infinite terror, that he was coming to speak to her himself on the next day. On the next day, still bundled up in my curious habiliments, I sat counting the time, flushed and heated by the conflict of sinking hopes and rising fears within me; and waiting to be startled by the sight of the gloomy face whose non-arrival startled me every minute.

My aunt was a little more imperious and stern than usual, but I observed no other token of her preparing herself to receive the visitor so much dreaded by me. She sat at work in the window, and I sat by, with my thoughts running astray on all possible and impossible results of Mr. Murdstone's visit, until pretty late in the afternoon. Our dinner had been indefinitely postponed; but it was growing so late, that my aunt had ordered it to be got ready, when she gave a sudden alarm of donkeys, and to my consternation and amazement, I beheld Miss Murdstone, on a side-saddle, ride deliberately over the sacred piece of green, and stop in front of the house, looking about her.

"Go along with you!" cried my aunt, shaking her head and her fist at the window. "You have no business there. How dare you trespass? Go along! Oh! you bold-faced thing!"

My aunt was so exasperated by the coolness with which Miss Murdstone looked about her, that I really believe she was motionless, and unable for the moment to dart out according to custom. I seized the opportunity to inform her who it was; and that the gentleman now coming near the offender (for the way up was very steep, and he had dropped behind), was Mr. Murdstone himself.

"I don't care who it is!" cried my aunt, still shaking her head, and gesticulating anything but welcome from the bow-window. "I won't be trespassed upon. I won't allow it. Go away! Janet, turn him round. Lead him off!" and I saw, from behind my aunt, a sort of hurried battle-piece, in which the donkey stood resisting everybody, with all his four legs planted different ways, while Janet tried to pull him round by the bridle, Mr. Murdstone tried to lead him on, Miss Murdstone struck at Janet with a parasol, and several boys, who had come to see the engagement, shouted vigorously. But my aunt, suddenly descrying among them the young malefactor who was the donkey's guardian, and who was one of the most inveterate offenders against her, though hardly in his teens, rushed out to the scene of action, pounced upon him, captured him, dragged him, with his jacket over his head and his heels grinding the ground, into the garden, and, calling upon Janet to fetch the constable and justices, that he might be taken, tried, and executed on the spot, held him at bay there. This part of the business, however, did not last long; for the young rascal, being expert at a variety of feints and dodges, of which my aunt had no conception, soon went whooping away, leaving some deep impressions of his nailed boots in the flower-beds, and taking his donkey in triumph with him.

Miss Murdstone, during the latter portion of the contest, had dismounted, and was now waiting with her brother at the bottom of the steps, until my aunt should be at leisure to receive them. My aunt, a little ruffled by the combat, marched past them into the house, with great dignity, and took no notice of their presence, until they were announced by Janet.

"Shall I go away, aunt?" I asked, trembling.

"No, sir," said my aunt. "Certainly not!" With which she pushed me into a corner near her, and fenced me in with a chair, as if it were a prison or a bar of justice. This position I continued to occupy during the whole interview, and from it I now saw Mr. and Miss Murdstone enter the room.

"Oh!" said my aunt, "I was not aware at first to whom I had the pleasure of objecting. But I don't allow anybody to ride over that turf. I make no exceptions. I don't allow anybody to do it."

"Your regulation is rather awkward to strangers," said Miss Murdstone.

"Is it?" said my aunt.

Mr. Murdstone seemed afraid of a renewal of hostilities, and interposing began:

"Miss Trotwood!"

"I beg your pardon," observed my aunt with a keen look. "You are the Mr. Murdstone who married the widow of my late nephew, David Copperfield, of Blunderstone Rookery?—Though why Rookery, I don't know!"

"I am," said Mr. Murdstone.

"You'll excuse my saying, sir," returned my aunt, "that I think it would have been a much better and happier thing if you had let that poor child alone."

"I so far agree with what Miss Trotwood has remarked," observed Miss Murdstone, bridling, "that I consider our lamented Clara to have been, in all essential respects, a mere child."

"It is a comfort to you and me, ma'am," said my aunt, "who are getting on in life, and are not likely to be made unhappy by our personal attractions, that nobody can say the same of us."

"No doubt!" returned Miss Murdstone, though, I thought, not with a ready or gracious assent. "And it certainly might have been, as you say, a better and happier thing for my brother if he had never entered into such a marriage. I have always been of that opinion."

"I have no doubt you have," said my aunt. "Janet," ringing the bell, "my compliments to Mr. Dick, and beg him to come down."

Until he came, my aunt sat perfectly upright and stiff, frowning at the wall. When he came, my aunt performed the ceremony of introduction.

"Mr. Dick. An old and intimate friend. On whose judgment," said my aunt, with emphasis, as an admonition to Mr. Dick, who was biting his forefinger and looking rather foolish, "I rely."

Mr. Dick took his finger out of his mouth, on this hint, and stood among the group, with a grave and attentive expression of face. My aunt inclined her head to Mr. Murdstone, who went on:

"Miss Trotwood. On the receipt of your letter, I considered it an act of greater justice to myself, and perhaps of more respect to you—"

"Thank you," said my aunt, still eyeing him keenly. "You needn't mind me."

"To answer it in person, however inconvenient the journey," pursued Mr. Murdstone, "rather than by letter. This unhappy boy who has run away from his friends and his occupation—"

"And whose appearance," interposed his sister, directing general attention to me in my indefinable costume, "is perfectly scandalous and disgraceful."

"Jane Murdstone," said her brother, "have the goodness not to interrupt me. This unhappy boy, Miss Trotwood, has been the occasion of much domestic trouble and uneasiness; both during the lifetime of my late dear wife, and since. He has a sullen, rebellious spirit; a violent temper; and an untoward, intractable disposition. Both my sister and myself have endeavoured to correct his vices, but ineffectually. And I have felt—we both have felt, I may say; my sister being fully in my confidence—that it is right you should receive this grave and dispassionate assurance from our lips."

"It can hardly be necessary for me to confirm anything stated by my brother," said Miss Murdstone; "but I beg to observe, that, of all the boys in the world, I believe this is the worst boy."

"Strong!" said my aunt, shortly.

"But not at all too strong for the facts," returned Miss Murdstone.

"Ha!" said my aunt. "Well, sir?"

"I have my own opinions," resumed Mr. Murdstone, whose face darkened more and more, the more he and my aunt observed each other, which they did very narrowly, "as to the best mode of bringing him up; they are founded, in part, on my knowledge of him, and in part on my knowledge of my own means and resources. I am responsible for them to myself, I act upon them, and I say no more about them. It is enough that I place this boy under the eye of a friend of my own, in a respectable business; that it does not please him; that he runs away from it; makes himself a common vagabond about the country; and comes here, in rags, to appeal to you, Miss Trotwood. I wish to set before you, honourably, the exact consequences—so far as they are within my knowledge—of your abetting him in this appeal."

"But about the respectable business first," said my aunt. "If he had been your own boy, you would have put him to it, just the same, I suppose?"

"If he had been my brother's own boy," returned Miss Murdstone, striking in, "his character, I trust, would have been altogether different."

"Or if the poor child, his mother, had been alive, he would still have gone into the respectable business, would he?" said my aunt.

"I believe," said Mr. Murdstone, with an inclination of his head, "that Clara would have disputed nothing which myself and my sister Jane Murdstone were agreed was for the best."

Miss Murdstone confirmed this with an audible murmur.

"Humph!" said my aunt. "Unfortunate baby!"

Mr. Dick, who had been rattling his money all this time, was rattling it so loudly now, that my aunt felt it necessary to check him with a look, before saying:

"The poor child's annuity died with her?"

"Died with her," replied Mr. Murdstone.

"And there was no settlement of the little property—the house and garden—the what's-its-name Rookery without any rooks in it—upon her boy?"

"It had been left to her, unconditionally, by her first husband," Mr. Murdstone began, when my aunt caught him up with the greatest irascibility and impatience.

"Good Lord, man, there's no occasion to say that. Left to her unconditionally! I think I see David Copperfield looking forward to any condition of any sort or kind, though it stared him point-blank in the face! Of course it was left to her unconditionally. But when she married again—when she took that most disastrous step of marrying you, in short," said my aunt, "to be plain—did no one put in a word for the boy at that time?"

"My late wife loved her second husband, ma'am," said Mr. Murdstone, "and trusted implicitly in him."

"Your late wife, sir, was a most unworldly, most unhappy, most unfortunate baby," returned my aunt, shaking her head at him. "That's what *she* was. And now, what have you got to say next?"

"Merely this, Miss Trotwood," he returned. "I am here to take David back; to take him back unconditionally, to dispose of him as I think proper, and to deal with him as I think right. I am not here to make any promise, or give any pledge to anybody. You may possibly have some idea, Miss Trotwood, of abetting him in his running away, and in his complaints to you. Your manner, which I must say does not seem intended to propitiate, induces me to think it possible. Now I must caution you that if you abet him once, you abet him for good and all; if you step in between him and me, now, you must step in, Miss Trotwood, for ever. I cannot trifle, or be trifled with. I am here, for the first and last time, to take him away. Is he ready to go? If he is not—and you tell me he is not; on any pretence; it is indifferent to me what—my doors are shut against him henceforth and yours, I take it for granted, are open to him."

To this address, my aunt had listened with the closest attention, sitting perfectly upright, with her hands folded on one knee, and looking grimly on the speaker. When he had finished, she turned her eyes, so as to command Miss Murdstone, without otherwise disturbing her attitude, and said:

"Well, ma'am, have *you* got anything to remark?"

"Indeed, Miss Trotwood," said Miss Murdstone, "all that I could say has been so well said by my brother, and all that I know to be the fact has been so plainly stated by him, that I have nothing to add except my thanks for your politeness. For your very great politeness, I am sure," said Miss Murdstone; with an irony which no more affected my aunt than it discomposed the cannon I had slept by at Chatham.

"And what does the boy say?" said my aunt. "Are you ready to go, David?"

I answered no, and entreated her not to let me go. I said that neither Mr. nor Miss Murdstone had ever liked me, or had ever been kind to me. That they had made my mama, who always loved me dearly, unhappy about me, and that I knew it well, and that Peggotty knew it. I said that I had been more miserable than I thought anybody could believe who only knew how young I was. And I begged and prayed my aunt—I forget in what terms now, but I remember that they affected me very much then—to befriend and protect me, for my father's sake.

"Mr. Dick," said my aunt; "what shall I do with this child?"

Mr. Dick considered, hesitated, brightened, and rejoined, "Have him measured for a suit of clothes directly."

"Mr. Dick," said my aunt triumphantly, "give me your hand, for your common sense is invaluable." Having shaken it with great cordiality, she pulled me towards her and said to Mr. Murdstone:

"You can go when you like; I'll take my chance with the boy. If he's all you say he is, at least I can do as much for him then, as you have done. But I don't believe a word of it."

"Miss Trotwood," rejoined Mr. Murdstone, shrugging his shoulders, as he rose, "if you were a gentleman—"

"Bah! Stuff and nonsense!" said my aunt. "Don't talk to me!"

"How exquisitely polite!" exclaimed Miss Murdstone, rising. "Overpowering, really!"

"Do you think I don't know," said my aunt, turning a deaf ear to the sister, and continuing to address the brother, and to shake her head at him with infinite expression, "what kind of life you must have led that poor, unhappy, misdirected baby? Do you think I don't know what a woeful day it was for the soft little creature when *you* first came in her way—smirking and making great eyes at her, I'll be bound, as if you couldn't say boh! to a goose!"

"I never heard anything so elegant!" said Miss Murdstone.

"Do you think I can't understand you as well as if I had seen you," pursued my aunt, "now that I *do* see and hear you—which I tell you candidly, is anything but a pleasure to me? Oh yes, bless us! who so smooth and silky as Mr. Murdstone at first! The poor, benighted innocent had never seen such a man. He was made of sweetness. He worshipped her. He doted on her boy—tenderly doted on him! He was to be another father to him, and they were all to live together in a garden of roses, weren't they? Ugh! Get along with you, do!" said my aunt.

"I never heard anything like this person in my life!" exclaimed Miss Murdstone.

"And when you had made sure of the poor little fool," said my aunt—"God forgive me that I should call her so, and she gone where *you* won't go in a hurry—because you had not done wrong enough to her and hers, you must begin to train her, must you? begin to break her, like a poor caged bird, and wear her deluded life away, in teaching her to sing *your* notes?"

"This is either insanity or intoxication," said Miss Murdstone, in a perfect agony at not being able to turn the current of my aunt's address towards herself; "and my suspicion is that it's intoxication."

Miss Betsey, without taking the least notice of the interruption,

continued to address herself to Mr. Murdstone as if there had
been no such thing.

"Mr. Murdstone," she said, shaking her finger at him, "you
were a tyrant to the simple baby, and you broke her heart. She
was a loving baby—I know that; I knew it years before *you* ever
saw her—and through the best part of her weakness you gave her
the wounds she died of. There is the truth for your comfort,
however you like it. And you and your instruments may make the
most of it."

"Allow me to inquire, Miss Trotwood," interposed Miss Murdstone, "whom you are pleased to call, in a choice of words in
which I am not experienced, my brother's instruments?"

Still stone-deaf to the voice, and utterly unmoved by it, Miss
Betsey pursued her discourse.

"It was clear enough, as I have told you, years before *you* ever
saw her—and why, in the mysterious dispensations of Providence,
you ever did see her, is more than humanity can comprehend—it
was clear enough that the poor soft little thing would marry
somebody, at some time or other; but I did hope it wouldn't
have been as bad as it has turned out. That was the time, Mr.
Murdstone, when she gave birth to her boy here," said my aunt;
"to the poor child you sometimes tormented her through afterwards, which is a disagreeable remembrance, and makes the sight
of him odious now. Aye, aye! you needn't wince!" said my aunt.
"I know it's true without that."

He had stood by the door, all this while, observant of her, with
a smile upon his face, though his black eyebrows were heavily
contracted. I remarked now, that, though the smile was on his face
still, his colour had gone in a moment, and he seemed to breathe
as if he had been running.

"Good day, sir," said my aunt, "and good-bye! Good day to you,
too, ma'am," said my aunt, turning suddenly upon his sister. "Let
me see you ride a donkey over *my* green again, and as sure as you
have a head upon your shoulders, I'll knock your bonnet off, and
tread upon it!"

It would require a painter, and no common painter too, to
depict my aunt's face as she delivered herself of this very unexpected sentiment, and Miss Murdstone's face as she heard it.

But the manner of the speech, no less than the matter, was so fiery, that Miss Murdstone, without a word in answer, discreetly put her arm through her brother's, and walked haughtily out of the cottage; my aunt remaining in the window looking after them; prepared, I have no doubt, in case of the donkey's reappearance, to carry her threat into instant execution.

No attempt at defiance being made, however, her face gradually relaxed, and became so pleasant, that I was emboldened to kiss and thank her; which I did with great heartiness, and with both my arms clasped round her neck. I then shook hands with Mr. Dick, who shook hands with me a great many times, and hailed this happy close of the proceedings with repeated bursts of laughter.

"You'll consider yourself guardian, jointly with me, of this child, Mr. Dick," said my aunt.

"I shall be delighted," said Mr. Dick, "to be the guardian of David's son."

"Very good," returned my aunt, "*that's* settled. I have been thinking, do you know, Mr. Dick, that I might call him Trotwood?"

"Certainly, certainly. Call him Trotwood, certainly," said Mr. Dick. "David's son's Trotwood."

"Trotwood Copperfield, you mean," returned my aunt.

"Yes, to be sure. Yes. Trotwood Copperfield," said Mr. Dick, a little abashed.

My aunt took so kindly to the notion, that some ready-made clothes, which were purchased for me that afternoon, were marked "Trotwood Copperfield," in her own handwriting, and in indelible marking-ink, before I put them on; and it was settled that all the other clothes which were ordered to be made for me (a complete outfit was bespoke that afternoon) should be marked in the same way.

Thus I began my new life, in a new name, and with everything new about me. Now that the state of doubt was over, I felt, for many days, like one in a dream. I never thought of anything about myself, distinctly. The two things clearest in my mind were, that a remoteness had come upon the old Blunderstone life—which seemed to lie in the haze of an immeasurable distance; and that a curtain had for ever fallen on my life at Murdstone and Grinby's. No one has ever raised that curtain since.

# WILLIAM MAKEPEACE THACKERAY

🜨 🜨

*In* The History of Pendennis, *a largely autobiographical novel, young Pen's uncle and guardian, Major Arthur Pendennis, attempts to rescue his nephew from an unfortunate romance.*

. . . And now let Mr. Pen come in, who has been waiting all this while.

Having strung up his nerves, and prepared himself, without at the door, for the meeting, he came to it, determined to face the awful uncle. He had settled in his mind that the encounter was to be a fierce one, and was resolved on bearing it through with all the courage and dignity of the famous family which he represented. And he flung open the door and entered with the most severe and warlike expression, armed *cap-à-pie* as it were, with lance couched and plumes displayed, and glancing at his adversary, as if to say, "Come on, I'm ready."

The old man of the world, as he surveyed the boy's demeanor, could hardly help a grin at his admirable pompous simplicity. Major Pendennis too had examined his ground; and finding that the widow was already half won over to the enemy, and having a shrewd notion that threats and tragic exhortations would have no effect upon the boy, who was inclined to be perfectly stubborn and awfully serious, the Major laid aside the authoritative manner at once, and with the most good-humored natural smile in the world, held out his hands to Pen, shook the lad's passive fingers gayly, and said, "Well, Pen, my boy, tell us all about it."

Helen was delighted with the generosity of the Major's good-humor. On the contrary, it quite took aback and disappointed poor Pen, whose nerves were strung up for a tragedy, and who felt that his grand *entrée* was altogether baulked and ludicrous. He blushed and winced with mortified vanity and bewilderment. He felt immensely inclined to begin to cry. "I—I—I didn't know that you were come till just now," he said: "is—is—town very full I suppose?"

If Pen could hardly gulp his tears down, it was all the Major could do to keep from laughter. He turned round and shot a comical glance at Mrs. Pendennis, who too felt that the scene was at once ridiculous and sentimental. And so, having nothing to say, she went up and kissed Mr. Pen: as he thought of her tenderness and soft obedience to his wishes, it is very possible too the boy was melted.

"What a couple of fools they are," thought the old guardian. "If I hadn't come down, she would have driven over in state to pay a visit and give her blessing to the young lady's family."

"Come, come," said he, still grinning at the couple, "let us have as little sentiment as possible, and Pen, my good fellow, tell us the whole story."

Pen got back at once to his tragic and heroical air. "The story is, sir," said he, "as I have written it to you before. I have made the acquaintance of a most beautiful and most virtuous lady; of a high family, although in reduced circumstances; I have found the woman in whom I know that the happiness of my life is centred; I feel that I never, never can think about any woman but her. I am aware of the difference of our ages and other difficulties in my way. But my affection was so great that I felt I could surmount all these;—that we both could: and she has consented to unite her lot with mine, and to accept my heart and my fortune."

"How much is that, my boy?" said the Major. "Has anybody left you some money? I don't know that you are worth a shilling in the world."

"You know what I have is his," cried out Mrs. Pendennis.

"Good heavens, madam, hold your tongue!" was what the guardian was disposed to say; but he kept his temper, not without a struggle. "No doubt, no doubt," he said. "You would sacrifice anything for him. Everybody knows that. But it is, after all, then, your fortune which Pen is offering to the young lady; and of which he wishes to take possession at eighteen."

"I know my mother will give me anything," Pen said, looking rather disturbed.

"Yes, my good fellow, but there is reason in all things. If your mother keeps the house, it is but fair that she should select her company. When you give her house over her head, and transfer her banker's account to yourself for the benefit of Miss What-d'-you-call-'em—Miss Costigan—don't you think you should at least have consulted my sister as one of the principal parties in the transaction? I am speaking to you, you see, without the least anger or assumption of authority, such as the law and your father's will give me over you for three years to come—but as one man of the world to another,—and I ask you, if you think that, because you can do what you like with your mother, therefore you have a right to do so? As you are her dependant, would it not have been more generous to wait before you took this step, and at least to have paid her the courtesy to ask her leave?"

Pen held down his head, and began dimly to perceive that the action on which he had prided himself as a most romantic, generous instance of disinterested affection, was perhaps a very selfish and headstrong piece of folly.

"I did it in a moment of passion," said Pen, floundering; "I was not aware what I was going to say or to do" (and in this he spoke with perfect sincerity). "But now it is said, and I stand to it. No; I neither can nor will recall it. I'll die rather than do so. And I—I don't want to burden my mother," he continued. "I'll work for myself. I'll go on the stage, and act with her. She—she says I should do well there."

"But will she take you on those terms?" the Major interposed. "Mind, I do not say that Miss Costigan is not the most disinterested of women; but, don't you suppose now, fairly, that your position as a young gentleman of ancient birth and decent expectations, forms a part of the cause why she finds your addresses welcome?"

"I'll die, I say, rather than forfeit my pledge to her," said Pen, doubling his fists and turning red.

"Who asks you, my dear friend?" answered the imperturbable guardian. "No gentleman breaks his word, of course, when it has been given freely. But after all, you can wait. You owe something to your mother, something to your family—something to me as your father's representative."

"Oh, of course," Pen said, feeling rather relieved.

"Well, as you have pledged your word to her, give us another, will you, Arthur?"

"What is it?" Arthur asked.

"That you will make no private marriage—that you won't be taking a trip to Scotland, you understand."

"That would be a falsehood. Pen never told his mother a falsehood," Helen said.

Pen hung down his head again, and his eyes filled with tears of shame. Had not this whole intrigue been a falsehood to that tender and confiding creature who was ready to give up all for his sake? He gave his uncle his hand.

"No, sir—on my word of honor as a gentleman," he said, "I will never marry without my mother's consent!" and giving Helen a bright parting look of confidence and affection unchangeable, the boy went out of the drawing-room into his own study.

"He's an angel—he's an angel," the mother cried out in one of her usual raptures.

"He comes of a good stock, ma'am," said her brother-in-law— "of a good stock on both sides." The Major was greatly pleased with the result of his diplomacy—so much so, that he once more saluted the tips of Mrs. Pendennis's glove, and dropping the curt, manly, and straightforward tone in which he had conducted the conversation with the lad, assumed a certain drawl, which he always adopted when he was most conceited and fine.

"My dear creature," said he, in that his politest tone, "I think it certainly as well that I came down, and I flatter myself that last *botte* was a successful one. I tell you how I came to think of it. Three years ago my kind friend Lady Ferrybridge sent for me in the greatest state of alarm about her son Gretna, whose affair you remember, and implored me to use my influence with the young gentleman, who was engaged in an *affaire de coeur* with a Scotch clergyman's daughter, Miss Mac Toddy. I implored, I entreated gentle measures. But Lord Ferrybridge was furious, and tried the high hand. Gretna was sulky and silent, and his parents thought they had conquered. But what was the fact, my dear creature? The young people had been married for three months before Lord Ferrybridge knew anything about it. And that was why I extracted the promise from Master Pen."

"Arthur would never have done so," Mrs. Pendennis said.

"He hasn't,—that is one comfort," answered the brother-in-law.
Like a wary and patient man of the world, Major Pendennis did
not press poor Pen any farther for the moment, but hoped the best
from time, and that the young fellow's eyes would be opened
before long to see the absurdity of which he was guilty. And
having found out how keen the boy's point of honor was, he
worked kindly upon that kindly feeling with great skill, discours-
ing him over their wine after dinner, and pointing out to Pen the
necessity of a perfect uprightness and openness in all his dealings,
and entreating that his communications with his interesting young
friend (as the Major politely called Miss Fotheringay) should be
carried on with the knowledge, if not approbation, of Mrs.
Pendennis. "After all, Pen," the Major said, with a convenient
frankness that did not displease the boy, whilst it advanced the
interests of the negotiator, "you must bear in mind that you are
throwing yourself away. Your mother may submit to your marriage as she would to anything else you desired, if you did but cry
long enough for it: but be sure of this, that it can never please
her. You take a young woman off the boards of a country theatre
and prefer her, for such is the case, to one of the finest ladies in
England. And your mother will submit to your choice, but you
can't suppose that she will be happy under it. I have often
fancied, *entre nous,* that my sister had it in her eye to make a
marriage between you and that little ward of hers—Flora, Laura—
what's her name? And I always determined to do my small
endeavor to prevent any such match. The child has but two
thousand pounds, I am given to understand. It is only with the
utmost economy and care that my sister can provide for the decent
maintenance of her house, and for your appearance and education
as a gentleman; and I don't care to own to you that I had other
and much higher views for you. With your name and birth, sir—
with your talents, which I suppose are respectable, with the
friends whom I have the honor to possess, I could have placed you
in an excellent position—a remarkable position for a young man of
such exceeding small means, and had hoped to see you, at least, try
to restore the honors of our name. Your mother's softness stopped
one prospect, or you might have been a general, like our gallant
ancestor who fought at Ramillies and Malplaquet. I had another

plan in view: my excellent and kind friend, Lord Bagwig, who is very well disposed towards me, would, I have little doubt, have attached you to his mission at Pumpernickel, and you might have advanced in the diplomatic service. But, pardon me for recurring to the subject; how is a man to serve a young gentleman of eighteen, who proposes to marry a lady of thirty, whom he has selected from a booth in a fair?—well, not a fair,—barn. That profession at once is closed to you. The public service is closed to you. Society is closed to you. You see, my good friend, to what you bring yourself. You may get on at the bar to be sure, where I am given to understand that gentlemen of merit occasionally marry out of their kitchens; but in no other profession. Or you may come and live down here—down here, *mon Dieu!* for ever" (said the Major, with a dreary shrug, as he thought with inexpressible fondness of Pall Mall), "where your mother will receive the Mrs. Arthur that is to be, with perfect kindness; where the good people of the county won't visit you; and where, by Gad, sir, I shall be shy of visiting you myself, for I'm a plain spoken man, and I own to you that I like to live with gentlemen for my companions; where you will have to live, with rum-and-water drinking gentlemen-farmers, and drag through your life the young husband of an old woman, who, if she doesn't quarrel with your mother, will at least cost that lady her position in society, and drag her down into that dubious caste into which you must inevitably fall. It is no affair of mine, my good sir. I am not angry. Your downfall will not hurt me farther than that it will extinguish the hopes I had of seeing my family once more taking its place in the world. It is only your mother and yourself that will be ruined. And I pity you both from my soul. Pass the claret: it is some I sent to your poor father; I remember I bought it at poor Lord Levant's sale. But of course," added the Major, smacking the wine, "having engaged yourself, you will do what becomes you as a man of honor, however fatal your promise may be. However, promise us on our side, my boy, what I set out by entreating you to grant,—that there shall be nothing clandestine, that you will pursue your studies, that you will only visit your interesting friend at proper intervals. Do you write to her much?"

Pen blushed and said, "Why, yes, he had written."

"I suppose verses, eh! as well as prose? I was a dab at verses myself. I recollect when I first joined, I used to write things in that way. I was talking to my old friend General Hobbler about some lines I dashed off for him in the year 1806, when we were at the Cape, and, Gad, he remembered every line of them still; for he'd used 'em so often, the old rogue, and had actually tried 'em on Mrs. Hobbler, sir—who brought him sixty thousand pounds. I suppose you've tried verses, eh, Pen?"

Pen blushed again, and said, "Why, yes, he had written verses."

"And does the fair one respond in poetry or prose?" asked the Major, eyeing his nephew with the queerest expression, as much as to say, "O Moses and Green Spectacles! what a fool the boy is."

Pen blushed again. She had written, but not in verse, the young lover owned, and he gave his breast-pocket the benefit of a squeeze with his left arm, which the Major remarked, according to his wont.

"You have got the letters there, I see," said the old campaigner, nodding at Pen and pointing to his own chest (which was manfully wadded with cotton by Mr. Stultz). "You know you have. I would give twopence to see 'em."

"Why," said Pen, twiddling the stalks of the strawberries, "I— I," but this sentence was never finished; for Pen's face was so comical and embarrassed, as the Major watched it, that the elder could contain his gravity no longer, and burst into a fit of laughter, in which chorus Pen himself was obliged to join after a minute: when he broke out fairly into a guffaw.

It sent them with great good-humor into Mrs. Pendennis's drawing-room. She was pleased to hear them laughing in the hall as they crossed it.

"You sly rascal!" said the Major, putting his arm gayly on Pen's shoulder, and giving a playful push at the boy's breast-pocket. He felt the papers crackling there sure enough. The young fellow was delighted—conceited—triumphant—and in one word, a spooney.

The pair came to the tea-table in the highest spirits. The Major's politeness was beyond expression. He had never tasted such good tea, and such bread was only to be had in the country. He asked Mrs. Pendennis for one of her charming songs. He then made Pen sing, and was delighted and astonished at the beauty of the boy's voice: he made his nephew fetch his maps and drawings, and praised them as really remarkable works of talent in a young fellow: he complimented him on his French pronunciation: he flattered the simple boy as adroitly as ever lover flattered a mistress: and when bed time came, mother and son went to their several rooms perfectly enchanted with the kind Major.

When they had reached those apartments, I suppose Helen took to her knees as usual: and Pen read over his letters before going to bed: just as if he didn't know every word of them by heart already. In truth there were but three of those documents: and to learn their contents required no great effort of memory.

# ANONYMOUS

☡ ☡

*An unsigned novel,* The Ordeal for Wives, *published in 1865, presents a worldly aunt who has undertaken to introduce her niece to a fashionable English seaside resort—and to a possible suitor as well.*

JOAN ENGLEHEART was right when she said that Mrs. Tudor did not like seeing people eat. But Mrs. Tudor, in spite of this little peculiarity, and several others of a like nature, was not a mean woman. She was too intensely selfish, too avid of the good opinion of others, to be essentially mean. In what she could be stingy, unseen, she was stingy; in liberality that showed she was liberal, liberal, occasionally, to excess.

"I have too much feeling for my own happiness," Mrs. Tudor would say, when a handsome parson or fashionable physician pleaded some case of misery to her. "I have always been led away by my heart—too much for my own good, perhaps." And then, notwithstanding her threescore years and ten, the recollection of so much self-sacrifice and vicarious suffering would make Mrs. Tudor weep—veritable tears, but promptly dried—with the delicacy of a woman who, though she feels, does not mean to parade that feeling to the world; and who remembers whereof the bloom of her cheeks is made!

She never subscribed to public charities even with the seductions of standing in print among lords and marchionesses. "The widow's mite should be given in secret" was one of Mrs. Tudor's axioms. "Let the great and rich give away in high places. Enough for me to cast my poor offering into the treasury unseen;" with only the handsome parson or fashionable doctor to act as recording angel.

What will you have? Twenty pounds a year among printed donations of twice, thrice, four times that amount go for nothing in the charitable city where Mrs. Tudor lived. But twenty pounds a year divided into widows' mites in private life keep up a handsome reputation for unostentatious alms-giving. Mrs. Tudor knew her generation, and was wise with its wisdom. Every one said Mrs. Tudor was a charming old woman: I think every one, except her family and dependents, really liked her. When she stabbed your absent friends she did it with a delicacy that belongs only to long and refined experience. The coarse blow of a common assassin for ever reminds you that if you too, have a purse, and take your eye from him, you shall fall. Mrs. Tudor always performed her cruel office out of the depth of her regard for her immediate listener. "With your dear girls visiting at her house, should I do right to conceal it from you?" "As the pastor and guardian of your flock, ought you not to be told?" "With your back garden close upon their area, should I—*should I* be a friend if I remained silent?" And all the slaughtered character forthwith rose up in the light of necessary victims offered up by Mrs. Tudor at the altar of Spartan principle and friendship.

Her flattery was as good as her scandal. The same delicate flavor of well-bred discrimination made it palatable, even in inordinately large doses. To tell a woman of forty that she is young and charming would be simply gross; but to say, "My dear friend, I have something I really grieve to talk to you about: I don't know how you will take it, but as an old woman who had done with life before you began it, I feel that I must speak. All the world is talking of that poor fellow's evident infatuation for you. He is but

a boy—spare him! tell his mother to send him to London—
anything. You are not offended, now, are you? No; I knew you
could not be!" To say this is to possess a charming refined nature
even when saying disagreeable things. This was Mrs. Tudor's style
of flattery.

She called herself old; and she was very old, even for the city of
*sempiternelles* where she lived; but she held old age at bay more
stoutly I really believe than any other woman of her age extant.
She was a model of good making-up. I can never see the justice of
condemning, wholesale, all women who paint. Condemn them
utterly if they paint badly; but give homage due to all successful
works of real art. Mrs. Tudor was extraordinarily well done. Her
hair was a dark iron-grey, not any of those blacks and chestnuts
that every shifting light can convert into prisms of red, green, and
purple; her eyebrows were marked by one dark yet perfectly
delicate line; her cheeks bore the faintest roseate tinge that the
genius of Paris (assisted by after processes of her own) could
supply; her teeth, her figure, were all triumphs of imitative art.
The most difficult part of the picture, and one in which so many
inferior artists fail, the old, wrinkled, sapless hands were never
shown without gloves. I repeat it, Mrs. Tudor was well done; and
whether she, or Wilson, or the mere artificers from whence her
charms came in gross, possessed the greater genius, I hold that the
result of so much thought, and choice, and patient, unfaltering
every-day labor was a thing to be respected.

But cultivation is required for all high taste in art. When Esther
Fleming first found herself again in Mrs. Tudor's presence, the
vision of a painted and galvanized corpse tottering forward to meet
her with deathly sprightliness came upon her with even more
awful clearness than it had used to do when she was a child. All
the painful processes by which Mrs. Tudor's rejuvenescence had
been won—the dentistry, the dyeing, the daily paddings and
powderings and paintings for well-nigh half a century, were
mysteries too occult for Esther's mind to unravel, or even marvel
over. She liked her Aunt Engleheart's face, white and still as
death itself: all passion and unrest quenched out of it by long
years of poverty and Miss Joan. She liked to see that old face,
with the venerable white hair and the little close-frilled cap, as the

evening light fell on it through the branches of the thorn-tree by the porch; to see the folded withered hands lying peacefully at rest; the whole little, worn, bent form just as though waiting, patient and quiescent for death to come. This was the poetry of extreme, helpless old age; and Esther often at such times had spoken under her breath, half in awe of the frail still life so barely withheld from the final stillness of death itself. But Mrs. Tudor! Mrs. Tudor, sprightly and roseate and alert! All the girl's old childish horror of "something coming off" rushed across her mind as she remembered she would have to kiss Mrs. Tudor's cheek; and every one of the little affectionate speeches she had been preparing on her journey forsook her memory.

Aunt Thalia's warmth of heart was equal, however, to all occasions—even domestic ones. "Esther my dear, *dear* child!" and then, much to Esther's relief, the greatest difficulty of meeting was got over by Mrs. Tudor herself depositing a very long but circumspect kiss upon her cheek. "So grown I should scarce have recognized you! Wilson, has not Miss Fleming grown? Two shillings for bringing you from the railway? Certainly not. Esther love, I insist upon your not paying more than eighteen-pence; and let him carry up Miss Fleming's luggage to her apartment before he's paid. Wilson, the small upper room that faces the sea. I knew my dear niece would not mind mounting a little high," she whispered to Esther, as Wilson, very rustling and dignified, marched out of the room. "Yon princess in black silk would have been sour to me for a month if I had dared dispossess her of hers; and my dear Esther's little feet are too young to know whether they run up one or two flights of stairs at a time."

Mrs. Tudor embraced her again, but without more kisses: these risks were only incurred under the indispensable press of affection at coming and going: and then Esther remarked that she did not care at all where she slept, and would be very sorry indeed to put Wilson out in any way.

"And how is my dear sister? Sit down, my love, and unloose your bonnet-strings. How is my dear sister Cecelia? You wouldn't have a glass of wine, Esther, after your journey, now—would you?"

"Oh, no! Aunt Thalia. I never take wine."

"Dear child! so natural! You are very little altered, love, except in height. I take an early dinner, you must know, Esther; my doctor here desires it, and so I obey, but it breaks in upon my habits sadly; then about seven I drink tea. Now *what* will you have?" Mrs. Tudor looked extraordinarily genial and hospitable. "What will you have? They can get you a chop in a minute." And she stretched her hand out, figuratively, towards the bell.

"I would much rather have nothing but tea," said Esther. "I am not hungry—I mean not very—I had my dinner on the road."

"Now do you mean it, my love? do you positively mean it? I will never forgive you if you don't make yourself perfectly at home while you are with me. Well, then, we will have tea at once. And, Wilson," to that potentate who had now re-entered the room, "bid Mrs. Sims send up the cold duck, if you please; it will be just the thing for my niece after her long journey. Wilson will take you to your room, Esther. I would go myself, only that my good doctor tells me I must refrain as much as possible from walking upstairs."

And then Mrs. Wilson, condescendingly bland, but still with the kind of manner which she, as a servant, naturally felt to Esther as a poor relation, conducted her to her room on the third floor—a three-cornered apartment with a sloping roof, a bed the size of a coffin, and a window from whence you had a very nice side-view of the sea if you sat upon the floor.

"You find your aunt a good deal changed, no doubt, Miss Fleming?" remarked the lady's-maid, fidgeting about the strings of one of Esther's cases, but obviously only giving herself a pretext to stop and talk. "Even I, that am with her constant, can see it only too plain. She's pitched away extraordinary the last three months, miss."

Esther could see no particular change, she answered. She thought, perhaps, that her Aunt Thalia's was not a face to show illness much.

"Perhaps so," said Wilson, drily. "Appearances are deceitful; but then you must remember I see missus at all times, Miss Fleming. Thinner! Why, bless you, she's gone away to half what she were before her last attack. I've took in all her dresses without her knowing it; and she thinks, sometimes, she's getting stout again, and tells the doctor so; but I know better. I wish some of them, or some one belonging to her, would tell her a little truth about her health, Miss Fleming, and then, perhaps she wouldn't kill herself —dressing and racketing and sitting up late at night as she do—kill herself, and I may truly say, kill all those who have to wait upon her too!"

Mrs. Wilson pressed her hand with much feeling upon the region of her left lung, and laid her head on one side with a sigh. It was evident that to her own mind her twenty-five pounds a year were no equivalent whatever to the disadvantages of being in Mrs. Tudor's intimate employ and favor.

"What sort of illness has she had?" she proceeded, when Esther had inquired into the nature of her mistress's last attack; "why you don't mean to say your aunt never wrote you word that she'd had a stroke?"

"A stroke!" interrupted Esther, looking grave and shocked. "Oh, Wilson! you surely can't mean—?"

"Yes, I do miss. I mean a stroke of paralysis. I lived with the old Countess of Davenport up to her death, and I knew directly I saw your aunt's face she was going to be taken like her ladyship. She *was* a mistress, if you like, Miss Fleming. Thirty-six pounds a year and the best of perquisites, and a under maid kept on purpose to set up and unlace the dresses at night; because her ladyship said from the first, 'Mrs. Wilson,' her ladyship says to me, 'I see that your 'ealths delicate, and—' "

"And Aunt Thalia, Wilson? Please tell me about Aunt Thalia's illness."

"Well, Miss Fleming, it was after an At Home at our own house; and missus and me was putting away some of the ornaments, when she cried out suddent, 'Wilson!' and tottered back a step or two, and fell on the sofa—so!" And Mrs. Wilson went through a little impromptu rehearsal, with great gusto upon the coffin bed! "I knew what it was in a minute, miss—the thick way of speaking, and dull eyes, and stiff hands, and all the rest of it—and I got her undressed; and Miss Whitty, the—the person who lodges underneath us, you know—sent for the doctor. And *he* knew what it was, Miss Fleming, just as well as I did; and Mrs. Tudor, she knew what it was, too; but we made light of the whole matter; and none of us ever called the attack by its right name, and we don't now. When missus speaks about it, she says, 'That time I was a little faint and giddy, you know, Wilson.' And I say the same; and so must you, of course, if your aunt should happen to mention it."

"And Aunt Thalia goes out to parties as much as ever?" cried Esther. "How can she care about them after such a fearful warning?"

"Ah!" ejaculated Mrs. Wilson, piously, and suddenly remembering the pain above her heart. "Ah! there's no saying what those that belong to this world wouldn't do to escape out of themselves and their own tempers and fancies! I agreed to accept your aunt's situation on the highest of recommendations, Miss Fleming. The Dean of Sarum's lady (who has known me since I was *that* high, and all my family, too), begged me herself to take it; and though I had never lived out of the first of establishments before, I was willing to do so because of all your aunt said about my having my time to myself. Time! why, I'd sooner live with the Countess of Davenport again on half the wages, and wait on the three young ladies besides, than be where I am, Miss Fleming. Morning, noon, and night, I haven't a moment to myself: your aunt wants a nurse, miss, as well as a maid. And though I'd do as much as my strength allowed for a fellow-creature"—Mrs. Wilson assumed the air of a trampled but forgiving martyr—"a fellow-creature in real illness, I don't consider myself called upon to set up o' nights for people that are out at routs and card-parties, and then to have to make their sick-messes, and carry their air-cushion, and put up with their humors by day! Not without extra wages, Miss Fleming! I read my Bible, and I hope I perform my 'umble duties as a Christian, but I know what service is."

"And this is the woman we have been told is such a treasure," thought Esther, when Mrs. Wilson, after this little exposition of her opinions respecting her own worth, had left her alone. "Her great, lonely, fine-furnished rooms, and this woman, with her heartlessness and discontent, are the nearest approach to a home that Aunt Thalia has. I am glad to think Mrs. Engleheart will die poor and quiet and unpretending at Countisbury, and have Joan, with all her faults, to wait upon her to the last."

She felt her heart almost warm towards Mrs. Tudor when she joined her again down stairs. There was something within her that instinctively recognized and respected the courage of this old woman of the world in neither shrinking from, nor seeking sympathy under, the dark shadow that had fallen upon her. If it was courage wrongly shown (cards, rouge, parties, instead of calm meditation and solemn retrospect), it was courage still; the same stout nerve that had upheld Joan Engleheart during so many years of unpitied, unassisted poverty; the same strong, enduring power that, simple and youthful though she was, lay dormant in Esther's own breast. Yes, she looked at the old bland face that had met the forerunner of a fearful death just with the same well-bred *insouciance* it would have shown to any other disagreeable but unavoidable visitor, and, for the first time in her life, felt that she and Mrs. Tudor were of one kin.

"You distress me, my love, by eating so little. Really you ought to have something more substantial after your long journey—a poached egg, now? You are quite sure? I meant you to have some cold duck, and, oh, my dear Esther! what do you think?"

Esther, of course, expressed her inability to have any idea whatever.

"I asked the woman of the house to send it up, and she informed me my maid had eaten it for her own early tea—the whole of one wing, and some delicious slices on the back. And she knows that if there's one thing more than another that is likely to tempt me it's a morsel of cold duck."

Esther laughed. "Wilson knows what is likely to tempt herself, no doubt," she remarked. "Most servants do."

"She is," Mrs. Tudor lowered her voice, and looked with meaning (as confidential persons upon the stage invariably look round, but fail to see the infernal villain crouched under the pasteboard portico, at least two yards and a half from their side) towards the door: "she is the greediest, the falsest, the most rapacious, odious woman that I verily believe ever drew breath even amidst servants. I keep her because the Dean of Sarum's wife recommended her, and because she understands her business, and does not rob me very outrageously; but her appetite! Oh, my dear child! I often think what I have to go through at the hands of all my maids is my punishment, in the flesh, for caring about worldly vanities in my old age. And, speaking of vanities, where did you have that dress made you have on?—not in the wilds of Devonshire, I am sure."

"Yes, Aunt Thalia, in the wilds of Devonshire. Joan and I made it from the pattern of the white one I had at school."

"Ah, dear, good Joan!" remarked Mrs. Tudor, evidently just remembering her niece's existence. "Dear, good, useful, industrious Joan! how is she? and my sister? You have not told me one word yet, love, as to how my dear sister is looking?"

"Aunt Engleheart never seems to change, to me," answered Esther. "She looks just as weak and pale and quiet as she did when I first went to Countisbury; but she can dress herself still; and twice this summer she has walked to church and back."

"Poor dear Cecelia! She was never very strong. I should like extremely to go and see her if I could; but I am afraid the excitement would be too much for her. We were always so passionately attached to each other!" They had not met, or sought to meet, for the last twenty years. "She was blonde, you know, and I brune; and the difference in age used not to show then as it must now. Blondes always fade all at once when they do fade. That is a *dédommagement* to dark women, my love; for, looking old when they are young, they wear better when their first *beauté du diable* is over. How old are you, Esther?—I forget—fifteen, sixteen? Which is it?"

"Oh, Aunt Thalia! I am past eighteen. And Joan and David both think I look two or three years older than that."

"David! What is David? Whom are you talking of, child? I thought you had no acquaintance among those savage wilds."

"But David Engleheart, ma'am; my cousin David!"

"Never say 'ma'am' again, Esther, I beg. It does not sound vulgar from you, but it is old-fashioned and provincial. Call me your Aunt Tudor, or your Aunt Thalia, or even Mrs. Tudor, but never ma'am. Will you remember?"

"Yes, Aunt Thalia."

"And now, if you have really eaten as much as you wish, love" (Esther had eaten nothing), "we will go and finish our chat by the open window. Yes, sit on the footstool. I like to see you so; the pose is good. Put your left arm a little lower, and turn your face up towards me. That is right. Do you know you are really very like your great-grandfather? You have just poor dear Garratt's eyes, but you have not the family chin. There you are a Vincent. Your poor mother was a pretty little woman, but without the slightest style. Do you remember her?"

"Only a little," answered Esther. "I remember she was very white and tired-looking, and hardly ever took me in her arms or had me in the sitting-room to play with her; but that is all. I remember my father much the best."

"Quite right, my dear Esther; quite right. Your mother's family were very nice people—very nice people indeed in their own way; but there is no occasion for us to remember them. I am glad to find you growing up such a complete Fleming. When I saw you last I was really distressed about your voice and manners, but you have immensely improved now. School has softened you down."

"I am glad you think so," said Esther. "I was afraid I learnt very little for all the money it cost. I am not brilliant, Aunt Thalia. Years ago I used to think I should be a genius, able to write books and do all sorts of things. I rate my own abilities much more truly now."

"I did not send you to school to learn lessons, Esther, but to acquire style and manner. You have learnt quite enough, I have no doubt, with Joan at home. What you want now is to know how to hide your learning and be agreeable in the world. Men don't like clever women; always remember that. Softness, liveliness, grace, are the qualities you must strive after."

Esther thought of Oliver, of her never-ceasing, uneasy sense of her own superiority to him, and sighed. "I am sure you are right there," she remarked. "I often wish I was more soft and yielding than I am."

"Then you wish a very foolish thing, let me tell you, Esther," said Mrs. Tudor. "Seem as soft as you choose, but thank Providence for having made you really strong. You will want all your strength some day, depend upon it. A graceful, feminine manner, and perfect reliance in herself are what a young woman needs to obtain success in society."

"I don't care a bit for success in society. I wish to have real success—I mean I wish to be really lovable."

Mrs. Tudor looked hard at her great-niece's candid, flushed

face, and laughed. "You are full of sentiment, I can see," she observed, "in spite of Joan having had you in her hands so long. Wait until you have seen a little more of the world, and you will become like the other young people of this generation—like your friends the Miss Dashwoods, for example. I wonder knowing them has not put all romantic fancies out of your head!"

"But Jane ought to be very romantic just now." Esther felt somewhat conscience-stricken as she put forth this remark. "I suppose you know she is engaged?"

"To whom?"

"To—to Mr. Chichester, I believe. I know nothing of him."

"What are you getting red for, child?"

"I am sure I don't know, Aunt Thalia. It is a dreadfully foolish habit of mine. I—I do wish I could get over it," Miss Fleming added, indignantly, and then she blushed crimson indeed.

"No sign of modesty looks ill in a young person," said Mrs. Tudor, complacently. "As long as you are under twenty no one will think worse of you for blushing, and you will find it a habit that time soon cures. Who told you Jane Dashwood was to marry Paul Chichester?"

"Her sister Millicent. She speaks of it in all her letters as a regular engagement. Colonel Dashwood lets Mr. Chichester come to the house as often as he chooses."

"Colonel Dashwood lets most unmarried men do that, Esther; and in the rare cases where he does not, the Miss Dashwoods save their lovers any trouble by meeting them elsewhere. I have seen a good many of Miss Dashwood's flirtations during the last five years, although my acquaintance with the family, child, is of the slightest description. Understand that. A formal offer and declension of civility once a year, an exchange of cards in the interval. The lad to whom she engaged herself when she first came out, Arthur Peel, is the nephew of one of my most intimate friends, and I happen to know exactly how the Dashwoods first entangled and afterwards discarded him. Then came George Lawless; then Major Burroughs. I know every particular about them both. Lawless paid old Dashwood eleven hundred pounds to get off at the last moment; and now this last ridiculous affair with Paul Chichester! I have seen her walking about with him, and looking up into his face as she has done with a dozen other men before him; but an engagement—bah! Paul Chichester may be eccentric, but he is not quite such a fool as to take one of Colonel Dashwood's daughters without a penny, and with their reputation, for his wife."

"And what is this Mr. Chichester like, himself? I—I feel a kind of interest in him, you know, as Jane's lover; but the Dashwoods give such conflicting accounts of him that I can form no picture to myself either of his manner or his face."

"Never speak of forming a picture to yourself, child: it sounds pedantic. You want to know what Paul Chichester is like? Well, you will be able to judge for yourself: he is here in Weymouth." Involuntarily Esther blushed again. "He was speaking to me on the walk today. A very good style he has; far better, in spite of his threadbare coat, than two-thirds of the young men one meets. I told him I was quite sure from the likeness about the upper part of his face that he was a son of Hildebrand Chichester, and, although he evidently shunned the subject, he did not deny it; and that convinces me that he *is* the son whom I believed to have been dead, or to have gone abroad, years and years ago. They were a strange family always, the Chichesters," went on Mrs. Tudor. "If the stories that go about them are true, Hildebrand Chichester and his son were about the strangest of them all."

"What are these stories, Aunt Thalia?"

"Nothing that can interest you, child; nothing, at all events, that it would profit you to repeat to the Miss Dashwoods."

Esther flushed up indignantly. "I repeat nothing that is told me. I should like to have heard, simply because I like listening to old family stories, and—and because you tell things in a way that interests one, Aunt Thalia. But don't say a word if you mistrust me. Never say anything of other people as long as I stay in your house if you think I am such a child that I cannot be trusted with a secret."

"And if I tell you what I know about Paul Chichester, you will never breathe a syllable of it to those little fools the Dashwood girls? never let the man himself, when you come to be acquainted with him, have the faintest idea that you know more of him than of a stranger? Don't answer: I read your face, child. You believe that you could be discreet as age, silent as death, and up to a certain point I believe you would. At all events, as a little test of your powers, also because I don't really care a straw whether it is repeated or not, I will tell you the story. There is madness in a good many of our old English families, Esther—I suppose that is a fact you have chanced to come across in some of your studies with Joan—more especially, I have noticed, amongst those of the extreme north and extreme south of the kingdom. The Chichesters come from the border, and are not without their share of the aristocratic inheritance—the 'skeleton,'" cried Mrs. Tudor, pleasantly, "that mews and crouches in the unseen closet of so many a rich man's house; the spectre that is sought in vain to be kept at bay by men of science and art and medicine, and yet that is ever hovering over every christening-feast, every marriage-breakfast, in which any child of the ill fated house has past."

"But not—not on him?" broke from Esther's lips as she leant forward and looked, almost with a shudder, into Mrs. Tudor's bland face. "This horrible calamity has not fallen upon Paul?"

"Don't look so excited, child, or I shall tell you no more. It doesn't matter to you. No Fleming has ever been known to be even eccentric; and as for the Vincents, families like the Vincents never *are* mad, I have remarked. Poor, good people, they are quite enough of everything else, I am sure, without that! Where had I got to? Ah! I know—the Chichesters have not been without their share of the aristocratic inheritance. They are a very old family— not in any way connected with the Dorsetshire Chichesters, Esther, remember that. I must impress upon you the absolute importance of a young woman who aspires to tone distinctly remembering who every human being is. Sir Hugh Chichester, of Newton, the great-grandfather of this young man, married the eldest daughter of Lord March, and from that time until the present there have, I believe, been only two decided cases of the hereditary complaint among them. One, Maria Chichester, a sister of Paul's father, who died quite young, and was indeed more weak of intellect than positively diseased or warped; the other—well, Esther, I will not shock your interest in the reputed lover of your friend's sister by calling Paul Chichester even eccentric. Hildebrand Chichester, his father, was, beyond all doubt, wrong in his mind for years."

"But are you sure he is this Hildebrand Chichester's son? That he did not deny the relationship does not actually prove that the relationship exists."

"Well reasoned, *ma petite;* but he not only did not deny, he virtually confessed it. When his father was dead, and his mother married again, I happened to stay with some friends of mine in Northumberland, not three miles from the place of his stepfather's uncle, old Lord Feltham; and speaking to Paul Chichester yesterday, the whole time and place came suddenly before me—the pink-and-white, silly beauty of his mother always lying on the sofa, and appealing to her husband for the sympathy he would not give; Paul himself, a dark, odd-looking child, running wild about the place, and utterly neglected for the sake of the heir of Newton, the child of the second marriage. 'Your Christian name is Paul?' I said. 'Then I recollect you well. When you were eight or nine years old you were the strangest, the most unchild-like child I ever came across. Have you forgotten?'

"He looked in my face steadily, and said 'No.' He had not forgotten one stone or one tree of Newton. Then he added, 'But I have not been there. I have not spoken of Newton for years, nor shall I ever do so again while I live. None of the people with whom I associate now belong to that time or place, or know that I belong to it.' And then he turned the subject resolutely, and we spoke of his family and of the past no more."

"And if Mr. Chichester is indeed so well connected, how comes it that he wears a threadbare coat? I am very ignorant, Aunt Thalia. I have always thought that to be a lord's son, or a lord's stepson, even, would insure one, at least, enough to live respectably upon."

"Then you have thought great nonsense, child; and Paul Chichester was never the stepson of a lord. His mother's second husband died, as far as I recollect, about six years ago, the title having in the mean time gone (on the old lord's death) to his cousin, from whom, if he continues childless, it will of course come to Paul's half-brother. The strange part of the story, the part illustrating the Chichester peculiarity, I am now going to tell you. Although Mrs. Chichester had brought nothing into the family but her pretty face and her imbecility, old Lord Feltham always made a great favorite of her, and on his death-bed requested his son to allow her—her husband was already ailing—to remain at Newton. This wish was carried out, and not only this; Paul Chichester received, I am told, an excellent education at the present Lord Feltham's expense (for the younger branches of the Chichesters, you must know, are absolutely penniless. When Paul's mother married again the bridegroom presented her with the very dress she was married in). Well, when the young man was about twenty years of age, his education finished, Lord Feltham about to present him with a commission in the army, some fearful domestic altercation took place, and Paul—the family blood showing—ran away from home, or, at all events, swore to them all, most solemnly, that they should see his face no more, and left them. From different sources I have heard of him afterwards as dead, or gone to the colonies, or roaming about, a ruined man, upon the Continent. But one thing I am certain of—neither his mother, nor Lord Feltham, nor any member of the family, have ever looked upon his face again from that day to this."

"And you know nothing more of the cause of this quarrel? It must have been no common thing that could make a young lad throw up all his prospects, all his ties, at the very beginning of life, and take of his own free will to loneliness and poverty."

"No common thing, if the young lad had been of perfectly sane mind, Esther; but with an hereditary tendency like that of the Chichesters, the slightest, the most unfounded suspicion might be enough to make him take up the notion that all his family were in league against him."

"And does his manner give any indication of his inheriting the family disease? When you remember him, years ago, was he like other children? Aunt Thalia, the story takes possession of me. I feel that, while I wish it, I shall yet dread to become acquainted with Mr. Chichester."

"In which feeling you show your extreme ignorance of the world, child. Half the people one meets have, probably, more of madness in their brain, certainly more in their manner, than Paul Chichester. What was he like as a child, did you ask me? Well, really, you know, the subject of children is one that never interests me. I could not bear to be in the room with you, my love, as you may recollect, until you had got well over the age of asking questions and upsetting things. Paul Chichester was like other children, I suppose—no, I recollect, by-the-way, he was not. He was taciturn. He used to come in after dinner at Newton when the nurse brought in his brother, and, none of the family ever paying him the slightest attention, he had a trick of standing apart from us all and staring with his great dark eyes at his mother's face until the young heir had been made enough of and fed, of course, with all the unwholesome things upon the table. Let us speak no more of him, child!" broke off Mrs. Tudor, abruptly, and accompanying the remark by the little deprecatory toss of her gloved hands with which it was her custom to throw off, as it were, the burthen of speaking of anything, or any person, the moment it no longer amused herself. "I have so much still to hear about my dear sister and her health. She should come here for a change—really you would not believe, Esther, how few people I have met here whom I know. Mrs. Strangways, and Paul Chichester, and poor good Whitty, who is coming to-night, are all. I have mentioned Miss Whitty to you, of course, have I not?"

"Yes, Aunt Thalia, I believe so. Is he—is Mr. Chichester, I mean—going to stop in Weymouth?"

"She lives in the dining-rooms under me. I call her my spaniel. She is a good creature in her way, but tiring—tiring and greedy. If she could, she would get me to give all my old dresses to her instead of to Wilson. Draw the curtain aside, Esther, and we shall see the people as they come up from the station. Who is that riding with Mrs. Strangways, I wonder!—hand me my opera-glasses, child, and I shall see better—young Orchard, again, positively. How ridiculous the poor lad is making himself with that woman! You have heard of Mrs. Strangways from the Dashwoods? She and Jane Dashwood are extremely intimate, and I should say extremely well matched."

"I have heard Milly say they are intimate. Do you—do you think Mr. Chichester will be likely to stay longer in Weymouth?"

"She is looking very thin; she has lost all her youth. That is invariably the way with blonde women; they fade in six months. Celia lost her complexion twenty years, at least, sooner than I did. I looked as young at five-and-thirty as you do now."

It was hopeless to think of turning aside the current of Mrs.

Tudor's thoughts, especially when the current had set back towards the all-delicious subject of her own youthful beauty. Esther gave herself up, resignedly, to listening to the chronicles of fifty-year-old charms and conquests, and strove, resolutely, but in vain, to turn away her thoughts from Jane Dashwood's lover and his sombre history.

And what, in good truth, was Paul Chichester to Esther Fleming? Why had Esther Fleming, in love with and engaged to Oliver Carew, colored guiltily at the mention of her friend's sister's lover?

The reasons for emotion so unwarrantable, and of which Miss Fleming herself felt so duly ashamed, were, she firmly believed, to be found in certain complex sentiments set forth by Miss Millicent Dashwood's last letter; and as I feel I should fail in expressing these sentiments at all accurately, save in the Dashwood language, I will record simply what Milly wrote.

"Jane is going on in her old way with Arthur Peel, who is hanging out at present at the Strangways. I think Mrs. Strangways makes a *catspaw* of Arthur Peel, and Miss Dashwood too; but don't repeat that I said so, for it would make Jenny furious. Paul Chichester is in Bath again, and seems to be rather relieved than otherwise at seeing Jane sitting out half the night with Arthur on the staircase at balls. I should not like my lover to be so amiable; but my own opinion is, there is no love at all between any of them—except, perhaps, where it would be better dispensed with. By-the-by, Jane says she is sure Paul would admire you extremely. She has learnt some very odd doctrines lately about 'elective affinities' (are there two ff's or one?) the results of which seem to be that everybody is obliged by some moral law to fall in love with precisely the people they can't marry. Paul is not your style: I mean, he is not broad-shouldered and chubby, like our Swindon Viking; but, for a dark man, he is very handsome. Jenny puts back the hair off his forehead, and says, 'Really, Mr. Chichester, you have quite a Vandyck face. I admire you extremely: how much I should like to be able to find some one worthy of you!' So like Jane. Then she will go to a party that same evening and talk half the night to Arthur Peel, and come back, poor Jenny! and cry till daylight. I dare say you and Paul won't like each other at all when you meet; but Jane relies on her 'elective' theories, and, I have no doubt will warn Paul to fall in love with you; the best way in the world, perhaps, to prevent him from doing so. You poor, dear, old Esther! how I do pity you, with only a tender recollection of Swindon, and a miraculously-proper flirtation with cousin David to keep you from stagnation!"

Esther had put down some of the nonsense to Milly's usual flighty style of writing; but she knew enough of the Dashwood girls to feel that, as likely as not, it had all been repeated to Mr. Chichester himself; and, as you have seen, she had not sufficient control to hinder her cheeks from burning at his name. What if she should meet him, be introduced to him! was her reflection when at last she had escaped from Mrs. Tudor's endless stories to the silence of her own little attic. Would she blush, with this same contemptible folly, in his presence? She who had been able to speak of Oliver without her face betraying the real emotions of her heart to color in this guilty way about a person she had never seen—a person with a Vandyck face, and whom Mrs. Tudor considered distinguished? No doubt, a pale, effeminate, vain creature, the exact reverse of all she considered manly and admirable. For the first time for weeks other thoughts than those of Oliver were floating through Esther's brain before she went to sleep; and when she woke next morning she was dimly conscious that something unconnected with Mr. Carew and Countisbury had mingled with her dreams.

"I am going to make you very useful," Mrs. Tudor remarked when, at eleven o'clock, blooming and airy in her fresh morning toilette, she joined her niece in the drawing-room. "I am going to make you carry my book and cushion to the beach; and then we can dispense altogether with the presence of Wilson. How are you, my love?" presenting Esther, for an icy second, two gloved fingers of her left hand; "Have you slept? have you recovered from your journey? That is well. Now run and put on your hat: anything will do for the beach, my love; you see how I am dressed."

At Countisbury, Miss Fleming's custom was to put on her hat without so much as looking in the glass; but of course, at a great place like Weymouth, any human being must naturally care more for personal appearance than among the lonely Devonshire moors. When she had put on her holland jacket, and her best black hat, and the narrow black velvet round her throat, and her dark neat-fitting gloves, she was conscious how well she looked in the extreme simplicity of her dress; and half-guiltily she started from the pleasure that consciousness awakened in her.

"You only want an umbrella to be perfectly well-dressed," Mrs. Tudor remarked, as she scanned her niece's appearance with satisfaction. "I told you to put on any thing, because I wanted to see you plainly dressed. It is the severest test of a young woman's taste. Every one can look well *en toilette,* very few in cotton and hollands. When you have a blue umbrella you will be the perfection of simple style. I will take you at once to a shop, and make you a present of one."

"But what am I to do with a blue umbrella, Aunt Thalia? the weather is perfectly fine."

"That is immaterial. All young persons of distinction carry blue umbrellas this season. You need not put it up unless you choose; but you must always carry it in the forenoon—indeed, I should say, you had better never put it up. It will last you longer."

So they went to a shop and spent sixteen shillings on this indispensable addition to a young person of distinction's dress, and then proceeded to the beach, where following her physician's advice, Mrs. Tudor forced herself to sit, for a couple or so of hours, every forenoon.

Now Esther Fleming was still of an age when to sit and dream silently at the waves is in itself a vague voluptuous delight. To watch the pale sky fading in the far horizon, to watch the fisherman's sails starting forth, like the trembling venture of young hope, across the bay, filled her with yearning thoughts, if not of Oliver, of something infinitely dearer in reality—the love she had herself built up for him! And, full of such visions, she would contentedly have sat out the two hours of stipulated sea-air without speaking a word; but Mrs. Tudor, in common, I fancy, with most other old persons, had no liking whatever for being out-of-doors and alone. What dreams had she? what did a fading horizon or departing sail say to her? Her ventures had been put forth half a century before. She had welcomed back to shore ships well-laden with substantial merchandise in lieu of that frail, worthless ballast, with which they first set sail. Whatever interest this Weymouth parade could yield her was on the side where people rode up and down, not on that where the morning sun glared on her face, and the fresh sea-wind despoiled her best artificial curls, and all the affluence of light, and air, and life told her, with the coarse ill-breeding of nature, how old, and weak, and sunless she, Thalia Tudor, was! She could care for Colonel Dash's new barouche and Mrs. Blank's shabby livery; but the sun, and wind, and dust, and heat, and cold by turns wearied and irritated her to death. At the end of an hour's complaining Esther found she could much more enter into Wilson's frame of mind respecting her aunt's requirements than she could have done the night before; and she was sensible of very considerable relief when Mrs. Tudor descried one of her Bath friends, the Miss Whitty already spoken of, approaching them along the promenade.

"My dearest Mrs. Tudor! such a delightfully-unexpected pleasure!" cried this lady in a tone of the most youthful excitement. "To think, when we last parted, that we should meet so soon again, and at the seaside: really now, it is *most* extraordinary! Miss Fleming, I'm sure, from the family likeness. How-do-you-do, Miss Fleming? I hope you left your friends in Devonshire quite well?" (Miss Whitty always held it a point of politeness to inquire after everybody's relations, whether she knew them or not. "It may please—It can't displease," was her way of reasoning to herself. "If I never see them, it does not signify; if I do, it is something like an introduction to have been constantly asking about them to their friends." And to make acquaintance with fresh people was the grand goal and winning point of Miss Whitty's life.) "I am so delighted we have met," she proceeded, when Esther had satisfied her as to the sanitary condition of the Countisbury household. "We can take such nice long walks together by the sea. Do you care for sea-anemones? I am a perfect child when I once find myself among the—the limpets and sea-weeds, and things, upon the rocks."

"I should think you had best stop with me on dry land, Whitty," remarked Mrs. Tudor, with a cutting laugh. "We old women are not fitted for scrambling among rocks, and wetting our feet, like girls of Esther's age. Where are you lodging? My woman tells me there is not a garret to be hired in Weymouth under thirty shillings a week."

"I have taken apartments in one of the smaller streets, Mrs. Tudor," answered poor Whitty, evidently with a great many high notes taken out of her by her patroness's first word. "The people are not very civil; and I am afraid they take the butter already; but I get the rooms on moderate terms, and perhaps, as I shall be out a great deal, the cooking and attendance won't matter."

"You can get your food with me when you will," said Mrs. Tudor. "I dine early here at the sea, and drink my tea at six. You are free to take both meals with me when you choose."

Remembering Mrs. Tudor's somewhat scant hospitality to herself the night before, Esther was a little surprised at this open-handed offer to any one so hungry-looking as Miss Whitty. She did not yet understand the system upon which Mrs. Tudor's reputation for liberality was based and kept up; but poor Whitty did. Years of poverty and humility, and petty toad-eating, and little deceitful gratitude, had taught her the precise value of all proffered favors from richer people—the exact sort of answer it was incumbent upon herself to give. "She would not for worlds intrude upon Mrs. Tudor. Nothing was more disagreeable, away from home, than having people dropping in at dinner-time. She would be delighted to come round any evening, or every evening, after tea, if Mrs. Tudor would permit her, and—"

"Very well, very well," interrupted Mrs. Tudor complacently ("'tis the creature's pride," she remarked afterwards to Esther. "Whenever I try to put bread in her mouth she makes excuses, as you saw; and she's starving, my dear, she's starving!") "You shall come to-night, Whitty. My niece and I will drink our tea early, and if you come in by seven we shall just have time for a game of piquet before bed-time. I am ordered to be in my bed by ten, and it tells upon me a great deal. I never shut my eyes before one. It tires me a vast deal more than being up."

"Perhaps the noise of the waves keeps you awake, mim," suggested Miss Whitty, with one of her faint little simpers. "I had an aunt once who was ordered to the sea, and—"

"Do you know who that is driving with old Lady Fanshawe? I know the woman's face. Who is she?"

"Lady Fanshawe—where, mim? Oh, yes! to be sure; in the

yellow barouche." Poor Whitty was always ready to merge her own stories or observations on the faintest interruption from any one else. "Now I see her face. It's Miss Garth, half-sister, you remember, to the late Lord Riversdale. There was a great talk about her once for Colonel Manners, mim: but he went to India suddenly, and she got a situation as companion, you may recollect; and she's had money left her since, and lives in very good style at Cheltenham—quite in the dinnering set."

"I know her; but do talk grammar, Miss Whitty; 'dinnering' means nothing. I knew Amelia Garth; I knew Amelia Garth's mother. She comes of bad blood. Old Lady Fanshawe would do better to mind her own needy flesh and blood than take up with such a woman as yon. Who is this coming along the walk? He has a distinguished air. Ah! now I recognize him. Esther, child," in a whisper, "this is your friend's lover, whom you were making so many inquiries about. Mr. Chichester, how do you do?"

And Esther, who had been listening with rather vacant attention to the conversation about Amelia Garth, started round, and positively trembled through all her frame on suddenly finding herself face to face with Paul Chichester.

"Mr. Chichester, my niece, Miss Fleming."

Esther bowed, very distantly and cold: Paul smiled. "I am quite accustomed to hear your name, Miss Fleming. I was entrusted with a great many messages for you, in case I should meet you here."

"Oh! I am much obliged;" and then Esther stopped, and felt more confused than she had ever done in her life before.

"You were at school with Miss Dashwood, Esther, were you not?" said Mrs. Tudor with a sharp look at her niece's downcast face. "Mr. Chichester has recently come from Bath, and can, no doubt, give you news of your young friends."

"Milly wrote me a day or two before I left Countisbury, and told me all they were doing, Aunt Thalia. She and Jane seem to have been very gay of late."

"Not so gay as usual, I imagine," said Paul. "I believe Bath is considered to be empty just at present."

"I heard of two balls and an archery-fete in one week; that sounds gay to me."

"But it would not to them. Miss Dashwood informed me in

the race-week that she had danced four-and-twenty hours in four days, in addition to all her morning fatigue on the course. That is pretty well, I think, even for one of the fastest young ladies in England."

"Do you mean Jane?"

"Certainly. Don't you know that to be considered fast is Miss Dashwood's own highest and most cherished ambition?"

"I thought you pretended to be engaged to her," almost rose indignantly to Esther's lips; but as she was going to speak she happened to look straight into Paul Chichester's eyes, and something she read there made her stop short. She forgot her shyness, she forgot her indignation, she forgot Oliver Carew. "I think Jane makes herself out worse than she is, sir. I could never believe that she was fast at heart."

"Have you seen many of your friends here, Mr. Chichester?" interrupted Mrs. Tudor, who was inwardly chafing over her niece's deplorable want of *aplomb* and self-possession. "I have been here a fortnight, and have scarce seen a dozen faces that I know. Weymouth is not what it was a few years ago. These railways fill every place with the same sort of company. I think I shall begin to spend my summers in Bath for the sake of change. Everything is bad here; the medical men worst of all."

And then Mr. Chichester has to listen for about a quarter of an hour to Mrs. Tudor's statements of all she had gone through at the seaside; varied only by occasional little echoes and notes of admiration on the part of Miss Whitty, whose eyes and hands and tongue always followed the sentiments of all wealthy persons with the regularity of clock-work.

"Can he really care for those long stories?" thought Esther to herself; "or is he waiting so patiently only to give me the Dashwoods' messages? How I wish Milly had never written me such nonsense! If the man were a coxcomb he might think anything of me from the absurd way I colored at meeting him!" And then she gave another stealthy look at Paul's face—I suppose to see if any of a coxcomb's attributes were to be found in its expression.

It was a strikingly handsome face: the forehead broad, the black, clear-marked eyebrows straight and delicate. Esther had sometimes laughed at hearing David descant from his old poets upon the beauty of greenish-grey eyes, but in Paul's face she was first sensible of the singular charm such eyes possess when accompanied by an olive-pale complexion and hair and lashes of jet. There hung in her own bedroom at Countisbury a little old engraving from one of Vandyck's pictures: it bore no name: it was simply the portrait of a cavalier in velvet coat and point-lace collar and ruffle: but from the time when she was six years old, and when she had to stand upon a chair to view her idol closely, Esther had bestowed a whole religion of secret veneration and love upon this engraving. When she first began to like Oliver a feeling of infidelity used to overcome her as she looked at her Vandyck— Mr. Carew's short British features being, as you may imagine, supremely unlike the pathetic, noble type of that unknown face; however pleasant in themselves when lit up with youth and health and the admiration that they expressed for her. But, as she looked at Paul, every detail of the picture rose, line by line, before her: the dark and delicate sweep of brow; the steady, deep-set eyes of hazel-grey; the clear-cut lips; the resolute chin—all, even to the jet-black hair, and olive-brown complexion with which her imagination had been wont to give the picture life, rose before her, just as on many a score of summer evenings she had seen them, half in fancy, half within the little old oak frame, upon the wall at Countisbury. Now she knew what had made her suddenly stop short, had made her suddenly feel that she and Paul were speaking together as old friends, not as strangers whose acquaintance might be reckoned up by minutes. She had met—alas! for the first time—her childish ideal clothed with life; had found, in Jane Dashwood's lover, the type with which she had so vainly striven to identify her own.

"You have seen Mrs. Strangways?" broke in Mrs. Tudor's voice. "She is a great deal aged, Mr. Chichester, is she not?"

"I don't see any difference in her," answered Paul, promptly. "To me Mrs. Strangways is always a very pretty woman indeed."

"Oh, of course! You young men are all wild about Mrs. Strangways. A boy is riding with her to-day who might be her son. Who is he, Whitty? They are coming here, to the right, on horseback. Who is that silly lad Mrs. Strangways has got hold of now?"

"A son of Colonel Ashton's, mim," returned Whitty with her preternatural, instantaneous capacity for answering everything and knowing everybody's history. "He left Eton at Christmas, and has got a commission in the Carbineers, but won't join the regiment till February."

"And which is Mrs. Strangways?" Esther asked, with an undefined sensation of curiosity to see the woman Mr. Chichester admired.

"The lady on horseback on our left," answered Miss Whitty. "Turn your head a little round from the sea, Miss Fleming; she will pass before us in a moment."

"Mrs. Strangways is an acquaintance of yours, then, Mr. Chichester?" remarked Mrs. Tudor, when the lady had gone past and bestowed a radiantly-sweet smile on Paul. "An old acquaintance, probably?"

"Oh, yes! a very old acquaintance," Paul answered, carelessly. "Every one who knows London well must know Mrs. Strangways."

"She's a very nice-looking person, sir, isn't she?" cried poor Miss Whitty, who, on the strength of Paul's last somewhat equivocal compliment, thought she might as well hazard something generally pleasing. "I believe she and Miss Dashwood were considered quite the two first beauties in Bath last winter."

"Indeed!" responded Paul, coolly: much too coolly to meet Esther's ideas respecting what was required of him as Jane's lover. "I should not myself, place Miss Dashwood and Mrs. Strangways in the same rank as regards beauty."

"I should think not!" replied Esther. "Jane Dashwood is fair and fresh and young; and that—that person who has ridden past us is older by years, and looks quite bold and worn and faded. Yes, Aunt Thalia, she does: and I don't like to hear Jane Dashwood named with her."

"Appearances are so very misleading, Miss Fleming," suggested Whitty, apologetically. "I have heard many people say how much they like Mrs. Strangways when they get to know her well."

"And it is never suitable for young persons, who know nothing on such matters, to pronounce judgment on their elders," said Mrs. Tudor, rising from her seat with difficulty. "Mr. Chichester, my lodging is at the red-brick house exactly opposite. I should be glad to see you at any time if you are going to stay in Weymouth."

Mr. Chichester answered that he was going back to London next morning early; but—and he looked at Esther—he had not yet delivered any of his messages to Miss Fleming.

"Then come and do so this evening," said Mrs. Tudor.

"We old ladies," with a glance at Whitty, "shall begin our game of cards at eight, and if you choose to encounter the stupidity of such an entertainment I shall be glad to see you. Esther, my love, you are anxious to receive the Miss Dashwoods' messages?"

"I—I—shall be very happy to see Mr. Chichester if he will come, Aunt Thalia."

And then she looked straight in his face, with her honest smile: and Paul, for the first time, thought her handsome.

# LOUISA MAY ALCOTT

*In* Eight Cousins, or "The Aunt-Hill," *Uncle Alec confers with the aunts as he undertakes his role as Rose's guardian.*

ALL DINNER-TIME Rose felt that she was going to be talked about, and afterward she was sure of it, for Aunt Plenty whispered to her as they went into the parlor,—

"Run up and sit awhile with Sister Peace, my dear. She likes to have you read while she rests, and we are going to be busy."

Rose obeyed, and the quiet rooms above were so like a church that she soon composed her ruffled feelings, and was unconsciously a little minister of happiness to the sweet old lady, who for years had sat there patiently waiting to be set free from pain.

Rose knew the sad romance of her life, and it gave a certain tender charm to this great-aunt of hers, whom she already loved. When Peace was twenty, she was about to be married; all was done, the wedding-dress lay ready, the flowers were waiting to be put on, the happy hour at hand, when word came that the lover was dead. They thought that gentle Peace would die too; but she bore it bravely, put away her bridal gear, took up her life afresh, and lived on,—a beautiful, meek woman, with hair as white as snow and cheeks that never bloomed again. She wore no black but soft, pale colors, as if always ready for the marriage that had never come.

For thirty years she had lived on, fading slowly, but cheerful, busy, and full of interest in all that went on in the family; especially the joys and sorrows of the young girls growing up about her, and to them she was adviser, confidante, and friend in all their tender trials and delights. A truly beautiful old maiden, with her silvery hair, tranquil face, and an atmosphere of repose about her that soothed whoever came to her!

Aunt Plenty was utterly dissimilar, being a stout, brisk old lady, with a sharp eye, a lively tongue, and a face like a winter-apple. Always trotting, chatting, and bustling, she was a regular Martha, cumbered with the cares of this world and quite happy in them.

Rose was right; and while she softly read psalms to Aunt Peace, the other ladies were talking about her little self in the frankest manner.

"Well, Alec, how do you like your ward?" began Aunt Jane, as they all settled down, and Uncle Mac deposited himself in a corner to finish his doze.

"I should like her better if I could have begun at the beginning, and so got a fair start. Poor George led such a solitary life that the child has suffered in many ways, and since he died she has been going on worse than ever, judging from the state I find her in."

"My dear boy, we did what we thought best while waiting for you to wind up your affairs and get home. I always told George he was wrong to bring her up as he did; but he never took my advice, and now here we are with this poor dear child upon our hands. I, for one, freely confess that I don't know what to do with her any more than if she was one of those strange, outlandish birds you used to bring home from foreign parts." And Aunt Plenty gave a perplexed shake of the head which caused great commotion among the stiff loops of purple ribbon that bristled all over her cap like crocus buds.

"If *my* advice had been taken, she would have remained at the excellent school where I placed her. But our aunt thought best to remove her because she complained, and she has been dawdling about ever since she came. A most ruinous state of things for a morbid, spoilt girl like Rose," said Mrs. Jane, severely.

She had never forgiven the old ladies for yielding to Rose's pathetic petition that she might wait her guardian's arrival before beginning another term at the school, which was a regular Blimber hot-bed, and turned out many a feminine Toots.

"I never thought it the proper school for a child in good circumstances,—an heiress, in fact, as Rose is. It is all very well for girls who are to get their own living by teaching, and that sort of thing; but all *she* needs is a year or two at a fashionable finishing-school, so that at eighteen she can come out with *éclat,*" put in Aunt Clara, who had been a beauty and a belle, and was still a handsome woman.

"Dear, dear! how short-sighted you all are to be discussing education and plans for the future, when this unhappy child is so plainly marked for the tomb," sighed Aunt Myra, with a lugubrious sniff and a solemn wag of the funereal bonnet, which she refused to remove, being afflicted with a chronic catarrh.

"Now, it is my opinion that the dear thing only wants freedom, rest, and care. There is a look in her eyes that goes to my heart, for it shows that she feels the need of what none of us can give her,—a mother," said Aunt Jessie, with tears in her own bright eyes at the thought of her boys being left, as Rose was, to the care of others.

Uncle Alec, who had listened silently as each spoke, turned quickly toward the last sister, and said, with a decided nod of approval,—

"You've got it, Jessie; and, with you to help me, I hope to make the child feel that she is not quite fatherless and motherless."

"I'll do my best, Alec; and I think you *will* need me, for, wise as you are, you cannot understand a tender, timid little creature like Rose as a woman can," said Mrs. Jessie, with a heart full of motherly good-will.

"I cannot help feeling that *I*, who have had a daughter of my own, can best bring up a girl; and I am *very* much surprised that George did not intrust her to me," observed Aunt Myra, with an air of melancholy importance, for she was the only one who had given a daughter to the family, and she felt that she had distinguished herself, though ill-natured people said that she had dosed her darling to death.

"I never blamed him in the least, when I remember the perilous experiments you tried with poor Carrie," began Mrs. Jane, in her hard voice.

"Jane Campbell, I will *not* hear a word! My sainted Caroline is a sacred subject," cried Aunt Myra, rising as if to leave the room.

Dr. Alec detained her, feeling that he must define his position at once, and maintain it manfully if he hoped to have any success in his new undertaking.

"Now, my dear souls, don't let us quarrel and make Rose a bone of contention,—though, upon my word, she *is* almost a bone, poor little lass! You have had her among you for a year, and done what you liked. I cannot say that your success is great, but that is owing to too many fingers in the pie. Now, I intend to try my way for a year, and if at the end of it she is not in better trim than now, I'll give up the case, and hand her over to some one else. That's fair, I think."

"She will not be here a year hence, poor darling, so no one need dread future responsibility," said Aunt Myra, folding her black gloves as if all ready for the funeral.

"By Jupiter, Myra, you are enough to damp the ardor of a saint!" cried Dr. Alec, with a sudden spark in his eyes. "Your croaking will worry that child out of her wits, for she is an imaginative puss, and will fret and fancy untold horrors. You have put it into her head that she has no constitution, and she rather likes the idea. If she had not had a pretty good one, she *would* have been 'marked for the tomb' by this time, at the rate you have been going on with her. I will not have any interference,—please understand that; so just wash your hands of her, and let me manage till I want help, then I'll ask for it."

"Hear, hear!" came from the corner where Uncle Mac was apparently wrapt in slumber.

"You were appointed guardian, so we can do nothing. But I predict that the girl will be spoilt, utterly spoilt," answered Mrs. Jane, grimly.

"Thank you, sister. I have an idea that if a woman can bring up two boys as perfectly as you do yours, a man, if he devotes his whole mind to it, may at least attempt as much with one girl," replied Dr. Alec, with a humorous look that tickled the others immensely, for it was a well-known fact in the family that Jane's boys were more indulged than all the other lads put together.

"*I* am quite easy, for I really do think that Alec will improve the child's health; and by the time his year is out, it will be quite soon enough for her to go to Madame Roccabella's and be finished off," said Aunt Clara, settling her rings, and thinking, with languid satisfaction, of the time when she could bring out a pretty and accomplished niece.

"I suppose you will stay here in the old place, unless you think of marrying, and it's high time you did," put in Mrs. Jane, much nettled at her brother's last hit.

"No, thank you. Come and have a cigar, Mac," said Dr. Alec, abruptly.

"Don't marry; women enough in the family already," muttered Uncle Mac; and then the gentlemen hastily fled.

"Aunt Peace would like to see you all, she says," was the message Rose brought before the ladies could begin again.

"Hectic, hectic!—dear me, dear me!" murmured Aunt Myra, as the shadow of her gloomy bonnet fell upon Rose, and the stiff tips of a black glove touched the cheek where the color deepened under so many eyes.

"I am glad these pretty curls are natural; they will be invaluable by and by," said Aunt Clara, taking an observation with her head on one side.

"Now that your uncle has come, I no longer expect you to review the studies of the past year. I trust your time will not be *entirely* wasted in frivolous sports, however," added Aunt Jane, sailing out of the room with the air of a martyr.

Aunt Jessie said not a word, but kissed her little niece, with a look of tender sympathy that made Rose cling to her a minute, and follow her with grateful eyes as the door closed behind her.

After everybody had gone home, Dr. Alec paced up and down the lower hall in the twilight for an hour, thinking so intently that sometimes he frowned, sometimes he smiled, and more than once he stood still in a brown study. All of a sudden he said, half aloud, as if he had made up his mind,—

"I might as well begin at once, and give the child something new to think about, for Myra's dismals and Jane's lectures have made her as blue as a little indigo bag."

Diving into one of the trunks that stood in a corner, he brought up, after a brisk rummage, a silken cushion, prettily embroidered, and a quaint cup of dark carved wood.

"This will do for a start," he said, as he plumped up the cushion and dusted the cup. "It won't do to begin too energetically, or Rose will be frightened. I must beguile her gently and pleasantly along till I've won her confidence, and then she will be ready for any thing."

Just then Phebe came out of the dining-room with a plate of brown bread, for Rose had been allowed no hot biscuit for tea.

"I'll relieve you of some of that," said Dr. Alec, and, helping himself to a generous slice, he retired to the study, leaving Phebe to wonder at his appetite.

She would have wondered still more if she had seen him making that brown bread into neat little pills, which he packed into an attractive ivory box, out of which he emptied his own bits of lovage.

"There! if they insist on medicine, I'll order these, and no harm will be done. I *will* have my own way, but I'll keep the peace, if possible, and confess the joke when my experiment has succeeded," he said to himself, looking very much like a mischievous boy, as he went off with his innocent prescriptions.

Rose was playing softly on the small organ that stood in the upper hall, so that Aunt Peace could enjoy it; and all the while he talked with the old ladies Uncle Alec was listening to the fitful music of the child, and thinking of another Rose who used to play for him.

As the clock struck eight, he called out,—

"Time for my girl to be abed, else she won't be up early, and I am full of jolly plans for to-morrow. Come and see what I have found for you to begin upon."

Rose ran in and listened with bright, attentive face, while Dr. Alec said, impressively,—

"In my wanderings over the face of the earth, I have picked up some excellent remedies, and, as they are rather agreeable ones, I think you and I will try them. This is an herb-pillow, given to me by a wise old woman when I was ill in India. It is filled with saffron, poppies, and other soothing plants; so lay your little head on it to-night, sleep sweetly without a dream, and wake to-morrow without a pain."

"Shall I really? How nice it smells." And Rose willingly received the pretty pillow, and stood enjoying its faint, sweet odor, as she listened to the doctor's next remedy.

"This is the cup I told you of. Its virtue depends, they say, on the drinker filling it himself; so you must learn to milk. I'll teach you."

"I'm afraid I never can," said Rose; but she surveyed the cup with favor, for a funny little imp danced on the handle, as if all ready to take a header into the white sea below.

"Don't you think she ought to have something more strengthening than milk, Alec? I really shall feel anxious if she does not have a tonic of some sort," said Aunt Plenty, eyeing the new remedies suspiciously, for she had more faith in her old-fashioned doses than all the magic cups and poppy pillows of the East.

"Well, ma'am, I'm willing to give her a pill, if you think best. It is a very simple one, and very large quantities may be taken without harm. You know hasheesh is the extract of hemp? Well, this is a preparation of corn and rye, much used in old times, and I hope it will be again."

"Dear me, how singular!" said Aunt Plenty, bringing her spectacles to bear upon the pills, with a face so full of respectful interest that it was almost too much for Dr. Alec's gravity.

"Take one in the morning, and a good-night to you, my dear," he said, dismissing his patient with a hearty kiss.

Then, as she vanished, he put both hands into his hair, exclaiming, with a comical mixture of anxiety and amusement,—

"When I think what I have undertaken, I declare to you, aunt, I feel like running away and not coming back till Rose is eighteen!"

# SAMUEL CLEMENS

🎍 🎍

*Aunt Polly is the sturdy guardian of duty and respecta-
bility all through* The Adventures of Tom Sawyer.
*Here she is taxing her nephew with what seems like
the cruelest trick he has ever played—pretending to her
that her glimpse of him when he was presumed dead
was a ghostly visit from the Other World.*

"TOM, I've a notion to skin you alive!"

"Auntie, what have I done?"

"Well, you've done enough. Here I go over to Sereny Harper,
like an old softy, expecting I'm going to make her believe all that
rubbage about that dream, when lo and behold you she'd found
out from Joe that you was over here and heard all the talk we had
that night. Tom, I don't know what is to become of a boy that will
act like that. It makes me feel so bad to think you could let me go
to Sereny Harper and make such a fool of myself and never say a
word."

This was a new aspect of the thing. His smartness of the
morning had seemed to Tom a good joke before, and very
ingenious. It merely looked mean and shabby now. He hung his
head and could not think of anything to say for a moment. Then
he said:

"Auntie, I wish I hadn't done it—but I didn't think."

"Oh, child, you never think. You never think of anything but
your own selfishness. You could think to come all the way over
here from Jackson's island in the night to laugh at our troubles,
and you could think to fool me with a lie about a dream; but you
couldn't ever think to pity us and save us from sorrow."

"Auntie, I know now it was mean, but I didn't mean to be

mean. I didn't, honest. And besides, I didn't come over here to laugh at you that night."

"What did you come for, then?"

"It was to tell you not to be uneasy about us, because we hadn't got drownded."

"Tom, Tom, I would be the thankfulest soul in this world if I could believe you ever had as good a thought as that, but you know you never did—and I know it, Tom."

"Indeed and 'deed I did, auntie—I wish I may never stir if I didn't."

"Oh, Tom, don't lie—don't do it. It only makes things a hundred times worse."

"It ain't a lie, auntie, it's the truth. I wanted to keep you from grieving—that was all that made me come."

"I'd give the whole world to believe that—it would cover up a power of sins, Tom. I'd 'most be glad you'd run off and acted so bad. But it ain't reasonable; because, why didn't you tell me, child?"

"Why, you see, when you got to talking about the funeral, I just got all full of the idea of our coming and hiding in the church, and I couldn't somehow bear to spoil it. So I just put the bark back in my pocket and kept mum."

"What bark?"

"The bark I had wrote on to tell you we'd gone pirating. I wish, now, you'd waked up when I kissed you—I do, honest."

The hard lines in his aunt's face relaxed and a sudden tenderness dawned in her eyes.

"*Did* you kiss me, Tom?"

"Why, yes, I did."

"Are you sure you did, Tom?"

"Why, yes, I did, auntie—certain sure."

"What did you kiss me for, Tom?"

"Because I loved you so, and you laid there moaning and I was so sorry."

The words sounded like truth. The old lady could not hide a tremor in her voice when she said:

"Kiss me again, Tom!—and be off with you to school, now, and don't bother me any more."

The moment he was gone, she ran to a closet and got out the ruin of a jacket which Tom had gone pirating in. Then she stopped, with it in her hand, and said to herself:

"No, I don't dare. Poor boy, I reckon he's lied about it—but it's a blessed, blessed lie, there's such a comfort come from it. I hope the Lord—I *know* the Lord will forgive him, because it was such goodheartedness in him to tell it. But I don't want to find out it's a lie. I won't look."

She put the jacket away, and stood by musing a minute. Twice she put out her hand to take the garment again, and twice she refrained. Once more she ventured, and this time she fortified herself with the thought: "It's a good lie—it's a good lie—I won't let it grieve me." So she sought the jacket pocket. A moment later she was reading Tom's piece of bark through flowing tears and saying: "I could forgive the boy, now, if he'd committed a million sins!"

# "SAKI"

The Unbearable Bassington *demonstrates that a certain rivalry often exists between cousins of the same age and sex.*

SUZETTE'S MOTHER welcomed her unexpected visitor with obvious satisfaction. Her daughter's engagement, she explained, was not so brilliant from the social point of view as a girl of Suzette's attractions and advantages might have legitimately aspired to, but Egbert was a thoroughly commendable and dependable young man, who would very probably win his way before long to membership of the County Council.

"From there, of course, the road would be open to him to higher things."

"Yes," said Elaine, "he might become an alderman."

"Have you seen their photographs, taken together?" asked Mrs. Brankley, abandoning the subject of Egbert's prospective career.

"No; do show me," said Elaine, with a flattering show of interest; "I've never seen that sort of thing before. It used to be the fashion once for engaged couples to be photographed together, didn't it?"

"It's *very* much the fashion now," said Mrs. Brankley assertively, but some of the complacency had filtered out of her voice.

Suzette came into the room, wearing the dress that she had worn in the Park that morning.

"Of course, you've been hearing all about *the* engagement from mother," she cried, and then set to work conscientiously to cover the same ground.

"We met at Grindelwald, you know. He always calls me his Ice Maiden because we first got to know each other on the skating-rink. Quite romantic, wasn't it? Then we asked him to tea one day, and we got to be quite friendly. Then he proposed."

"He wasn't the only one who was smitten with Suzette," Mrs. Brankley hastened to put in, fearful lest Elaine might suppose that Egbert had had things all his own way. "There was an American millionaire who was quite taken with her, and a Polish count of a very old family. I assure you I felt quite nervous at some of our tea-parties."

Mrs. Brankley had given Grindelwald a sinister but rather alluring reputation among a large circle of untravelled friends as a place where the insolence of birth and wealth was held in precarious check from breaking forth into scenes of savage violence.

"My marriage with Egbert will, of course, enlarge the sphere of my life enormously," pursued Suzette.

"Yes," said Elaine; her eyes were rather remorselessly taking in the details of her cousin's toilette. It is said that nothing is sadder than victory except defeat. Suzette began to feel that the tragedy of both was concentrated in the creation which had given her such unalloyed gratification till Elaine had come on the scene.

"A woman can be so immensely helpful in the social way to a man who is making a career for himself. And I'm so glad to find that we've a great many ideas in common. We each made out a list of our idea of the hundred best books, and quite a number of them were the same."

"He looks bookish," said Elaine, with a critical glance at the photograph.

"Oh, he's not at all a bookworm," said Suzette quickly, "though he's tremendously well-read. He's quite the man of action."

"Does he hunt?" asked Elaine.

"No, he doesn't get much time or opportunity for riding."

"What a pity!" commented Elaine. "I don't think I could marry a man who wasn't fond of riding."

"Of course that's a matter of taste," said Suzette stiffly; "horsey men are not usually gifted with overmuch brains, are they?"

"There is as much difference between a horseman and a horsey man as there is between a well-dressed man and a dressy one," said Elaine judicially; "and you may have noticed how seldom a dressy woman really knows how to dress. As an old lady of my acquaintance observed the other day, some people are born with a sense of how to clothe themselves, others acquire it, others look as if their clothes had been thrust upon them."

She gave Lady Caroline her due quotation marks, but the sudden tactfulness with which she looked away from her cousin's frock was entirely her own idea.

A young man entering the room at this moment caused a diversion that was rather welcome to Suzette.

"Here comes Egbert," she announced, with an air of subdued triumph; it was at least a satisfaction to be able to produce the captive of her charms, alive and in good condition, on the scene. Elaine might be as critical as she pleased, but a live lover outweighed any number of well-dressed straight-riding cavaliers who existed only as a distant vision of the delectable husband.

Egbert was one of those men who have no small talk, but possess an inexhaustible supply of the larger variety. In whatever society he happened to be, and particularly in the immediate neighbourhood of an afternoon-tea table, with a limited audience of womenfolk, he gave the impression of someone who was addressing a public meeting, and would be happy to answer questions afterwards. A suggestion of gaslit mission-halls, wet umbrellas, and discreet applause seemed to accompany him everywhere. He was an exponent, among other things, of what he called New Thought, which seemed to lend itself conveniently to the employment of a good deal of rather stale phraseology. Probably in the course of some thirty odd years of existence he had never been of any notable use to man, woman, child, or animal, but it was his firmly announced intention to leave the world a better, happier, purer place than he had found it; against the danger of any relapse to earlier conditions after his disappearance from the scene, he was, of course, powerless to guard. 'Tis not in mortals to ensure succession, and Egbert was admittedly mortal.

Elaine found him immensely entertaining, and would certainly have exerted herself to draw him out if such a proceeding had been at all necessary. She listened to his conversation with the complacent appreciation that one bestows on a stage tragedy, from whose calamities one can escape at any moment by the simple process of leaving one's seat. When at last he checked the flow of his opinions by a hurried reference to his watch, and declared that he must be moving on elsewhere, Elaine almost expected a vote of thanks to be accorded him, or to be asked to signify herself in favour of some resolution by holding up her hand.

When the young man had bidden the company a rapid business-like farewell, tempered in Suzette's case by the exact degree of tender intimacy that it would have been considered improper to omit or overstep, Elaine turned to her expectant cousin with an air of cordial congratulation.

"He is exactly the husband I should have chosen for you, Suzette."

For the second time that afternoon Suzette felt a sense of waning enthusiasm for one of her possessions.

# IRVING BACHELLER

*Rural American life at the close of the nineteenth cen-
tury is pictured in* Eben Holden—*and with it a time
when an uncle skilled in horse-trading has valuable
lessons for an impetuous young man.*

THE HORSE played a part of no small importance in that country. He was the coin of the realm, a medium of exchange, a
standard of value, and exponent of moral character. The man
that traveled without a horse was on his way to the poorhouse.
Uncle Eb or David Brower could tell a good horse by the sound
of his footsteps, and they brought into St. Lawrence County the
haughty Morgans from Vermont. There was more pride in their
high heads than in any of the good people. A Northern Yankee
who was not carried away with a fine horse had excellent self-
control. Politics and the steed were the only things that ever woke
him to enthusiasm, and there a man was known as he traded.
Uncle Eb used to say that one ought always to underestimate
his horse "a leetle fer the sake of a reputation."

We needed another horse to help with the haying, and Bob
Dean, a tricky trader, who had heard of it, drove in after supper
one evening, and offered a rangy brown animal at a low figure.
We looked him over, tried him up and down the road, and then
David, with some shrewd suspicion, as I divined later, said I could
do as I pleased. I bought the horse and led him proudly to the
stable. Next morning an Irishman, the extra man for the haying,
came in with a worried look to breakfast.

"That new horse has a chitterin' kind of a coff," he said.

"A cough?" said I.

" 'Tain't jist a coff, nayther," he said, "but a kind of *toom!*"

With the last word he obligingly imitated the sound of the cough. It threw me into perspiration.

"Sounds bad," said Uncle Eb, as he looked at me and snickered.

" 'Fraid Bill ain't much of a jockey," said David, smiling.

"Got a grand appetite—that hoss has," said Tip Taylor.

After breakfast Uncle Eb and I hitched him to the light buggy and touched him up for a short journey down the road. In five minutes he had begun to heave and whistle. I felt sure one could have heard him half a mile away. Uncle Eb stopped him and began to laugh.

"A whistler," said he, "sure's yer born. He ain't wuth a bag o' beans. But don't ye never let on. When ye git licked ye musn't never fin' fault. If anybody asks ye 'bout him tell 'em he's all ye expected."

We stood waiting a moment for the horse to recover himself. A team was nearing us.

"There's Bob Dean," Uncle Eb whispered. "The durn scalawag! Don't ye say a word now."

"Good mornin'!" said Dean, smiling as he pulled up beside us.

"Nice pleasant mornin'!" said Uncle Eb, as he cast a glance into the sky.

"What ye standin' here for?" Dean asked.

Uncle Eb expectorated thoughtfully.

"Jest a lookin' at the scenery," said he. "Purty country, right here! Alwus liked it."

"Nice lookin' hoss ye got there," said Dean.

"Grand hoss!" said Uncle Eb, surveying him proudly. "Most *ree*markable hoss."

"Good stepper, too," said Dean soberly.

"Splendid!" said Uncle Eb. "Can go a mile without ketchin' his breath."

"Thet so?" said Dean.

"Good deal like Lucy Purvis," Uncle Eb added. "She can say the hull mul'plication table an' only breathe once. Ye can learn sumthin' from a hoss like thet. He's good as a deestric' school—thet hoss is."

"Yes, sir, thet hoss is all right," said Dean, as he drove away.

"Righter'n I expected," Uncle Eb shouted, and then he covered his mouth, shaking with suppressed laughter.

"Skunk!" he said, as we turned the animal and started to walk him home. "Don't min' bein' beat, but I don't like t' hev a man rub it in on me. I'll git even with him mebbe."

And he did. It came about in this way. We turned our new purchase into the pasture, and Uncle Eb and I drove away to Potsdam for a better nag. We examined all the horses in that part of the country. At last we chanced upon one that looked like the whistler, save that he had a white stocking on one hind foot.

"Same age, too," said Uncle Eb, as he looked into his mouth.

"Can pass anything on the road," said his owner.

"Can he?" said Uncle Eb, who had no taste for slow going. "Hitch him up an' le's see what he can do."

He carried us faster than we had ever ridden before at a trot, and coming up behind another team the man pulled out, let the reins loose on his back, and whistled. If anyone had hit him with a log chain the horse could not have moved quicker. He took us by the other team like a flash, on the dead run and three in the buggy.

"He'll do all right," said Uncle Eb, and paid for the horse.

It was long after dark when we started home, leading him behind, and near midnight when we arrived.

In the morning I found Uncle Eb in the stable showing him to the other help. To my surprise the white stocking had disappeared.

"Didn't jes' like that white stockin'," he said, as I came in. "Wondered how he'd look without it."

They all agreed this horse and the whistler were as much alike as two peas in appearance. Breakfast over, Uncle Eb asked the Irishman to hitch him up.

"Come Bill," said he, "le's take a ride. Dean'll be comin' 'long bym bye on his way t' town with that trotter o' his'n. 'Druther like to meet him."

I had only a faint idea of his purpose. He let the horse step along at top speed going up the road and when we turned about he was breathing heavily. We jogged him back down the road a mile or so, and when I saw the blazed face of Dean's mare, in the distance, we pulled up and shortly stopped him. Dean came along in a moment.

"Nice mornin'!" said he.

"Grand!" said Uncle Eb.

"Lookin' at the lan'scape ag'in?"

"Yes; I've jes' begun t' see what a purty country this is," said Uncle Eb.

"How's the hoss?"

"Splendid! Gives ye time t' think an' see what yer passin'. Like t' set 'n think once in a while. We don't do enough thinkin' here in this part o' the country."

"Y'd orter buy this mare an' learn how t' ride fast," said Dean.

"Thet one," said Uncle Eb, squinting at the mare, "why she can't go fast 'nough."

"She can't, hey?" said Dean, bridling with injured pride. "I don't think there's anything in this town can head her."

"Thunder!" said Uncle Eb, "I can go by her with this ol' plug easy 'twixt here an' our gate. Ye didn't know what ye was sellin'."

"If ye pass her once I'll give her to ye," said he.

"Mean it?" said Uncle Eb.

"Sartin," said he, a little redder in the face.

"An' if I don't I'll give ye the whistler," said Uncle Eb as he turned about.

The mare went away, under the whip, before we had fairly started. She was going a fifty shot but in a moment we were lapping upon her hind wheel. Dean threw a startled glance over his shoulder. Then he shouted to the mare. She quickened her pace a little but we kept our position. Uncle Eb was leaning over the dasher his white locks flying. He had something up his sleeve, as they say, and was not yet ready to use it. Then Dean began to shear over to cut us off—a nasty trick of the low horseman. I saw Uncle Eb glance at the ditch ahead. I knew what was coming and took a firm hold of the seat. The ditch was a bit rough, but Uncle Eb had no lack of courage. He turned the horse's head, let up on the reins and whistled. I have never felt such a thrill as then. Our horse leaped into the deep grass running like a wild deer.

"Hi there! hi there!" Uncle Eb shouted, bouncing in his seat, as we went over stones and hummocks going like the wind.

"Go, ye brown devil!" he yelled, his hat flying off as he shook the reins.

The mare lost her stride; we flashed by and came up into the road. Looking back I saw her jumping up and down a long way behind us and Dean whipping her. Uncle Eb, his hands over the dasher, had pulled down to a trot. Ahead of us we could see our folks—men and women—at the gate looking down the road at us waving hats and handkerchiefs. They had heard the noise of the battle. Uncle Eb let up on the reins and looked back snorting with amusement. In a moment we pulled up at our gate. Dean came along slowly.

"Thet's a purty good mare," said Uncle Eb.

"Yer welcome to her," said Dean sullenly.

"Wouldn't hev her," said Uncle Eb.

"Why not?" said the trader a look of relief coming over his face.

"Can't go fast enough for my use," Uncle Eb answered. "Ye can jest hitch her in here awhile an' the first day ye come over with a hundred dollars ye can hev her 'n the whistler, both on 'em. Thet whistler's a grand hoss! Can hold his breath longer'n any hoss I ever knew!"

The sum named was that we had paid him for the highly accomplished animal. Dean had the manhood to pay up then and there and said he would send for the other horse, which he never did.

"Guess he wont bother us any more when we stop t' look at the scenery," said Uncle Eb, laughing as Dean drove away. "Kind o' resky business buyin' hosses," he added. "Got t' jedge the owner as well as the hoss. If there's anything the matter with his conscience it'll come out in the hoss some where—every time. Never knew a mean man t' own a good hoss. Remember, boy, 's a lame soul thet drives a limpin' hoss."

"No use talkin'; Bill ain' no jedge uv a hoss" said David Brower. "He'll hev t' hev an education er he'll git t' the poor house some day sartin."

"Wall he's a good jedge o' gals anyway," said Uncle Eb.

As for myself I was now hopelessly confirmed in my dislike of farming and I never traded horses again.

# W. SOMERSET MAUGHAM

*Of Human Bondage shows a nephew rebelling
against the authority of a guardian aunt and uncle.*

MR. PERKINS soon saw that his words had had no effect on
Philip, and for the rest of the term ignored him. He wrote a re-
port which was vitriolic. When it arrived and Aunt Louisa asked
Philip what it was like, he answered cheerfully:

"Rotten."

"Is it?" said the Vicar. "I must look at it again."

"Do you think there's any use in my staying on at Tercanbury?
I should have thought it would be better if I went to Germany for
a bit."

"What has put that in your head?" said Aunt Louisa.

"Don't you think it's rather a good idea?"

Sharp had already left King's School and had written to Philip
from Hanover. He was really starting life, and it made Philip more
restless to think of it. He felt he could not bear another year of
restraint.

"But then you wouldn't get a scholarship."

"I haven't a chance of getting one anyhow. And besides, I don't
know that I particularly want to go to Oxford."

"But if you're going to be ordained, Philip?" Aunt Louisa
exclaimed in dismay.

"I've given up that idea long ago."

Mrs. Carey looked at him with startled eyes, and then, used to
self-restraint, she poured out another cup of tea for his uncle.
They did not speak. In a moment Philip saw tears slowly falling
down her cheeks. His heart was suddenly wrung because he
caused her pain. In her tight black dress, made by the dressmaker
down the street, with her wrinkled face and pale tired eyes, her

gray hair still done in the frivolous ringlets of her youth, she was a ridiculous but strangely pathetic figure. Philip saw it for the first time.

Afterwards, when the Vicar was shut up in his study with the curate, he put his arms round her waist.

"I say, I'm sorry you're upset, Aunt Louisa," he said. "But it's no good my being ordained if I haven't a real vocation, is it?"

"I'm so disappointed, Philip," she moaned. "I'd set my heart on it. I thought you could be your uncle's curate, and then when our time came—after all, we can't last for ever, can we?—you might have taken his place."

Philip shivered. He was seized with panic. His heart beat like a pigeon in a trap beating with its wings. His aunt wept softly, her head upon his shoulder.

"I wish you'd persuade Uncle William to let me leave Tercanbury. I'm so sick of it."

But the Vicar of Blackstable did not easily alter any arrangements he had made, and it had always been intended that Philip should stay at King's School till he was eighteen, and should then go to Oxford. At all events he would not hear of Philip leaving them, for no notice had been given and the term's fee would have to be paid in any case.

"Then will you give notice for me to leave at Christmas?" said Philip, at the end of a long and often bitter conversation.

"I'll write to Mr. Perkins about it and see what he says."

"Oh, I wish to goodness I were twenty-one. It is awful to be at somebody else's beck and call."

"Philip, you shouldn't speak to your uncle like that," said Mrs. Carey gently.

"But don't you see that Perkins will want me to stay? He gets so much a head for every chap in the school."

"Why don't you want to go to Oxford?"

"What's the good if I'm not going into the Church?"

"You can't go into the Church; you're in the Church already," said the Vicar.

"Ordained then," replied Philip impatiently.

"What are you going to be, Philip?" asked Mrs. Carey.

"I don't know. I've not made up my mind. But whatever I am,

it'll be useful to know foreign languages. I shall get far more out of a year in Germany than by staying on at that hole."

He would not say that he felt Oxford would be little better than a continuation of his life at school. He wished immensely to be his own master. Besides he would be known to a certain extent among old schoolfellows, and he wanted to get away from them all. He felt that his life at school had been a failure. He wanted to start fresh.

It happened that his desire to go to Germany fell in with certain ideas which had been of late discussed at Blackstable. Sometimes friends came to stay with the doctor and brought news of the world outside; and the visitors spending August by the sea had their own way of looking at things. The Vicar had heard that there were people who did not think the old-fashioned education so useful nowadays as it had been in the past, and modern languages were gaining an importance which they had not had in his own youth. His own mind was divided, for a younger brother of his had been sent to Germany when he failed in some examination, thus creating a precedent, but since he had there died of typhoid it was impossible to look upon the experiment as other than dangerous. The result of innumerable conversations was that Philip should go back to Tercanbury for another term, and then should leave. With this agreement Philip was not dissatisfied. But when he had been back a few days the headmaster spoke to him.

"I've had a letter from your uncle. It appears you want to go to Germany, and he asks me what I think about it."

Philip was astounded. He was furious with his guardian for going back on his word.

"I thought it was settled, sir," he said.

"Far from it. I've written to say I think it the greatest mistake to take you away."

Philip immediately sat down and wrote a violent letter to his uncle. He did not measure his language. He was so angry that he could not get to sleep till quite late that night, and he awoke in the early morning and began brooding over the way they had treated him. He waited impatiently for an answer. In two or three days it came. It was a mild, pained letter from Aunt Louisa, saying that he should not write such things to his uncle, who was very much distressed. He was unkind and unchristian. He must know they were only trying to do their best for him, and they were so much older than he that they must be better judges of what was good for him. Philip clenched his hands. He had heard that statement so often, and he could not see why it was true; they did not know the conditions as he did, why should they accept it as self-evident that their greater age gave them greater wisdom? The letter ended with the information that Mr. Carey had withdrawn the notice he had given.

Philip nursed his wrath till the next half-holiday. They had them on Tuesdays and Thursdays, since on Saturday afternoons they had to go to a service in the Cathedral. He stopped behind when the rest of the Sixth went out.

"May I go to Blackstable this afternoon, please, sir;" he asked

"No," said the headmaster briefly.

"I wanted to see my uncle about something very important."

"Didn't you hear me say no?"

Philip did not answer. He went out. He felt almost sick with humiliation, the humiliation of having to ask and the humiliation of the curt refusal. He hated the headmaster now. Philip writhed under that despotism which never vouchsafed a reason for the most tyrannous act. He was too angry to care what he did, and after dinner walked down to the station, by the back ways he knew so well, just in time to catch the train to Blackstable. He walked into the vicarage and found his uncle and aunt sitting in the dining-room.

"Hulloa, where have you sprung from?" said the Vicar.

It was very clear that he was not pleased to see him. He looked a little uneasy.

"I thought I'd come and see you about my leaving. I want to know what you mean by promising me one thing when I was here, and doing something different a week after."

He was a little frightened at his own boldness, but he had made up his mind exactly what words to use, and, though his heart beat violently, he forced himself to say them.

"Have you got leave to come here this afternoon?"

"No. I asked Perkins and he refused. If you like to write and tell him I've been here you can get me into a really fine old row."

Mrs. Carey sat knitting with trembling hands. She was unused to scenes and they agitated her extremely.

"It would serve you right if I told him," said Mr. Carey.

"If you like to be a perfect sneak you can. After writing to Perkins as you did you're quite capable of it."

It was foolish of Philip to say that, because it gave the Vicar exactly the opportunity he wanted.

"I'm not going to sit still while you say impertinent things to me," he said with dignity.

He got up and walked quickly out of the room into his study. Philip heard him shut the door and lock it.

"Oh, I wish to God I were twenty-one. It is awful to be tied down like this."

Aunt Louisa began to cry quietly.

"Oh, Philip, you oughtn't to have spoken to your uncle like that. Do please go and tell him you're sorry."

"I'm not in the least sorry. He's taking a mean advantage. Of course it's just waste of money keeping me on at school, but what does he care? It's not his money. It was cruel to put me under the guardianship of people who know nothing about things."

"Philip."

Philip in his voluble anger stopped suddenly at the sound of her voice. It was heart-broken. He had not realised what bitter things he was saying.

"Philip, how can you be so unkind? You know we are only trying to do our best for you, and we know that we have no experience; it isn't as if we'd had any children of our own: that's why we consulted Mr. Perkins." Her voice broke. "I've tried to be like a mother to you. I've loved you as if you were my own son."

She was so small and frail, there was something so pathetic in her old-maidish air, that Philip was touched. A great lump came suddenly in his throat and his eyes filled with tears.

"I'm so sorry," he said. "I didn't mean to be beastly."

He knelt down beside her and took her in his arms, and kissed her wet, withered cheeks. She sobbed bitterly, and he seemed to feel on a sudden the pity of that wasted life. She had never surrendered herself before to such a display of emotion.

"I know I've not been what I wanted to be to you, Philip, but I didn't know how. It's been just as dreadful for me to have no children as for you to have no mother."

Philip forgot his anger and his own concerns, but thought only of consoling her, with broken words and clumsy little caresses. Then the clock struck, and he had to bolt off at once to catch the only train that would get him back to Tercanbury in time for call-over. As he sat in the corner of the railway carriage he saw that he had done nothing. He was angry with himself for his weakness. It was despicable to have allowed himself to be turned from his purpose by the pompous airs of the Vicar and the tears of his aunt. But as the result of he knew not what conversations between the couple another letter was written to the headmaster. Mr. Perkins read it with an impatient shrug of the shoulders. He showed it to Philip. It ran:

Dear Mr. Perkins,

Forgive me for troubling you again about my ward, but both his Aunt and I have been uneasy about him. He seems very anxious to leave school, and his Aunt thinks he is unhappy. It is very difficult for us to know what to do as we are not his parents. He does not seem to think he is doing very well and he feels it is wasting his money to stay on. I should be very much obliged if you would have a talk to him, and if he is still of the same mind perhaps it would be better if he left at Christmas as I originally intended.

Yours very truly,
William Carey.

# PATRICK DENNIS

꙳ ꙳

*A nephew with his own memories of Auntie Mame takes his young son to meet this fabulous relative.*

## "Auntie Mame Revisited"

READING about the Unforgettable Character was so spellbinding that I dozed off. It was four o'clock when I was awakened by the ringing of the telephone. I got up to answer it but Pegeen already had.

"It's for you," she said, covering the mouthpiece. "And it's that mad aunt of yours."

"That's impossible," I whispered. "She's in India."

"Then it's a remarkably clear connection. Here."

"Hello?" I said cautiously.

"Darling, darling boy! *Here* I am!" Auntie Mame sang.

"But where?"

"At the St. Regis. I just landed this morning and I'm only here for a day or so. Didn't I write to tell you I was coming?"

"No, you didn't," I said.

"Well, I meant to."

"How *was* India?" I asked inanely.

"Divine, darling. Absolutely divine! I can't *wait* to tell you about my important work there. Why, Nehru said that I've done more to get India's mind off communism than any single . . ."

"I'll bet even Pakistan looked pretty good to them while you were there," I said.

"What, darling?"

"Nothing."

"Well, darling, I want to *see* you. You and Pegeen and your sweet little baby. Here you go and have this lovely little boy and

I've never laid eyes on him, what with helping to tidy up Europe and Asia for all these years. Couldn't you put him in a basket and bring him down?"

"Auntie Mame," I said, "he's seven years old. He's so big he could put *me* in a basket and . . ."

"Heavens! How the time flies when one is busy. But do come! I'm giving a little welcome home party for myself."

"When?"

"Why, just as soon as you get here. I'm having some of the most interesting people—a real international flavor! Hurry, darling, do. I can't *contain* myself until I see the three of you."

"We'll try. We'll be along in about an hour."

"*À bientôt*, love!" She rang off.

"*Now* what?" Pegeen asked.

"It was Auntie Mame."

"So I gathered."

"She's at the St. Regis. She just got back. She wants us to come right down."

"I knew it was too good to last," Pegeen said. "The last seven or eight years have been so peaceful."

"Well, come on. Put on your hat. Let's get going. She wants to see the kid, too."

"Had you planned to sweep into the St. Regis in that old bathrobe?" Pegeen asked.

"Oh, God, I forgot. Well, get the kid ready and by that time I'll be dressed."

"But just remember one thing," Pegeen said, looking unusually serious. "She may be a real character, a sketch, a charmer, and all that sort of thing, but she's not going to get her hands on my child. She can see him and say kitchy-coo and how big he is and how much he looks like you and all the things that aunts are supposed to say, but she's not . . ."

"Oh, Pegeen, she won't even *want* to. She's already got a dozen irons in the fire, without messing around with children."

When we got to the door of Auntie Mame's suite, Pegeen said once more: "Now just remember." I rang the buzzer and the door opened. Ito, his head swathed in a turban, salaamed.

"Ito!" I said, grasping his hand. His hair peeping out from under the turban was grizzled, but Ito giggled delightedly and I could see that only his costume had changed.

"You come in. Madame having affair. Madame very anxious see little boy."

Our kid's eyes were almost popping out of his head. He tugged at my hand. "Is he like Punjab in *Little Orphan Annie?*"

"No, Mike," I said, "he just works for your aunt."

For a short stay in town, Auntie Mame had taken a considerable number of rooms and they were filled with a kind of UN delegation. There were lots of Indian men in business suits and turbans and Indian women in floating saris. Mike had never seen anything like it before in his life.

About the first person I bumped into was Vera, her hair dyed an aggressive golden. On her sixtieth birthday she had conceded that her ingénue days were over and she was now playing young matrons of thirty-five and still packing them in at the matinees. Death having taken its toll in the FitzHugh family, the Honorable Basil was now a belted earl and Vera was very much her ladyship. What with being authentically British, her interpolations on the English language had soared to a new art form. "Pittrick, dalling," she said, extending a hand, "fency fainding yew haa eftah ull these years. But yew've *aged* sao, daa boy."

"Hi, Vera," I said. "Seen anything of Auntie Mame?"

"Aoh, but yais, dalling. End she *looks* revishing. Haow well she keddies hugh yaas."

"But where . . ."

Coming toward me was a vision I knew could only be Auntie Mame. She was wearing an elaborate sari, extravagantly draped to make the most of her still slim figure. Her hair, which had all gone to gray, was rinsed to a delicate periwinkle blue. She wore a lot of kohl around her eyes and a caste mark on her forehead.

"Hello, Fatima," I said.

"Patrick! Darling, darling boy!" She threw herself into my arms and covered my face with kisses. "And Pegeen!" She and Pegeen, whose relationship had been brief and little more than politely cordial, exchanged a chaste kiss. "And now *where* is the baby?"

"He's right here," I said, laying a hand on Mike's red head.

"Darling!" she said dramatically, "*I'm* your Auntie Mame!" She put her arms around him and kissed him.

"Your *Great*-Auntie Mame," Pegeen said.

"And he's named Michael for the Archangel Michael!" Auntie Mame trilled.

"No," Pegeen said flatly, "for my father, Mickey the Mick."

"Oh, but Patrick, he's just divine. He looks exactly the way you did when *you* were a little boy, except that he has Pegeen's beautiful, beautiful hair. Even *more* beautiful than Pegeen's, I think." She pressed her nose against Mike's and looked into his eyes. "I've never *seen* hair the color of yours, my little love. It's so red!"

"I've never seen hair the color of yours, either," Mike said. "It's . . . it's so *blue!*"

Auntie Mame gave out with a silvery laugh. "You *are* an observant young man, aren't you?"

"What did you say?" Mike asked her, wide-eyed.

"I said, you're observant, aren't you?"

"I'm afraid I don't know what that means."

"Heavens, child. Has your father done *nothing* for your vocabulary?"

"My what?"

"Your vocabulary. That means the words people use when they speak. And, darling, a large and flexible vocabulary is the hallmark of every truly cultivated person."

"I don't understand most of those big words."

"Of course you don't, my little love. How can you, if you're never given a chance to use them? I'm going to get you a vocabulary pad, just as I did for your father, and every time you hear a word you don't understand, you simply write it down and then I'll tell you what it means and how to use it in speech. That'll be ever so much fun, won't it?"

"I—I guess so," Mike said.

"Listen, Auntie Mame," I said nervously, "if you'll be dusting right out of town again, I don't think you'll have much time to be building Mike's vocabulary or . . ."

"Who knows? Although I'm needed in India, I *do* say that

blood is thicker than water and . . . Oh, Michael, darling, *do* you know about India? Do you know where it is?"

"Sort of," Mike said.

"Ah, my little love, if only I could show it to you—the color, the splendor, the mystery!"

"I like mysteries."

"So do I, my little love. And to see it all through your young blue eyes. Do you know that there are jungles with leopards and lions and you can see elephants right on the streets?"

"Like the circus, Auntie Mame?" Mike said, brightening.

"Yes, darling, like the circus. Only much better, because you can touch them and ride on them."

"Ride on an *elephant?*" Mike squeaked.

"Why, certainly, darling. When I was staying with the Maharajah of Ghitagodpur we went *everywhere* on elephants. I had an elephant of my own all the time I was visiting him."

"Your own *elephant?*"

"Of course, darling. I'll bet you'd like that, wouldn't you?"

"Oh, boy! Maybe when you're in India again I could get on the train and come and visit you. I've been on a train alone before. I went all the way from Verdant Greens to Grand Central Station to have lunch with Daddy and go to a play."

"Why, of course you could come and visit me, my little love. Although I usually fly when I go to India."

"In an *airplane?*"

"On a broomstick," Pegeen murmured.

"Gee! Well, maybe I could visit you pretty soon. School's out now and . . ."

"Mike," I said, "stop fishing."

"I'm sorry, Auntie Mame," he said. Then he added: "That's a very pretty dress."

"Thank you, darling! I can see you already have quite a way with the ladies. Yes, the sari *is* the most truly becoming costume a woman can wear. I have dozens of them in my trunk and . . . oh, and I have something else there, too. Something I think a little boy like you might enjoy."

"What is it, Auntie Mame?" Mike asked.

"It's a scimitar, darling."

"What's that?"

"Well, it's a kind of curved sword. I found it one day while I was poking about in the bazaars. It's really a Moslem weapon rather than Hindu, but the tracery on the handle intrigued me so that I . . ."

Mike wasn't understanding much of what Auntie Mame was saying, but once he heard the word sword, he could hardly contain himself.

"Would you like it, darling?"

"Oh, boy! *Would* I!"

"Don't you think it's kind of dangerous for a child of . . ." Pegeen began.

"Oh, my dear, it's so dull you couldn't cut cheese with it. But it *does* have glamour. Why don't you two just circulate, and I'll take this darling little boy into my room and . . ." Auntie Mame and Mike were gone before I could say a word.

"Now listen," Pegeen said. "Just remember that this family reunion is *one* thing, but that crazy woman isn't going to get her hands on Mike. He's a perfectly normal, unexceptional little boy—although his I.Q. *is* high—and I want to keep him that way. She's not going to ruin him with a lot of . . ."

"Well, I don't know quite what you mean by the word 'ruin,'" I said with some indignation. "She raised *me*, didn't she? Do *I* do anything that strikes you as eccentric? It seems to me that we've led a perfectly happy, commonplace sort of . . ."

"Exactly. And that's the way I want to keep it."

We circulated among Auntie Mame's old friends from her New York days and her new ones from her Bombay nights. It was a party in the Grand Manner, recalling Auntie Mame's crushes of the late twenties. Everybody you ever heard of was there, and I must admit that, compared to the standardized cocktail gatherings and dinners in Verdant Greens, it was brilliant. It even gave me a momentary twinge of nostalgia for the old bootleg-gin days in Beekman Place and the gracious rooms in Auntie Mame's house in Washington Square—long since torn down. Even Pegeen was impressed, despite her dark suspicions of Auntie Mame.

"Well, Pegeen," I said, "say what you will, but you've got to admit that the old girl can still drag 'em in."

"She could charm the birds off the trees," Pegeen said. "That's the trouble with her. I like her, I really do like her, but . . . My God!"

I followed Pegeen's horrified stare to see Mike and Auntie Mame emerging from her bedroom. His head was bound up in a white turban and he dragged a huge scimitar behind him.

"Look, darlings! Look at my little Indian boy! Now salaam for them, Michael, just the way Auntie Mame taught you to."

Mike salaamed. All the Indian gentlemen salaamed right back and the Indian ladies giggled shrilly and fluttered their saris. "Of course, we're Parsis," one of them said to me, "and we've been Christianized for five generations, but the little American boy with the dear Miss Mame is so . . ."

"Well, it's all settled!" Auntie Mame said matter-of-factly, coming to us.

"What's all settled?" I asked.

"Our trip back to India. All he needs is a couple of inoculations and we'll be ready to leave at the end of the week. I must say he's an adorable child. You've done a splendid job on him, Pegeen. Perfectly splen . . ."

"*What* trip to India?" I thundered.

"That's right, Daddy. Auntie Mame and I are going on a big airplane and visit a king who has elephants and shoots tigers and plays polo and I'm going to meet a kind of religious man who teaches Auntie Mame how to breathe and concentrate—that's a new word, Daddy—and he's going to teach me and . . . What did you call that man, Auntie Mame?"

"Yogi, darling, but I wouldn't bother your father with that just now . . ."

"That's it, a yogi, and we're going to . . ."

"You're going to do no such thing," I said calmly.

If I'd slapped him he couldn't have looked more wounded. "B-but Daddy . . ."

"Mike, dear, it's just out of the question," Pegeen said. "I mean the distance, the danger. I wouldn't be happy with you away."

"You were happy with me away last summer," Mike said. "You said you couldn't wait to get me out from under your feet and off to crummy old Camp Yahoo. You said . . ."

"Mind your manners, Mike," I said.

"B-but Daddy . . ."

"Patrick, darling, how could you deprive the child of this adventure?" Auntie Mame said. "It's almost like slamming the door of knowledge in his face. Here he has this perfectly splendid opportunity to see one of the most interesting countries in the world—filled with color and history and mystery and political unrest —really see it from the *inside* as no tourist ever does, and you . . ."

"Auntie Mame," I began, "it's just that he's so young and . . ."

"It's awfully good of you," Pegeen said. "It's one of the most generous things I've ever heard of, but . . ."

"Mother," Mike said. His lower lip was trembling and his eyes were bluer than Auntie Mame's hair. "Couldn't I *please* go? I've never been any place away before except Bermuda and Maddox Island and Camp Yahoo. *Please* couldn't I go?" Well, Mike has a way of breaking your heart with a single look.

"Mike, I-I . . . Well, let me talk it over with Daddy."

"A *splendid* idea," Auntie Mame said briskly. "Couples *should* talk over their problems. Get them right out in the open and face them fairly and squarely. If *everyone* did that there wouldn't be so much wrangling and divorce. Go right into my bedroom and have this out *now*." She pushed us into her room and shut the door.

"Well," I said.

"Well," Pegeen said, "I just don't know. On the one hand I can see just about ten thousand strong objections to the whole fantastic scheme. Your aunt is frivolous and scatterbrained and possessive and dominating, and Mike is an impressionable little boy . . ."

"There's also a lot of danger in India," I said. "Poisonous insects and reptiles, I believe. Yet I've never been there and I'll admit that it sounds . . ."

"Of course it's a wonderful opportunity for Mike. I'd be the last to deny that. It'll be an experience that he can carry with him for the rest of his life. But still . . ."

"Well, I know he couldn't get into much trouble. Auntie Mame *is* dependable in her own peculiar fashion. Yet it's so far away and . . ."

"That doesn't worry me so much, Pat, it's just that . . . Well, if I say *no* and stick to it, I'll feel like a terrible heel and all of his life he can confront me with . . ."

"Well," I said, "if *anybody* says no, it's going to be you. I think his heart would snap right in two. He *does* like Auntie Mame and of course he . . ."

"Oh, all *right!*" Pegeen sighed. "She's really got us where the hair grows shortest. We'll say this: He can go, but *only* on one condition, that he be back here by Labor Day. One thing he's *not* going to do is miss a lot of schooling while she . . ."

"And he's not to learn yoga either," I said. "I want to make that very clear."

"No yoga *whatsoever*," Pegeen said. "I know that this is just crazy but . . ."

The door eased open and the two of them stood there—Mike in his turban and Auntie Mame in her sari. Mike gave us the big blue eyes treatment. "I can go?" he asked. I knew they'd been listening, but I wasn't going to give Auntie Mame the satisfaction of confronting her with it.

"Yes, you can go."

"*Gee!*" Mike was all over us, kissing Pegeen and me.

"But just one or two points I want made *crystal clear*, Auntie Mame," I said.

"Yes, darling?" she said with dewy-eyed innocence.

"He's *got* to be back by Labor Day in time for school . . ."

"Oh, but *naturally*, Patrick, Labor Day in the suburbs is always *such* fun!"

". . . and he's not to be put in touch with a lot of crackpot swami stuff . . ."

"There's a sweet little Episcopal Church where I'll send him every Sunday morning. However, to deprive him of the chance of meeting an intellect such as my guru's and not to allow him to draw strength and wisdom from . . ."

"And, last of all, you're to behave yourself with Mike."

"*Behave* myself? I? A woman past forty *behave*? What do you . . ."

"You know exactly what I mean. No nonsense. Just get him to India and back and no side trips to scenic Tibet or opium dens or . . ."

"So like your father, Patrick dear. Sometimes I think I've accomplished nothing with you."

"That's just what I want you to do with Mike. Nothing. He's living a conservative, quiet life in a conservative, quiet atmosphere. He's going to a good conservative school and . . ."

"I'll just bet he is. Can you have him ready to leave Friday?" Auntie Mame asked Pegeen.

"Friday? Well, I . . ."

"Bully! We'll take the noon plane."

"You mean I can *really* go?" Mike said.

"Yes, but only for the summer. Your Auntie Mame understands that you're to be back in time for school—come hell or high water."

Auntie Mame took Mike by the hand and looked lovingly into his eyes. "Tell me, my little love, do you like the school you go to?"

"No, I don't," Mike said.

"There's such an interesting man here from Madras. He has a whole new conception of education, Michael. It's an interracial school for boys and girls of all nations and colors. It's held in the out-of-doors, and instead of books . . ."

"I said I wanted him back *before* Labor Day!" I sputtered.

"This man is right here at the party now, my little love," she said to Mike, "and I'm sure he'd like to meet you. Come along with me and we'll find him. Enjoy yourselves, darlings," she said over her shoulder.

"My God," Pegeen gasped, "she's the Pied Piper."

Holding Mike's hand, Auntie Mame drifted into the crowd, her sari floating out behind her.

# LANGSTON HUGHES

ℳ ℳ

*Jesse B. Semple, familiarly known as Simple, remembers the aunt who raised him in this nostalgic sketch from* The Best of Simple.

## "Last Whipping"

WHEN I went by his house one Sunday morning to pick up my Kodak that he had borrowed, Simple was standing in the middle of the floor in his shirttail imitating a minister winding up his Sunday morning sermon, gestures and all.

He intoned, " 'Well, I looked and I saw a great beast! And that great beast had its jaws open ready to clamp down on my mortal soul. But I knowed if it was to clamp, ah, my soul would escape and go to glory. Amen! So I was not afraid. My body was afraid, a-a-ah, but my soul was not afraid. My soul said whatsoever you may do to my behind, a-a-ah, beast, you *cannot* harm my soul. Amen! No, Christians! That beast *cannot* tear your immortal soul. That devil in the form of a crocodile, the form of a alligator with a leather hide that slippeth and slideth through the bayous swamp —that alligator *cannot* tear your soul!' "

"You really give a good imitation of a preacher," I said. "But come on and get dressed and let's go, since you say you left my Kodak at Joyce's. I didn't stop by here to hear you preach."

"I am saying that to say this," said Simple, "because that is the place in the sermon where my old Aunt Lucy jumped up shouting and leapt clean across the pulpit rail and started to preaching herself, right along with the minister.

"She hollered, 'No-ooo-oo-o! Hallelujah, no! It cannot tear your soul. Sometimes the devil comes in human form,' yelled Aunt Lucy, 'sometimes it be's born right into your own family. Sometimes the devil be's your own flesh and kin—and he try your soul—but your soul he cannot tear! Sometimes you be's forced to tear his hide *before* he tears your soul. Amen!'

"Now, Aunt Lucy were talking about *me* that morning when she said 'devil.' That is what I started to tell you."

"Talking about you, why?" I asked.

"Because I had been up to some devilment, and she had done said she was gonna whip me come Monday. Aunt Lucy were so Christian she did not believe in whipping nobody on a Sunday."

"What had you done?"

"Oh, I had just taken one of her best laying hens and give it to a girl who didn't even belong to our church; to roast for her Sunday school picnic, because this old girl said she was aiming to picnic *me*—except that she didn't have nothing good to eat to put in her basket. I was trying to jive this old gal, you know—I was young—so I just took one of Aunt Lucy's hens and give her."

"Why didn't you pick out a pullet that wasn't laying?"

"That hen was the biggest, fattest chicken in the pen—and I wanted that girl to have plenty to pull out of her basket at that picnic so folks would make a great big admiration over her and me."

"How did your Aunt Lucy find out about the hen?"

"Man, you know womenfolks can't keep no secret! That girl told another girl, the other girl told her cousin, the cousin told her mama, her mama told Aunt Lucy—and Aunt Lucy woke me up Sunday morning with a switch in her hand."

"Weren't you too old to be whipped by then?"

"Of course, I was too old to whip—sixteen going on seventeen, big as a ox. But Aunt Lucy did not figure I was grown yet. And she took her duty hard—because she always said that the last thing my mother told her when she died was to raise me right."

"What did you do when you saw the switch?"

"Oh, I got all mannish, man. I said, 'Aunt Lucy, you ain't gonna whip me no more. I's a man—and you ain't gonna whip me.'

"Aunt Lucy said, 'Yes, I is too, Jess. I will whip you until you gets grown enough to know how to act like a man—not just *look* like one. You know you had no business snatching my hen right off her nest and giving it to that low-life hussy what had no better sense than to take it, knowing you ain't got nowhere to get no hen except out of *my* henhouse. Were this not Sunday, I would whale you in a inch of your life before you could get out of bed.' "

"Aunt Lucy was angry," I commented.

"She was," said Simple. "And big as I was, I was scared. But I was meaning not to let her whip me, even if I had to snatch that sapling out of her hand."

"So what happened on Monday morning?"

"Aunt Lucy waited until I got up, dressed, and washed my face. Then she called me. 'Jess!' I knowed it were whipping time. Just when I was aiming to snatch that switch out of her hand, I seed that Aunt Lucy was crying when she told me to come there. I said, 'Aunt Lucy, what you crying for?'

"She said, 'I am crying 'cause here you is a man, and don't know how to act right yet, and I done did my best to raise you so you would grow up good. I done wore out so many switches on your back, still you tries my soul. But it ain't *my* soul I'm thinking of, son, it's yourn. Jess, I wants you to carry yourself right and 'sociate with peoples what's decent and be a good boy. You understand me? I's getting too old to be using my strength like this. Here!' she hollered, 'bend over and lemme whip you one more time!' "

"Did she whip you?"

"She whipped me—because I bent," said Simple. "When I seen her crying, I would have let her kill me before I raised my hand. When she got through, I said, 'Aunt Lucy, you ain't gonna have to whip me no more. I ain't gonna give you no cause. I do not mind to be beat. But I do not *never* want to see you cry no more—so I am going to do my best to do right from now on and not try your soul. And I am sorry about that hen.'

"And you know, man, from that day to this, I have tried to behave myself. Aunt Lucy is gone to glory this morning, but if she is looking down, she knows that is true. That was my last whipping. But it wasn't the whipping that taught me what I needed to know. It was because she cried—and cried. When peoples care for you and cry for you, they can straighten out your soul. Ain't that right boy?"

"Yes," I said, "that's right."

# PHYLLIS McGINLEY

Times Three *has some lyrical comments from a young girl's point of view, praising aunts and appraising cousins.*

### "In Praise of Aunts"

OF ALL that tribe the young must do
Familial obedience to,
Whom we salute on anniversaries,
Whose names we learn while new in nurseries
Or borrow at baptismal fonts,
The soothingest are aunts.

Aunts are discreet, a little shy
By instinct. They forbear to pry
Into recesses of the spirit
Where apprehensions lie.
Yet, given a tale to hear, they *hear* it.

Aunts spinster pamper us with praise,
And seats for worldly matinées
With coffee after. Married aunts,
Attentive to material wants,
Run rather to the shared comestible,
Taboo or indigestible;
Are lenient but cool;
And let us, if we must, play fool.

Aunts carry no duty in their faces.
Their letters, mailed from far-off places,

Are merely letters meant to read
(Answerable at a moderate speed),
Not cries of need
Or vessels heavy with their hopes.
Aunts also send,
Tucked into casual envelopes,
Money entirely ours to spend.

At night they do not lie awake
Shuddering for our sorrows' sake.
Beneath our flesh we seldom wear
Their skeletons, nor need we stare
Into a looking glass and see
Their images begin to be.
Aunts care, but only mildly care,
About our winter moods,
Posture, or social attitudes,
And whether we've made a friend or dropped one.

All should have aunts, or else adopt one.

## "The Turn of the Screw"

GIRL COUSINS condescend. They wear
Earrings, and dress like fashion's sample,
Have speaking eyes and curly hair.
And parents point to their example.
But the boy cousins one's allotted
Are years too young for one. Or spotted.

# Grandmothers and Grandfathers

# JOHANNA SPYRI

⚔ ⚔

*In* Heidi, *a little girl is taken up to the Alpine meadows and entrusted to the care of her grandfather.*

## "Up To Meadow Nuncle's"

A PATH LEADS from the cheerful old market town of Mayenfeld through green and wooded fields to the very foot of the mountains whose tall slopes gaze sternly down upon the valley. The first part of this narrow trail has no great interest for the traveler, but the moment it begins to climb, the whole moor sends forth the sweet smells of its plants and grasses until the air is heavy with them. And suddenly the path strikes sharply up and goes straight to the Alps.

On one bright and sunny June morning a tall and stoutly built girl of this highland country was toiling up the road, leading a child by the hand. The cheeks of this small lassie were in such a glow that it flamed even through the deep tan of her skin. Nor was this after all so strange a thing, for, although the June sun burned hotly, the poor child was all bundled up, as if for protection from a bitter frost.

You would hardly think the little mite was more than five years old, but just what she really did look like you could never guess, because she was covered by two different dresses that anyone could plainly see. They were put on in layers, one above the other. And, to make matters worse, a big scarf of red cotton was so wound about her tiny form that she did not seem to have any shape at all as she trudged wearily along in her rough and heavy tramping shoes.

These two people had climbed some three or four miles up from the valley when they came to the group of houses which lies halfway on the long Alpine slope and which is called The Hamlet. And here they were shouted at from almost every house, now from an open window, now from a doorway or the roadside. For the highland girl had at last reached her home village. She made no stop, however, but on her way by kept calling back answers to all the questions that were asked of her. And so they came to the far end of The Hamlet and to the last of its scattering cottages. A voice hailed her—

"Oh Dete, wait a minute! If you're going farther up, I'll walk along with you."

The highland girl halted. The child who was with her quickly drew away her hand and sank down upon the ground.

"Are you so very tired, Heidi?" her companion asked.

"No-o-o, but I'm hot," the child said.

"You just wait, we'll be up there before long now. Only, you must try harder and take great big steps, and then we'll be at the top in an hour," her guide said, to encourage her.

At this moment a fat, good-natured woman stepped out of the house and joined them. The child got to her feet again and walked along behind the two older people. And these, who were old friends, began to talk at a great rate about the different people of The Hamlet and of the many other dwellings in its neighborhood.

"Say, Dete, where are you taking the youngster?" the fat woman asked. "That's the child of your dead sister, isn't it?"

"She's the one," answered Dete. "I'm going up to Nuncle's with her. And she'll have to stay with him, too."

"What's that? The child's going to live with Meadow Nuncle? You can't be in your right mind, Dete! How can you even think of such a thing? The old man will just pack you and your fine plan off home again, you'll see!"

"Oh, no, he can't do that. For, after all, he's her grandfather, and it's his business to look after her. I have been supporting the child so far. And I'll tell you one thing, Barbel—I am not going to lose such a place as I have now found for the sake of any youngster. It's time Nuncle steps in and does his share."

"Of course it is," broad Barbel agreed eagerly. "Or at least it would be if he were like other people. But you know his sort. What on earth will he do with the child, and with such a tiny one, too? She won't last it out in his house. But where is it you are planning to work?"

"In Frankfort," said Dete, "and an extra good job it is. My new employers were at the baths last summer, their rooms were on my floor, and I looked after them. They were determined to carry me off with them then, but I couldn't get away. And now they want to hire me again, and I'm going, no matter what anyone says."

"I shouldn't like to be that child," declared Barbel, with a shudder. "For nobody knows what's wrong with the old man up there. He never speaks to a living soul. From one end of the year to the other he never sets foot in the church. And when, once a season, he and his thick staff do come down to us, everybody runs away from him and is afraid. Those bushy gray eyebrows of his, and that awful beard! He looks so much like an old heathen and Indian that I can tell you you're glad not to run across him when you're alone."

"Suppose he does look queer," said Dete defiantly, "he's her grandfather just the same and has to take care of the child. He probably won't do her any harm. And if he does, *he* will have to answer for it, not I."

"And still," the prying Barbel said, "I'd awfully like to know what sin is on the old man's conscience. Why does he frown so? Why does he live up there on the mountain meadow, shut off from all the world? Why does he almost never show himself among people? They tell all sorts of stories about him, but I suppose you've heard them all from your sister, haven't you, Dete?"

"Indeed I have, but that is my business. If he found that I had been gossiping, I'd get myself into trouble."

Barbel had for ever so long been curious to know what was the matter with Meadow Nuncle. Why did he glare at people as if he hated them? Why did he live on the mountain like a hermit? Why did folks always speak of him curtly, as if they did not want to be against him and still were afraid to speak a good word for him? Barbel also thought it queer that all the people in The Hamlet should call the old man Meadow Nuncle, for of course he could not be the real uncle of every one of them. But, because they called him that, she followed their lead and never spoke of him except as Nuncle, which was the local way of saying Uncle.

Just a little while before our story opens, Barbel had married and come to The Hamlet from her girlhood's home in Prättigau, and this is why she did not yet know all the strange things that had happened in the small village and all about its odd characters and surroundings. Her friend Dete, however, had been born in

The Hamlet and had lived there with her mother until the old lady had died the year before. Then Dete had gone to work in the summer resort Ragaz as chambermaid in the great hotel there. And this morning she had come back with the child from Ragaz. They had ridden as far as Mayenfeld on a hay cart which a friend of hers was driving home, and he had been glad to give her and her little charge a lift.

Barbel was not the one to let so good a chance to learn about things slip. So she took tight hold of Dete's arm and said slyly—

"You see, dearie, one can get the truth from you about what people are saying, because of course you know the whole story. Do tell me what's wrong with the old fellow. Was he always so feared? Did he always hate everybody so?"

"How do I know how he used to be? I'm only twenty-six years old, and he is seventy at least. You can't expect me to have seen him when he was young. Still, if I knew it wouldn't be gossiped all over Prättigau afterward, I could tell you a few things, believe me! Mother was from Domleschg, you know, and so was he."

"Bah, Dete, what are you afraid of?" asked Barbel, a little offended. "Don't be so hard on the poor gossips down in Prättigau. And I guess I can keep a secret if I have to. Go on and tell me, that's a good girl! You won't be sorry for it."

"All right then, I will. But see that you keep your promise!" Dete warned her. First she turned around to make sure the child was not close enough to hear what she was going to say, but the youngster was nowhere to be seen. She must have stopped some time before this, only the two companions had been too interested in their chattering to notice the fact. Although the footpath made several windings, still one could see most of it all the way down to The Hamlet, and there was no one in sight.

"Oh, now I see her!" cried Barbel. "Look over yonder!" and she pointed far to one side of the mountain trail. "She is climbing the slope with the young goatherd Peter and his goats. I wonder why he's bringing his beasts so late today. But it's all right. He can look after the child, and you can tell me all the better about things."

"Peter won't have any trouble with her," said Dete. "She's anything but stupid for a five-year-old. She has her eyes open and sees what is going on in the world, I tell you! She'll do the old man good, for he has nothing left but his two goats and the thatch on the mountain meadow."

"He used to have more, didn't he?" asked Barbel.

"I should say he did!" answered Dete eagerly. "He owned one of the finest farms in Domleschg. He was the elder son and had only one brother, who was a quiet and steady fellow. Now, Nuncle wanted to do nothing except play the gentleman, travel around the country, and be friends with bad people whom nobody else wanted to know. He gambled and drank until the farm was all gone. And then the news came that his father and mother had died one right after the other because of their grief. And the brother, who had been made a beggar, got angry and ran away, nobody knew where. And Nuncle himself disappeared, leaving nothing but a bad name behind him."

"Where had he fled to?"

"They weren't sure. Some said he went off with the army to Naples. Anyway, nothing more was heard from him for almost fifteen years. And then suddenly he appeared, one day, with a half-grown boy, whom he tried to leave with his relatives."

"And they took the lad in, did they, Dete?" Barbel asked excitedly.

"Not they! Every door was closed against Nuncle. No one wanted to have any dealings with him. This made him very bitter. He swore he would never set foot in Domleschg again, and he came up here to The Hamlet to live with his boy. The mother must have been some Swiss girl that he had met down below and soon lost again."

"But, Dete, the old man had no money!"

"There must have still been some money left, for he had the boy Tobias learn how to be a carpenter. Tobias was a nice lad and well liked by all the people in The Hamlet, but nobody placed any trust in the father. They said he had run away from the army in Naples and that he would have been put in jail if he had not fled, because he had killed a man—not in war, of course, but in a fight. Still, we had to speak to him, since my mother's grandmother and his had been sisters. So we called him Nuncle. And, because through our father we are related to almost all the folks in The Hamlet, they called him the same. That is why, ever since he moved up to the mountain pasture, he has been known as Meadow Nuncle."

"But whatever became of Tobias?" Barbel asked curiously.

"Have a little patience and you'll hear," said Dete. "I can't tell you everything all at once. Well, Tobias was an apprentice off in Mels. And when his term was over he came home to The Hamlet and married my sister Adelheid, for they had always been fond of each other. And they got along finely after their marriage, but it did not last very long. Not more than two years later, when Tobias was helping to build a house, a beam fell on him and killed him. When they brought her husband home so badly hurt, Adelheid's grief threw her into a violent fever from which she never quite recovered. She was never very strong after that. She was so weak that often you could scarcely tell whether she was awake or sleeping. A few weeks after the death of Tobias they buried Adelheid, too."

"People must have pitied Nuncle then," said Barbel.

"Oh, no, they didn't. Far and near everyone was talking of the sad fate of the young couple. And they said as well as hinted that this was the punishment which Nuncle got because of his godless life. They told him to his face, too—the pastor had a straight talk with him about begging God for forgiveness. But Nuncle just grew more sullen and no longer had a good word for anybody. They took good care to avoid him, anyway."

"And is that why he left The Hamlet, Dete?"

"I suppose. Suddenly it was reported that Nuncle had gone up to the mountain meadow and sworn never to come down again. And since that time there he has stuck and lived at odds with God and men. Mother and I took Adelheid's child in with us; it was a year old. And when Mother died last summer, I wanted to earn my living down at the baths. So I took the child along and put her out to board at old Ursula's up in Pfäfferserdorf. It turned out that I could stay at the baths during the winter, for there was a lot of work to do, because I knew how to sew and mend."

"And you met your new employers there?"

"Yes. They came from Frankfort again, early last spring. They were the ones I had waited on the previous year and who want to take me back with them. Day after tomorrow we go. And the place is a good one, I'll tell you that."

"And you're leaving the child with the old man up there? Oh Dete, I wonder what you can be thinking of!" Barbel said in a tone of deep reproach.

"And why not?" Dete demanded. "I guess I've done my duty by the child. And what else is there left for me to do now? I surely can't take a youngster five years old to Frankfort. But—where are you going, Barbel? We're hardly halfway up to the meadow."

"I—why, I'm right where I started for," Barbel answered. "I must have a talk with Goat Peter's mother. She is to spin for me this winter. So good-by, Dete, and good luck!"

Dete gave her hand to Barbel and then stood watching her as she walked toward the small, dark brown hut which stood a few steps to one side of the trail in a hollow that protected it somewhat from the mountain winds. The hut was situated halfway up to the summit pasture, if one measured the distance from The Hamlet. And it was a good thing that it stood in a sheltered nook of the mountain side. For it did look so shaky and tumble-down that it must have been dangerous to live in it when the storm wind blew so madly across the Alps that doors and windows rattled. At such a time all the decaying timbers of the cottage trembled and creaked. If the little house had stood out on the level pasture, it would have surely been swept down into the valley far below.

In this hut dwelt Goat Peter.

This was the eleven-year-old boy who each morning went down to The Hamlet to fetch the villagers' goats. He drove them to the highland pastures, where they could graze on the short meadow grass of the slopes until evening came. Then Peter would run down the slopes again with his nimble flock, would pause at the edge of The Hamlet to whistle shrilly through his fingers, and each owner would come to the village green to get his own goat.

It was usually the small boys and girls who would be sent on this errand, for there was nothing to fear from the gentle little animals. And these short moments at sunset were the only time during the whole summer when Peter associated with his playmates. The rest of the days he spent with his goats.

To be sure, his mother and his blind grandmother lived with him at home. But as he was forced to leave the hut very early in the morning and never returned to it until late in the evening, spending, as he did, every minute possible in play with The Hamlet children, he saw but little of his home. In fact, there was just time enough to swallow his bowl of bread and milk at dawn and at dusk, and then off to his cot for sleep. His father, like himself, had been called Goat Peter, because in his childhood years he had also tended the flocks, but some years before this he had been killed by a falling tree which he was chopping down. The real name of young Peter's mother was Brigitte, but because of family associations everybody called her Goat Peter's wife, and the blind grandmother was known to old and young as just Grandmother.

Now Dete had been waiting some ten minutes or more to see if she could find the children. She had climbed a little higher to a spot where she had a better view of the downward sweep of the meadow lands, and from this new place she peered about her in every direction. She was becoming very impatient, for the youngsters were coming slowly the long way around. Peter knew many a hidden spot where there were shrubs and bushes good for his goats to nibble at, so he and his herd were taking their own time and not hurrying.

At first Heidi had tramped painfully along after Peter, for the heat made her gasp, and her heavy clothes were so uncomfortable that it took all her strength to keep up with the boy. She said nothing, but she kept eyeing the young goatherd, who with bare feet and in thin trousers was jumping about here and there without the least effort. And then she looked at the goats, whose slender legs were climbing so lightly over the thin bushes and the rocks of the steep cliffs. Suddenly Heidi sat down on the ground, peeled off her shoes and stockings quickly, pulled the thick red scarf away from her throat, and unbuttoned her little dress to wriggle hurriedly out of it.

But this, alas, was not all she had to do. There was another dress for her to unhook, because Aunty Dete, in order to make short work of dressing Heidi and to avoid an extra bundle, had drawn the child's Sunday clothes on over her everyday ones. Quick as light the old gown was off, too, and now Heidi stood dressed only in her thin underskirt and blouse and was stretching her bare arms happily forth from her short sleeves. Then she rolled her things up in a neat bundle and leaped and climbed after the goats at Peter's side, as light of foot as any in all the company.

Peter had paid no heed to what the child was doing when she had fallen behind. But later, when he saw her running along after him in her new costume, his whole face twisted into a merry grin as he turned around to look. And when he caught sight of the small heap of clothes lying down below, his grin became if possible even wider still and his mouth seemed to reach clear from one ear to the other, but he said nothing.

Now that Heidi felt so much more easy and comfortable, the two children started to talk with each other. Peter had many a question to answer, for Heidi wished to know how many goats he had, and where he was going with them, and what he was going to do when he got there. And so it was that they and the goats at last arrived at the hut and came to the sight of Aunt Dete.

The moment Dete saw this straggling company, she cried, "Heidi, whatever are you doing? My, how you do look! Where is your Sunday dress, and the other dress, and your scarf? And the brand new shoes I bought you and the new stockings I knit for you? They are gone, every one of them! What have you done with them all?"

The little girl pointed calmly down the mountain side and said, "There they are."

The aunt looked where she was pointing. Sure enough! Something was lying there, and on top of it was a red spot that must be the scarf.

"You naughty little imp!" the aunt cried in great vexation. "What got into your head, Heidi? Why did you take your things off? What do you mean by such actions?"

"I don't need them," the child said. Nor did she seem to be sorry in the least for her deed.

"You wretched, silly Heidi, where is your common sense?" her aunty went on to scold her. "Who's to go down and get them, more than a mile away? Quick, Peter, run and fetch the things for me, and don't stand there goggling as if you were stuck fast to the ground."

"I am already too late with my goats," said Peter slowly. And he stood right where he was without budging, his hands thrust into his pockets, listening with a grin to Dete's scolding.

"Just standing and staring won't get you very far in life," Aunty Dete called to him. "Come here. I've got something nice to show you."

She held out to him a penny so new that it flashed in his eyes.

Without a word Peter ran off and tore in a straight line down the hillside. He took such big jumps that he reached the pile of clothing in a short time. He seized it and appeared with it again so quickly that Dete could not help praising him and giving him the promised penny. Like a flash Peter stuck it deep in his trousers' pocket, and his face shone and was wreathed in smiles. For such a treasure did not come his way often.

"Now carry the pack to Nuncle's for me, because you're going up there anyway," Aunty Dete said.

And they made ready to climb the steep trail that rose straight upward behind the cottage of Goat Peter.

The boy did willingly as he was asked and followed his guide as she strode swiftly on ahead of him. In his left hand he clutched the bundle of clothes, in his right he swung his goat whip. Heidi and the little animals leaped gaily on by his side.

In this way, almost an hour later, the small procession arrived at the mountain meadow. Here the cabin of old Nuncle stood on a great overhanging rock, open to all the winds that blew, but also where every ray of sunshine would strike it, and with a fine view far down into the valley. Behind the hut three old fir trees towered aloft with their long, thick branches. And still farther on, in the rear of the meadow, the trail again wound its way up the mountain side until it reached the old gray cliffs. First the road crossed heights that were rich with grass and plants, then a great patch of tangled shrubs strewn everywhere with stones, until at last the trail was lost in the bald crags that stood sharply out against the sky.

Fast to the cottage on its valley side Nuncle had nailed a bench. Here he was sitting, with a pipe in his mouth and his hands on his knees, looking calmly on as the children, the goats, and Aunt Dete climbed up the path. Heidi led. She walked right up to the old gentleman, stretched out her hand, and said, "Good evening, Grandfather!"

"Well, well, and what does this mean?" Nuncle asked. He grasped the child's hand and gazed at her from under his bushy eyebrows with a long and rather fierce look. Heidi looked steadily back at him without once winking, for Grandfather, with his thick gray eyebrows that grew together in the middle, seemed somehow so strange to her that Heidi had to stare at him quite closely. In the meantime Dete arrived with Peter, who stood still for a while and waited to see what would happen.

"I wish you good day, Nuncle," said Dete, coming forward. "Here I am bringing you the child of Tobias and Adelheid. Of course you don't recognize her, because you haven't seen her since she was a year old."

"And what is the child to do in my house?" the old man asked. "As for you yonder," he called to Peter, "run along with your goats. You're none too early. Take my goats with you."

Peter disappeared at once, for Nuncle had given him a look that was all he wanted.

"Heidi's going to stay with you, Nuncle," Dete said. "I guess I've done my share for her these last four years. It's now your turn to see what you can do."

"O-ho!" said the old man, and flashed a look at Dete. "And when the child begins to whimper, as silly youngsters will, what am I going to do then?"

"That is your business," Dete said. "There was no one to tell me how to handle the child when she came to me barely a year old. And I already had my hands full looking after Mother and myself. I have my own work to go to now, and you are the child's nearest relative. If you can't keep her with you, then you must do whatever you want with her. But it's your fault if anything bad happens to her. And I guess you've got enough to answer for already in that respect."

Dete's mind was far from easy in this matter of getting rid of Heidi. That is why she grew so excited and said more than she meant to. At her last words, Nuncle rose up quickly and looked at her so that she fell back a step or two. He stretched out his arm and said fiercely—

"Go back to where you came from. And don't you show up here again!"

Dete did not wait to be told twice.

"Well, good-by then, Nuncle, and you too, Heidi," she said quickly.

And she ran all the way downhill to The Hamlet at a fast trot, for her excitement kept driving her on like a steam engine. As she passed through the village this time, she was hailed more often than before, because everyone was wondering what she had done with the child. They were all acquainted with Dete, knew who the child was, and remembered everything that had happened in the past.

But when from every door and window the questions flew, "Where is the child, Dete?" and "Where did you leave the young one?" she kept answering back ever more and more crossly—

"Up at Meadow Nuncle's. Ye-e-es! At Meadow Nuncle's, I said. You're not deaf, are you?"

The reason she was so rude was that the women on every hand were calling to her—

"Oh, how could you do such a thing!" and—

"The poor little kitten!" and—

"Leaving that helpless little midget up there!" and—

"The poor little angel!" over and over again.

Dete ran on and on as fast as ever she could, and was glad enough when she finally got out of hearing of their words. For she was not quite easy about the whole business, since her mother on her death bed had given Heidi to her to care for. But she comforted herself with the thought that she could help the child all the more now that she was earning good wages. And so she was glad to escape from anybody who argued against her act, and at last be on her way to take a good position.

## "At Grandfather's"

AFTER DETE HAD GONE, Nuncle had sat down again on the bench, and now he was blowing great clouds of smoke from his pipe, and all the time he was staring at the ground and saying never a word. Meanwhile Heidi looked about her happily. She discovered the goat shed that was built beside the cottage and peered into it. There was nothing inside.

The child continued her search and came to the old fir trees behind the hut. There the wind was blowing so hard through the branches that it whistled and roared up in the tree tops. Heidi stood still and listened. When it grew a little quieter, the child walked around the other side of the cottage and came back to her grandfather in front. As she found him still in the same position as when she had left him, she placed herself before him, put her hands behind her back, and gazed at him. The grandfather looked up.

"What do you want to do now?" he asked as the child kept standing before him without moving.

"I'm going to see what you have in the cottage," said Heidi.

"Come on, then!" And the grandfather got up and walked ahead of her into the hut. "Bring your bundle of clothes along with you," he called to her as she entered.

"I don't need them any more," Heidi explained.

The old man turned around and looked sharply at the child, whose black eyes were shining as she thought of what would be inside.

"She can't be lacking in common sense," he said half to himself. "Why don't you need your clothes any longer?" he added aloud.

"I'd soonest go like the goats. They have swift little legs."

"And you can, too, but get your things," Grandfather told her. "We'll put them in the chest."

Heidi did as she was told. The old man now opened the door, and Heidi followed him into a fairly large room which took up all the space of the cottage. There was a table, and a chair beside it.

In one corner was the bed where Grandfather slept. In another corner a great kettle hung above the fireplace. On the other side of the room there was a big door in the wall. Grandfather opened it. It led into the cupboard.

In there his clothes were hanging. On one shelf lay his shirts, his stockings, and his linen, and on another one were several plates, cups, and glasses, and on the topmost shelf a round loaf of bread, with smoked meat and cheese. Everything the Meadow Nuncle had in the world and needed for his housekeeping was in this closet. As soon as he had opened the cupboard, Heidi ran quickly up with her things and thrust them inside as far back of Grandfather's clothes as she could, so they would not be easy to find again.

Then she looked carefully around the room and said, "Where must I sleep, Grandfather?"

"Where you want to," he answered.

That just suited Heidi. She hunted in every nook and corner to see which was the best place for her to sleep. Over in the corner beyond Grandfather's couch a little ladder was standing. Heidi climbed this and came to the hayloft. There lay a fresh, sweet-smelling heap of hay, and through a round window one could look far down into the valley beneath.

"I want to sleep here," Heidi called down, "it's fine! Just come and see how nice it is here, Grandfather."

"I know well enough," came the voice from below.

"I'm making the bed now," the child called again, as she moved busily to and fro, "but you must come up and bring me a linen sheet, for there's a sheet on every bed, and that's what you lie on."

"So that's the way it is," the grandfather said below, and after a while he went to the cupboard and rummaged around a bit in it. Then he drew out from under his shirts a long coarse cloth that looked as if it might be something like a sheet. He came up the ladder with it. A very neat little bed had been made up there in the loft. At the top of it, where the head would come, the hay had been piled up high, so that one could look right through the open round window.

"That is done just right," the grandfather said. "Now comes the sheet, but wait a second"—and he snatched up a good armful of hay from the stack and made the couch twice as thick, so that the hard floor could not be felt through it—"there, now come here with the sheet."

Heidi had quickly grasped the linen sheet, but it was so heavy that she almost could not carry it. But that was a good thing, too, for then the sharp hay-straws could not stick through the firm material. Then the two of them spread the sheet over the hay, and where it was too wide or too long Heidi hastily stuffed the ends under the bed. At last it looked very trim and neat, and Heidi stood before it and looked at it thoughtfully.

"There's one thing we've forgotten, Grandfather," she said.

"What can that be?" he asked.

"A coverlet. For when you go to bed, you creep in between the sheet and the coverlet."

"Oh, you do? But what if I haven't got one?" the old man said.

"That's all right then, Grandfather," Heidi said gently. "We can take some more hay for our coverlet," and she started to go to the haymow again, but Grandfather put up his hand.

"Wait a minute," he said, climbed down the ladder, and walked over to his couch. Then he came back with a large, heavy linen sack and laid it on the floor.

"Isn't that better than hay?" he asked. Heidi tugged at the bag as hard as ever she could to unfold it, but her little hands could not master the heavy material. Grandfather helped, and when at last it was spread out on the bed everything looked quite neat.

Heidi stood admiring her new couch and said, "That is a splendid coverlet, and the whole bed is beautiful! And now I only wish it was night, so I could lie down on it."

"I think we'd better have something to eat first," said Grandfather. "Is that your idea?"

Heidi had been so excited about making the bed that she had forgotten everything else. But now that she came to think about food she at once grew very hungry, for she had had nothing except a piece of bread and a small cup of thin coffee early that morning, and since that time she had made a long journey.

So she said very heartily, "Yes, that's my idea, too."

"Go down then, since we're both agreed," said the old man, and he followed right on her heels.

Then he went to the kettle, pushed the big one aside, and drew forward the small one that hung on the chain, sat down before it on the three-legged wooden stool with the round seat, and blew the fire into flames. The water in the kettle began to boil, and below it the old man held a large piece of cheese on the end of a long iron fork over the fire, turning it this way and that until it was as yellow as gold on every side. All this Heidi had watched eagerly.

Suddenly a new thought had come into her mind, for she ran off to the cupboard and kept going back and forth. Then Grandfather brought the teapot and the toasted cheese to the table, and it was already neatly set with the round loaf of bread on it, and two plates and two knives, for Heidi had quickly found where everything was in the closet and knew that it would all be needed right away for the meal.

"That's nice that you think things out for yourself," said the grandfather as he laid the cheese down on the bread, "but there's something still lacking from the table."

Heidi saw how invitingly the steam was coming out of the teapot and ran quickly back to the cupboard. But there was only a single small bowl to be seen. Heidi was not at a loss for long, as two glasses were standing right behind it. The child came back at once and set the bowl and a glass on the table.

"That's the way, you know how to help yourself. But where are you going to sit?"

Grandfather was himself sitting on the only chair. Heidi ran straight as an arrow to the fireplace, brought back the little three-legged stool, and sat down on it.

"Well, there's a seat for you at any rate," the grandfather said, "only it's down a good way. But my chair would be too short for you to reach the table, too. And now you must have something to eat, so come ahead!"

Thereupon he got up, filled the small bowl with milk, set it on the chair, and drew this quite close to the stool, so that Heidi now had a table before her. Grandfather laid a big slice of bread and a piece of the golden cheese on the chair and said, "Eat away!"

He sat down on a corner of the table and began his own noonday meal. Heidi seized her bowl and drank and drank without stopping, for all the thirst from her long journey had returned to her. Then she drew a long breath—for she had been drinking so hard she couldn't breathe for a long time—and set down her bowl.

"Do you like the milk?" Grandfather asked.

"I never drank such good milk in all my life," Heidi answered.

"Then you must take some more."

And Grandfather filled the bowl to the very top again and placed it before the child, who was eating happily away at her bread after this had been spread with the soft cheese. For the cheese had been toasted until it was as soft as butter, and it tasted very good indeed. She took frequent sips of milk and seemed quite gay.

When the meal was ended, Grandfather went out to the goat shed and was busy putting it in order, and Heidi watched carefully as he first swept it out with a broom and then scattered fresh straw for the animals to sleep on. She followed him later into the shop next door, where he cut round sticks and shaped up a board. He bored holes in it, put in the round sticks, and set it up, and there was suddenly a chair like Grandfather's, only much higher. Heidi stared at the thing, speechless with wonder.

"What is that, Heidi?" her grandfather asked.

"That's my chair, because it's so high—you did it like lightning," said the child, not yet able to get over her surprise.

"She knows what things are. Her eyes are in the right place," her grandfather muttered to himself as he walked around the cottage and drove a nail here and there. Then he fixed something about the door and wandered from one place to another with hammer and nails and pieces of wood, patching or knocking things off, just as seemed best. Heidi followed his every step, watching him closely, and everything he did seemed to amuse her.

Thus the evening drew near. There was a louder rustling in the old fir trees, and a mighty wind came along and whistled and roared in the thick tree tops. It sounded so beautiful in Heidi's ears that it made her very happy. She hopped and danced about outside under the firs as if some strange joy had come to her.

Grandfather stood in the doorway of the shop and watched her play.

And then a shrill whistle was heard. Heidi put a stop to her jumping. Grandfather stepped outside. Down from above, goat after goat came leaping, like a pack of hunters, and Peter in their midst. With a cry of joy, Heidi rushed into the midst of the flock and, one after another, greeted her friends of the morning.

When the flock reached the hut, they all came to a halt, and two fine, slender goats, one white and one brown, came up to Grandfather and licked his hands, for he had some salt in them to welcome them with, as he did every evening. Peter disappeared with his troop. Heidi stroked gently first one goat and then the other, running around to pat them on the other side. She was quite mad about the small creatures.

"Are they ours, Grandfather? Are they both ours? Do they go into the shed? Are they to stay with us always?"

Heidi asked one question after another in her excitement, so that Grandfather could hardly get a word in edgewise. "Yes, yes, yes," he said. And when the goats had licked up all their salt, he added, "Go and bring out your bowl and the bread."

Heidi did as she was told and came right back. Then Grandfather milked the white goat and filled the little bowl with its milk, and cut off a slice of bread.

"Now eat your supper," he said, "and then run off to bed. Your Aunty Dete left a bundle for you—there are some nightgowns and other things in it. You'll find it downstairs in the chest when you need it. I must go and see to the goats now, so sleep well!"

"Good night, Grandfather. Good night—oh, what are their names, Grandfather? What do you call them?" the child cried as she ran after the old man and the goats, who were disappearing into the shed.

"The white one's name is Little Swan, the brown one is called Little Bear," Grandfather answered.

"Good night, Schwänli, good night, Bärli!" Heidi called with all her might, because they were just vanishing into the stable. Then she settled down on the bench and ate her bread and drank her milk, although the wind was so strong that it almost blew her from her seat. So she finished as fast as she could, and went in to climb up to bed. And she went right off to sleep and slept as soundly as if she were lying on the most beautiful bed of some princess.

Not long afterward, before it was yet wholly dark, Grandfather, too, lay down upon his couch, for he was always up with the sun mornings, and it peered over the mountain top very early in the summer time. During the night the wind blew with such force that it made the whole cottage tremble, and all the beams were creaking. It howled and groaned in the chimney like the voice of one in pain. And outside in the fir trees it raged so terribly that here and there a branch was broken off.

In the middle of the night Grandfather got out of bed and said to himself softly, "She is probably scared."

So he climbed up the ladder and went to Heidi's side. Out of doors the moon was shining brightly just then, but a moment later it hid again behind the driving clouds and all was dark. Then the moonlight shone a second time clearly through the round opening and fell right on Heidi's bed. Her cheeks were as red as fire from sleeping under the heavy coverlet. She lay quite peaceful and still on one round little arm and was dreaming of something pleasant, for a look of happiness was on her small face. Grandfather stood a long time to gaze at the gently sleeping child, until the moon again went behind a cloud and it was dark.

Then he returned to his own couch.

# GLENWAY WESCOTT

※ ※

*A longer view of life—and death—can be given by
grandparents than any other relatives. But* The Grandmothers *shows that no age is a guarantee against heart-
break.*

FOR ALWYN the cemetery at Hope's Corner took the place of a city child's park. In certain evergreens there were sparrows' nests which resembled untidy blond wigs; butcher birds lived in a cedar, and once or twice he found a dead mouse which they had hung on the thorn of a honey locust or a hawthorn. Old-fashioned roses, lying smothered in the grass, pricked his ankles. Lilies of the valley spread in a light green blanket, so that the graves on which they had been planted seemed to grow larger year by year. The headstone of a girl with a lovely name, Drusilla John, had fallen down; the coffin had collapsed, hollowing the sod above it; and Alwyn sat there by the hour, his legs under the marble slab as if it were a table, reading his favorite books, writing letters to his only friend.

The lots of his relatives were well kept, in proportion to the degree of kinship. The original families, with the single exception of his own, having left the community, the rest of the graveyard was a thicket of weeds, lilies, bushes, roses, and birds' nests; the conquered wilderness had reasserted itself, in miniature, over the conquerors' bodies.

Alwyn's grandmother said, "The neglect of the graveyard is a shame to the present generation," and held herself responsible for its general upkeep. So in the autumn she drove about the country in search of a man not too busy with the harvest to mow it, offering to pay him well, even willing to have the work done on the Sabbath. As the community filled up with German Catholic immigrants who bought the farms of the old settlers, she made it her business to see that the latter were not forgotten; as one of a proud, subjugated race would try to teach the history of the land and the names of its heroes to ignorant invaders. Eleven Civil War veterans, including her husband, were buried at Hope's Corner; and every year she persuaded the teacher of the school across the road to arrange a Decoration Day program of recitations and old songs. She took bands of children to the woods to make wreaths and bouquets, and attended the exercises, shepherding the scholars from grave to grave, speaking to those who showed a little rever-ence, often laughed at by those who had been badly brought up.

These were the dead of a great period of the nation's history, eleven heroes; she honored their graves as a lesson to the living. Her own departed ones—she scarcely knew where some of them were buried, and it did not matter. She never thought of them as asleep under blocks of marble and granite and drooping bunches of trilliums, mandrake blossoms, and anemones. They were awake somewhere, doing their duty, whatever it was, nobly, invisibly. . . . Probably they had forgotten her—life was remembrance, so death must be forgetfulness; but she could not forget them for a minute. Left alone at last amid the scenes of their youth, she clasped her souvenirs to her breast, and yearned for all the dead as a mother yearns for children who are living, but no longer children.

She scarcely differentiated between absence and death. She was not likely to see again with living eyes those who were the breadth of America away—each year one or more was added to their number. The others, the dead, were separated from her only by the fact that she herself was still alive. At her age all good-bys were alike.

But according to her faith the phases of the moon took place above their heads, the absent and the dead alike. When the new moon appeared, other old men and women prophesied the weather according to an Indian tradition: a warm, dry spell if the two horns pointed to the sky, rain if the crescent, like a dipper, seemed to spill water on the earth. But she was indifferent to the weather; for her that slight heavenly body swung like a lantern above the house, above the old farm, high enough to be seen from every State in the Union and every foreign land, high enough to be visible even to those who had crossed the boundaries of the world.

So once a month she walked under the cherry trees in the dusk, startling the white pullets and cockerels which burdened the branches. She lifted her eyes to the lovely sickle, sharpened almost out of sight by the luster which continued to rise over the hills from the sun; and wiped away her unwelcome tears with a corner of her apron.

Then she would say to her grandson, who, believing that she was lonely, followed her: "You know, I always think of those who are dear to me when there is a new moon. It is my custom. The same moon shines on them all, the same new moon." In spite of her tears she spoke firmly, indeed contentedly.

But when her daughter Flora died in 1914, this fortitude came to an end, and serenity gave way to despair. Death was acceptable twice during life: before it began in earnest, and after it was over.

Little children died—death deprived them of nothing; their mothers were strong and could bear it. Those who were old belonged to death, as if by contract; she was willing that nature should take its course. But the death of a lovely, unmarried girl was intolerable and against nature. She herself should have been allowed to go instead; life had had its way with her for more than half a century; she could have said Amen.

Hitherto, time had been given her in which to recover, to develop new habits and enjoy new hopes. Now it was too late; she would not live to see the end of this anguish; she could never begin again. She had always accepted things as they were; having protested, she had folded her arms and given in; but her will would never be at peace with the Will which had determined Flora's death. There was nothing to do but leave the world, unreconciled, and, because of the insubordination of her heart, half ashamed.

She had been proud of her life, the masterpiece of the divine Hand which had guided her hand, a vast and somber picture. The gesture which had drawn certain lines had hurt her; certain colors had been her life's blood; but looking back she had been able to view the result without much pain and with approbation. Now the giant Hand, with a final stroke, with the stain of a final wound, had spoiled their work.

In the past it had seemed natural for those who had the same sorrows to weep together. Now she could not bear to be seen weeping, apparently ashamed; it was not her fault—but those who have been strong, when they are crippled, want to hide their deformities. She would say to the children, "I can't have you here now; run off and play," and sit alone by the window, weeping without covering her face, her cheeks red and shining with the continual tears, her worn-out eyelids fluttering, her lips moving as she repeated to herself the fact that her last-born child was dead.

When she had been happy she had been able to endure the thought of all her former griefs. Now these wounds, suffered and healed long ago, burned with sympathetic pain; and the story of her life, the whole history of the family, seemed unmentionably sad. If young people realized how life ended, they would not want to live; so she would hide her despair and say nothing. Therefore, during the last years, she said very little about Leander, or her husband, or their close relatives, or her sons. Instead she drew near to those who had never been near her heart, and preferred to talk about them.

Accompanied by her grandson, she made a round of afternoon visits to old men and women whom she had known indifferently for years, who had never been more than neighbors. Before them she could pose as a wise woman, strong enough to endure the afflictions which God in His violence had imposed. Distracted by their weaknesses, she could ignore for a few hours her own weakness and dismay. She defended herself from their questions with a hard good nature—the humor of her rude ancestors, hunters and soldiers and vagabonds, masking her heart and hiding the wreckage which death had left in it at last.

She talked to her grandson with a startling sardonic gayety about these people and others like them who were dead: relatives whom she had happened not to love, his grandfather's friends, the friends of her friends. The disastrous comedies of their lives diverted her from the grief which was all that was left of hers; she could be as brave about their troubles as she had once been about her own. She dwelt without pity on their paradoxical characters, their avowals and frauds, their astonishing whims and failures; and at Alwyn's request identified among her photographs many of their faces.

There were two albums of embossed leather studded with buttons which resembled shoe buttons, and one with celluloid roses glued upon a velvet binding. There were daguerreotypes in cases closed by a metal clasp or a loop of worn cord, which Alwyn opened and tried to read as if they were a library of miniature books. At the left a leaf of red satin, at the right in a mat of beaded gilt the portraits: heads and busts and family groups, pygmy men and women as if seen through a telescope—the men in a daydream, the women anxious about their children, their lovers, their clothes. Mouths like bits of carved wax, nostrils of an insatiable arrogance; eyes long closed in death—or the young, suspicious eyes of men and women who were now old and patted Alwyn's head and peered at him dimly and beneficently—staring out of the picture frames as if he were an enemy in disguise.

. . . The lifeless light (in which innumerable photographers had covered their heads with large, black handkerchiefs and imitated a bird with their hands) half hid and half revealed all the possible combinations of all the motives there were—greed and sensuality and courage and compassion and cruelty and nostalgia; all the destinies there were—manias, consolations, regrets.

The same motives and similar destinies existed still; but these people whose playground they had been were gone. Nothing came back from the oblivion into which they had vanished (for old age and death were equally oblivion) not a sound came back but a little slightly exultant, unhappy laughter—Alwyn's grandmother laughing for them.

He listened to her comments—old-fashioned maxims, scraps of tragi-comic narrative, implicitly mocking, explicitly compassionate —and what she told revealed little more than the photograph albums themselves: another set of pictures, photographs of actions and opinions, also noncommittal and badly focused. But he knew what she knew and tried to forget: that each picture was a tomb where a dead heart (or merely the youth and freshness of a heart which was now old) lay buried—buried with its affections, its apathy, its fury. He knew that on each insignificant grave there stood (though he could only guess what it was) a secret like hers, wild and perfect as a wild flower, nodding in its everlasting leaves, or dangling from a broken stem. . . .

# BERTHA DAMON

*An especially individualistic grandmother appears in* Grandma Called It Carnal.

AFTER THE FUNERAL the house was empty of all but a few relatives, and they had stopped dabbing their eyes with handkerchiefs, and sympathizing out loud. There was a strange hot supper I didn't care for. It seemed to be settled by everyone that Mama's family, Grandma Griswold and Aunt Martha, would take us two children, for a while, anyway.

So Alice and I went to the small town of North Stonefield, Connecticut, and to Grandma's house. The family consisted of Grandma, her unmarried daughter Aunt Martha, Alice, and me. Aunt Martha did most of the work, but she was so overshadowed by Grandma's stronger will and keener interests, that it always seemed to be Grandma who brought us up.

It was not a light matter to be brought up by Grandma. Not for her and not for us. Alice and I were about six and five when it began, and Grandma was getting on toward seventy. The bringing-up went on for nine years, and those nine years made a deeper impression on all three of us than any other period in our lives. For better, for worse, we none of us ever got over it.

I used to look at Grandma and feel sorry for her that she had it to do. It was not that she was getting too old to bring up children: Grandma never seemed old. It was not that she had practically nothing to live on: Grandma was superior to popular delusions as to what were material necessities. But her life was so important to her, so filled with the somewhat unusual satisfactions she valued. For achieving and enjoying these satisfactions time was all Grandma Griswold needed. We two children used up or spoiled a lot of that.

I ought to have felt sorry for Aunt Martha. The real brunt, the practical thing, fell on her, as it always had. Whether or not Boston was the Athens of America, in at least one respect New England must be like Greece. The fairest flowers of Hellenic civilization bloomed in the soil of slavery and the subjection of women. Such has been the basis of considerable of our own culture. Many a seeming leisure-class parent—the distinguished father, the celebrated mother—has been made so by the self-sacrifice, the obscure hard domestic toil of some daughter over whose unfulfilled life the gray years passed.

Grandma gave the impression of leisure and of a sort of austere spiritual superiority. She had early decided, with Thoreau, not merely "to hear and tell the news, to bring wood and water, to count how many eggs the hens lay" but to see what it was she would be after; to be "unanimous"; in all the labyrinth to lead a *thread* of life. It was Martha who had to go round and round in the domestic labyrinth. Since the day when Martha in her eighteenth year had come back from her first term in boarding school and had seen how small and frail her mother looked and had thought her mother's years were surely few and that it was her duty to make these easy, since that day whatever work there was to do Martha had stayed at home and done.

Grandma never did any of the ordinary cooking. She would pare the apples and potatoes, sitting by the fire in winter or in the garden in summer, holding them in her oval hands and making them into shapely sculptured spheroids with no harsh angles; and she would make the "injun porridge"—as our neighbors called it. To make "injun porridge" perfectly—a very little "injun" meal boiled a very long while in a vast amount of water till all was of the consistency of whipped cream—was an art, and Grandma would undertake this herself, not trusting it to Aunt Martha. She would use only corn meal ground by the Bower brothers in their old-fashioned grist mill, ground between great stone wheels run by water power. She said, and she was right, that such meal had a consistency and a flavor that "store" meal from Deacon Parker's General Store lacked. Into the salted, violently bubbling water, she would patiently drop invisible pinches of the meal from her thumb and finger. So good was her method that this "injun porridge" never had to be stirred until at the very end, and never had any lumps. Long after the last grain of mealy powder had dropped from her hand the boiling continued gently. The entire process took at least two hours. And Grandma always had to be read aloud to all the time she was making "injun porridge."

Grandma never sewed anything. She knit: sometimes a mitten or perhaps a stocking, but preferably fine thread edging, for presents and as an aid to enduring the sometimes tedious conversations of her callers.

Aunt Martha had given up several good "chances" (is there a cynical wisdom in that word of ours for marriage?), given them up first, because she felt her mother needed her at home, and second, because her mother had always been unable to see that the man who wanted Martha was worthy of her, and had so advised her.

By the time we orphan nieces came along, Aunt Martha had turned thirty. She began to look what is called—at that age—tired most of the time. Already she was getting a few gray hairs, which she pulled out thoroughly. She still did her hair up in curlpapers every night, and when she trimmed her hats she contrived to give to the loop of a ribbon, coquetry and to the slant of a feather, appeal. The class she chose to teach in Sunday school was one of young men. Sometimes, though Aunt Martha no longer had a steady beau, a man would walk home with her from church Sunday night and would be invited to sit apart from the rest of us in the parlor with Aunt Martha, who, even to our childish eyes, was suppressing a sort of flutter.

To Aunt Martha the bringing-up duty was most unwelcome. And we children knew it. Why should she like us? There was all that extra work to do. Besides she had her reservations about Mama—that sister who had graduated from normal school, and she had not; married, and she had not; had two children, and she had not; and who, having done and had so much, had finally achieved the freedom and the lasting distinction of death. There Aunt Martha was, left to go on taking care of us two young residual burdens. It is tragic that some gifts have to be made so costly, so damaging to the giver that there remains no small part of the giver to go with the gift, which must therefore remain bare. Poor Aunt Martha!

For us children Aunt Martha, in New England parlance, worked her fingers to the bone. In general I did not feel grateful. I remember just once when I had been crying from loneliness, I ventured to get up into Aunt Martha's lap and bury my face in her shoulder. She did not say a word but she did not put me down, and for that I felt grateful. I think, free from insistences, I might have felt from time to time that much-demanded emotion. But little seedlings never flourish in the soil they have been given, be it ever so excellent, if they are continually pulled up to see if the roots are grateful yet.

Though something kept Grandma from speaking as if she loved

us, I knew, somehow, she did. Children, we reminded her of her own two little girls who had died so many years before. And we were children of the daughter who had grown up to be congenial, witty, and, in spite of housework and two little children, a writer of stories Mr. Samuel Bowles had printed in his *Springfield Republican*. Always her mother's secret pride, she was valued more than ever now she was gone. Yet Grandma could not, any more than Aunt Martha, ever say right out that she had loved our mother.

Sometimes it seemed to ease Grandma to speak of her, and never as if she was dead—only of how she used to be when she was a little girl. Every June fifteenth as long as Grandma lived, she used to fill the house with flowers, to get up extra early on Ethel's birthday to go out into the gray, half-awake garden to gather more flowers than she ever picked other times, and then to place them, dewy and not quite opened, upstairs and down as if there were going to be a party.

And Grandma besides being fond of us, was interesting. She was interesting even to look at. Grandma's manner, though I cannot imagine where in her environment she could have found example, was dignified and yet gracious; even when she was brushing the hearth or leading Juno the cow around the flower beds she somehow looked distinguished.

Though she was not tall, she seemed so; her slender body was remarkably straight, with never a drooping shoulder; and when she sat down, she never crossed her knees nor even her ankles. "In my youth young ladies were taught that crossing the limbs is immodest," she would say.

Her face was old, but it kept charm and power. Grandma's was one of those full-looking heads with the high brow that you see in the portraits of intellectual women of the early nineteenth century —somehow vanished now along with the strong oratorical mouth the public men wore. Her gentle brown eyes were wide apart, like a deer's; her nose straight and delicate; her jaw and chin, in spite of her persistence in doing without "modern" teeth, forceful-looking.

Almost always she wore a plain old black dress, basque button-ing down the front, white fichu at neck, white apron with knit edging, and shoes uncommonly common-sense. Despite her ideal in shoes her feet looked slender. She walked like an Indian, toes not turned out, easy, lithe. Her hands were long and beautiful, used with unconscious but remarkable grace. I remember watching her wind yarn; she made it seem an accomplishment, elegant as playing the harp.

It was with real anticipation and relish that you came into the room that held Grandma, and sat down on your little stool and folded your hands around your knees. For pretty soon Grandma would drop some remark—perhaps a very wilful remark—and begin opening up her mind.

Just the same, I used to feel a little sorry for Alice and me then. We were like little plants that manage to maintain a foothold in a crannied wall, or like Arizona birds who must make their nests in a high cactus, not that it isn't prickly but that there is no other safety to be chosen. However interesting it was to live with Grandma, it was not easy.

Grandma Griswold was—well, what her neighbors called "different." Grandma purposed to be different in more ways than one, and, for her, differentness began at home. The amazing thing about Grandma's housekeeping was that, even to the close of the first quarter of the twentieth century, every utensil, every way of doing, was just as purely eighteenth century as Grandma could manage to keep it. She was ninety-six when she died in 1925, and throughout her life—almost a century long—Grandma held back "modern improvements"—you could hear the ironical quotation marks she always spoke into the phrase—from contaminating her home.

For her departed parents Grandma had an almost Chinese reverence. She must often have heard them regretting, living as they did in the early phases of the Industrial Revolution, that the good old days had passed and were passing, heard them prophesying that the newfangled ways would bring only evil, moral and material, to those who took up with them. She had seen her parents clinging to the old ways, unshaken in their belief that in doing things by hand and slowly there was virtue. As they had lived, she resolved she would live, and her household with her. All her life she was willing to go to any amount of trouble herself and even more to put others to it, in order to preserve the ways of her childhood and that of her mother.

That wasn't all. Grandma would persist in reading John Ruskin. I drew a "Picker of Granma" once, and the picker showed that instead of a hand Grandma's right arm had sprouted a large volume labeled *John Ruskin*. There must have been a long period previous to my coming to live with her when such a volume seemed one of her members. Ruskin's bitter hatred of increasing mechanization Grandma heartily shared, and his nostalgia for the old romantic past when life was better.

Grandma was forever quoting such perverse Ruskinisms as this:

> By hand-labour, therefore, and by that alone, we are to till the ground. By hand-labour also to plough the sea; both for food, and in commerce, and in war; not with floating kettles there neither, but with hempen bridle, and the winds of heaven in harness.

And she was forever trying to carry these out. She could devise no way of employing the hempen bridle whose passing Ruskin deplored, but to restoring the ideal past in her housekeeping she dedicated herself with all her mind and all her strength. She was especially determined to hold modern inventions at bay. She set herself against the deplorable American tendency to act as if happiness and efficiency are increased by mechanical possessions. Quite early almost every woman in North Stonefield had got herself an eggbeater, and a great many were buying sewing machines. Grandma would have none of such devices. When, later, the automobile came along, Grandma always tried to stand in the way of it, literally and figuratively.

Ruskin would probably have approved the way she heated her house—if that phrase is not too ironic—through the Connecticut winters. "Airtight stoves," she used to say, "are another of those diabolical modern inventions. Iron when heated gives off a poisonous gas injurious to health." So the health of her children and later of us two grandchildren was strictly preserved by fireplace heat only, downstairs or up. And to have any heat upstairs you first had to be ill—from some other cause than modern heat.

A slight concession to modernity was embodied, in the parlor, in the shape of a tall oblong soapstone stove with the gloomy dignity of a mausoleum. Such a stove she countenanced because, being of soapstone, it could be relied upon never to give off poisonous gas or anything, least of all heat. However, only on state occasions was fire lighted in it, when it generated an inner warmth which it kept to itself and brooded over. I never saw that stove too hot to sit on.

Grandma, though distrusting the innovations, the inventions of others, was strong for her own. Grandma's life being extremely necessitous, the flock of inventions, makeshifts, and contraptions her fertile mind hatched was countless. To conserve the all too frugal heat from the soapstone stove she devised a quaint way of setting it against the wall farthest from the chimney and having the stovepipe go all across the room close to the ceiling; unhappily green wood caused sap to collect in the pipe and drip, so Grandma kept several pails hung up along the pipe, for all the world as on a maple tree in sugaring-off time. Once, when a tall elegant guest was shaking hands good-by with Grandma, just as he bowed gallantly, he hit a pail, and down it came, and all in a second the elegance and dignity of the scene vanished; black sooty sap hit the ceiling, the walls, the floor, the faces—it was in a splash, like the devastation in Kundry's garden when the spell was broken.

But Grandma's open fires! Nowadays fireplace fires seem commercial, without rich background. Then it was thrilling to know that all the wood in the hearthfires that kept us—well, not warm but focused, was a part of Grandma and the family, so to speak. It had all grown in our ancestral wood lot. History was in its flames; memory of spring walks there with Grandma when, under the rustling oak leaves that were scarcely changed by a winter's freezings, the early hepaticas, indescribably blue, stem and calyx wrapped in silvery pussy fur, curled among their three-lobed leaves; and trailing arbutus (so frail you scarcely dared speak) nestled on the south side of a stone, with perhaps a snowbank on the other side, and smelled of woods-earth and honey. Once when little Alice found the first arbutus, she just looked up solemnly and said, "It has happened." In those lighted logs, too, were memories of the wood-lot brook in spring freshet, swirling on the mossy brinkstones and wetting the skunk cabbage and the new ferns coiled like bishops' croziers in the picture books, and of black turtles with bright yellow well-spaced freckles hurrying along with the expressive haste a turtle can show. Memories too of winter walks when the architecture of the trees could be enjoyed, and each tint of rose or gray-violet in twigs was precious to the eye. In every open fire we read such history.

There was technique, too, efficient, orderly, beautiful. Who now understands the essential "building" of firewood in a fireplace? Who knows, for instance, that a backlog is not meant to burn; that it is to last, its object being to fill in the back of the fireplace to prevent cold air from the chimney settling and driving smoke into the room, and also to thrust forward the other wood so that heat will be driven outward? Therefore a backlog, green and huge, was placed not on the andirons, for that would make a draft and help the log to burn, but flat on the ashes well against the chimney back. On top of this basic log another green log, somewhat smaller, was piled.

Next to be laid in its place well to the front, on the andirons, was the forestick. This, too, must not burn quickly, as its purpose was to hold the burning fuel in place. But the lastingness of the forestick must depend not on its greenness, for green wood smokes. The forestick was selected for hardness, then; hornbeam or "ironwood" was best.

In between backlogs and forestick the combustible wood was piled, any sort, so that it was well cured and not snappy. Chestnut was snappy and, if any accidentally appeared, was snatched out. The hearth must have been brushed a hundred times a day with Grandma's turkey wing. "A clean hearth is a clean room," she used to say.

Cooking, what there was of it, was done in iron pots on a crane over the open fire, or in "bake-kettles," large heavy iron pots with iron covers, that sat on the hearth and, when functioning, were pushed nearer the fire and also had coals of fire heaped on their heads. Great-grandmother's baking had, of course, been done in the big brick oven built in the chimney, its hinged iron door almost opposite the low mantel; but Grandma admitted that her mother had been too good a cook and had perhaps allowed the sin of eating for pleasure to creep into the family life. So Grandma didn't let any baking be done except in this hearth arrangement which she knew could be relied upon not to tempt any cook into overelaborateness. A great deal of the time it was occupied with baked beans—not Boston style, but Connecticut—baked till the "innards" were a fine adhesive mass and there was a good brown crackly crust on top. A hunk of this durable comestible could indeed be hidden under one's pillow for night emergency. Once in a great while Grandma allowed Aunt Martha to bake in the stove which stood on sufferance in the lean-to, but very rarely. Grandma's mother had cooked only in fireplaces; that was best.

Gas and electricity had of course not yet traveled so far as to our small remote village. Kerosene lamps, however, had arrived, but not in Grandma's household. Tallow candles for every common night, wax for company. On every mantelpiece stood a vase filled with "lamplighters." These were cunningly twisted papers (no envelope fell to the floor that Grandma did not take notice of it), the making of which was one of the daily stints for us children. Even if matches had not been a "modern invention containing sulphur injurious to health," I doubt if Grandma would have allowed them to supplant devices so conducive to thrift and to discipline as were those twisted papers. A lot of them were required, for if too tight, they wouldn't light; if too loose, they burned up before you could get anywhere. They were misnamed lamplighters, for they ministered only to candles and open fires. All winter Grandma could boast that no match was harbored in her house, for the coals in the fireplace were never allowed to die out. In the summer she had to capitulate and use one match, but only one, to an evening. Her mother's flint she must have lost, or she would have used that.

As for plumbing, now that I come to think of it, though all our folk seemed reasonably civilized and clean—almost all—there probably was not a bathroom in any house in our village. (Despise us, but despise also the young Abraham Lincoln and Queen Guinevere, young and old.) There were, however, kitchen sinks; there were pumps. But not for us. The old romantic way, when the world was far better, had been to draw water for all household purposes from an outside well and to carry it out again in pails. So draw and carry water we did. As Arnold Bennett has said of similar arrangements in his youth in England, "Godliness was child's play compared with cleanliness in that house."

Under Grandma's administration a bath was no fillip to begin the day on. It was a stern duty, an almost impossible achievement, the final hardship of a week of hardships.

First, the water must be drawn from the old well, sixty feet from the kitchen door and twenty feet deep. Grandma's husband had, in his brief career as a husband, put in so modern an improvement as a wheel and chain above the well, but as soon as Grandma could have her way, she had removed that enervating device and reinstalled the old well sweep. "Old ways are best," she said, "and also a well sweep is far more picturesque." It is. Besides, Grandma never drew water. Often she used to look down her deep well, admire the dripping green mosses that grew on its old stones, and identify botanically the five kinds of fern that flourished there; but she stopped at that.

Full five months of the year it was winter. The snow had to be shoveled from the path, and the ice in the bucket broken out while iron chain froze to mittens. Down, between the walls hung with icicles, the heavy bucket sank till the tiptop of the wooden pole, usually way up in the sky with the shivering Lombardy poplars, was under your straining hand. After floating obstinately on the dark water, the bucket gradually sank and filled. Then you could release the pole and with quick upward grasps of the chain, help the heavy counterweight at the far base of the sweep to raise the oak bucket in its jerky dripping ascent. The precious water must be tipped out through the well spout into the wooden "house pail" and carried into the kitchen. This water-drawing you repeated as many times as the size of your bath might require. I do not get as much sentimental pleasure as others profess from a song called "The Old Oaken Bucket."

Next, all these pails of water must be emptied into great iron kettles and hung on the iron crane to heat. The fire will need replenishing. Out the back door, around the corner of the house, down the flag walk to the side gate, and across the road, is the woodpile. It is where it is because there it is handy for men folks to dump loads of wood direct from the cart when they are hauling it once a year. Saves them and the horse. Of course, it is most unhandy for women folks to fetch from, several times a day, but unhandiness for women folks never influenced the layout of country barns or houses.

Grandma had her best callers trained to stop by the woodpile and bring in an armful of wood as they came. This scheme often relieved them from the necessity of rapping on the door; when they attempted that, the sticks fell down and made such a clatter even on the windiest nights, that it was heard inside, and the callers were let in just as promptly as if they had succeeded in rapping.

For this wintry bath probably the snow had to be swept off the wood with an old broom, and the logs, frozen together, whacked hard with a heavy stick. You made as many trips with arms full of wood as might meet your caloric requirements.

"Bring in some for tomorrow morning," Aunt Martha would say, putting her head, wrapped in an old red crocheted cape, out the sitting-room door into the freezing back entry. "You should learn to look ahead."

That was a way Aunt Martha had, of handing out maxims while you were on the run, of getting a little assistance from you by surprise. She was forced into this because though she tried to get help in the housework from Alice and me, often the help didn't last long or come to much because Grandma would interrupt with some plan of her own for our time—and Grandma's plans in her own and everyone else's mind always had the right of way. Aunt Martha was left to finish the dishes or make the beds because Grandma needed a child to go to walk with her or to read to her some improving book.

Next, a room in which to bathe apart from the family must be warmed. More wood brought in for the fireplace there. Then must be assembled the big tin bathtub in the form of a pear-shaped coffin, towels, a mat, and homemade soap maintaining through strong sassafras overtones a dominant odor of household grease. Finally, the big iron kettles of hot water are lugged in and poured into the tub; the door is shut tight; the moment has come. Make of it what luxury you may before the water gets cold and your emergency fire goes out.

But your bath is not over; do not think it. All this soapy water must be emptied into pails, carried outdoors and emptied again. Then for a week all you have to do is to anticipate the next bath holiday or, if you prefer, six days' holiday from baths.

Do not misjudge us. In spite of all, we never skipped our baths, when and if we regarded them as due. We had New England character; perhaps taking baths was one way in which we acquired and expressed it.

Our bedgoing on winter nights when you could hear the ice on Cheney's Pond cracking like thunder and the snow lay drifted on our windowpanes, might have seemed picturesque to Ruskin. Along toward nine o'clock the first line of offense against the frigidity of the upstairs chambers was brought into action. From a closet near the fireplace were mobilized many slabs of soapstone and marshaled in the hot ashes; also tall narrow jugs, each with a little handle like an ear above its shoulder. Some said these jugs had been used for rum, but that would have been long before they came into Grandma's possession. Many families displayed them as parlor ornaments, gilded and tied with a bow of ribbon; ours had a use more serious. So the black iron teakettle was filled with water from one of the wooden water pails and hung on the crane over the blaze.

The bedtime curfew was never disregarded. The loud ringing of the "nine o'clock bell" in Thomson's old shop, long a town monitor, caused us to look up and wait for a somewhat uncertain confirmation of the hour by our funny old mantel clock with the pointed Gothic towers. Then Grandma rose. Cloths were wrapped around the heated soapstones; boiling water was poured into the jugs; corks were resolutely jammed down their necks, and pieces of old kid glove tied over the corks.

In spite of all these precautions, employing those jugs as bedfellows was what life insurance companies term "extra-hazardous occupation." Oft in the stilly night ere—or more often after—slumber's chain had bound you, a cork would creep out, adding to the danger of frost that of flood. These warm jug companions were specially prized by single sleepers—they who must embark alone in the frozen deeps of our spare beds. I well remember one of our guests who had an affair with one of these jugs. She came down in the morning and hung up her wrung-out cotton-flannel nightgown over a chair by the kitchen fireplace. But there was a bright, interested expression on her spinsterish face.

"Do you know," she said gratefully, "I never understood till last night when I was trying to get warm with that jug and the scalding water came out all over my feet, I never understood till then what St. Paul means when he says, 'It is better to marry than to burn.' When you have to sleep alone you're put to it, of course, to keep warm, and St. Paul must have had some unfortunate experience. That's a text that's never made any sense to me till now."

But to live well, one must live dangerously, so every night, unmindful of past casualties, we filled our jugs. Then the fire was put to bed. Probably there would be no considerable amount of wood to salvage, for always as bedtime drew near Grandma stayed her hand in putting on fuel. Any unconsumed logs were stood up on end in the corners so that the flames might die down, and the remainder be left for morning use. The backlog was too heavy to be stood up, so water from the teakettle was poured over it, and a great smoking and hissing it made. Sometimes a layer of fine ash would come out all over the mantel and hearth as if Vesuvius had sleepily erupted. All the embers were drawn together by the fire shovel and buried well with ashes. Next, the big braided rug was turned back and the wide zinc under it exposed in case any spark should snap out during the night. Finally we wrapped shawls around our shoulders, tucked under each arm a soapstone, took jug in one hand, candlestick in the other, and so, as Pepys says, always with relish, "so to bed."

And Grandma's household went with relish too. If you think that this bedgoing was hardship for us, that is the personal construction you put on our cold facts. To us bed in those icy chambers was an adventure and a triumph. The fun of a game or of a fight is to overcome something, and we were overcoming right and left. The greater the desire, says the psychologist, the greater the satisfaction; if no desire, no satisfaction. We desired supremely to be warm, and by our own high resolve and heroic efforts we were getting warm. In brief, our adaptive faculties were at their optimum—and this, Alexis Carrel says, is fundamental to the good life.

To burrow under drifts of patchwork quilts in those sweet and faintly rustling straw or cornhusk ticks (feathers universally used by our neighbors were forbidden by Grandma as being too luxurious), to deploy hot soapstones and bring up reinforcements of hot jugs to the most shivery outposts of your body, now here, now there; cautiously to make pedal excursions farther and farther into the wide glacial territory, conquering as the Romans did first inch by inch the near and then the distant realms, to feel warmth and ease gradually creeping through you, relaxing your knees, uncurling your toes—this was triumph.

And you would be hearing outside the wind blowing and the maple boughs whacking the big sturdy roof, and sometimes an icicle falling in a little showery crash from tree or house. Sometimes it was snowing softly and secretly. Sometimes the moon shone, supernaturally whitening the perfect whiteness of the hill back of the house and making our low ceiling look pearly. Always on our walls there were examples of an art lost nowadays—frost pictures on the windowpanes.

There were little cracking sounds inside the house as the downstairs rooms cooled off; a mouse gnawed in the wall, or ran with rippling feet across the floor in the attic where big sacks of popcorn and butternuts were hanging safely from the rafters. All the mouse could get at were old New England love letters in the worn trunk, and there was satisfaction in thinking he would find them spare diet. You looked, listened, gave a too ardent jug a last poke, snuggled, and sank into delicious sleep that was not a negation, not a blankness, but joy in itself, and all drifted through with pungent smells of the blown-out candlewick, the new-mown-hay smell of sheets dried in fresh air and never ironed, and from the small pillow Grandma had tucked under your ear the honey smell of dried everlasting.

# HENRY BELLAMANN

❦ ❦

*Kings Row describes the reactions of a boy when he first realizes his beloved grandmother is old.*

PARRIS MITCHELL'S MOTHER had died when he was born, his father less than a year later. Since then he had been cared for by his maternal grandmother. She adored him, and he adored her. Doubtless she spoiled him in some ways, but she had trained him to the observance of an old-fashioned, Old World courtesy that made him somewhat conspicuous. Because of this he appeared older than he was, and sometimes a shade theatrical. Children, for the most part, thought him a bit queer, but adults approved of him.

His grandmother, Marie Arnaut von Eln, was wholly French. Her family came originally from Lorraine. She had been twice married, the second time to a wandering German aristocrat who had come to America to make a fortune. He did not make a fortune, but after various enterprises had bought lands at Kings Row because of some fancied similarity of the soil to that of his native German province. He built a house of foreign fashion, laid out elaborate grounds, and planted extensive vineyards. He manufactured sufficient wine to drink himself to death, and left his widow with debts and unpaid taxes far beyond the value of the land.

Marie von Eln was a resourceful woman. She employed French and German labor and turned the vineyards into a nursery. It had prospered, and she was now, twenty years after her husband's death, accounted a wealthy woman. Not so rich as the Sansomes, or the Skeffingtons, or the St. Georges, but more than comfortable.

Kings Row had never known quite what to make of her. She

was a "foreigner," but obviously did not fit into the usual categories of what were always derogatorily referred to as "the foreign elements." She had the bearing and manner of an aristocrat, and her sense of humor was of the kind that often made the women of Kings Row uncomfortable. One could never be sure what it was that amused her. Everybody knew her, and everybody called her "Madame."

She was slight and quick of movement. She had black hair, threaded with gray, a high Roman nose, and extremely delicate hands. Her face was lined with innumerable thin crisscross wrinkles—like the cracks in an old glaze—but her high cheeks, faintly rose, were apple-smooth. Her dark blue eyes under the heavy bands of her almost masculine brows were deeply set in tragic shadows. Their grave expression was partly due to affliction: Madame was almost blind. She habitually wore a few fine diamonds set in black enamel.

Madame von Eln spoke French or German by preference. She emphasized, underscored, and generally illumined her discourse with graphic movements of hands, shoulders, and eyebrows.

Parris bore a striking resemblance to her.

She was waiting now for him to come home from school. Laying aside the thick reading glass, she thrust a sheaf of papers into a drawer and closed it. She patted the waves over her ears, gave a twist to the taffeta bow at her throat, and waited. She smiled a little. It was almost a smile of coquetry. Her quick ears had caught the sound of running steps on the lower terrace.

"*Bon soir, grand'mère.*" He held her very tight and kissed her four times on each smooth cheek. He rubbed his face against her hair. "*Ma belle grand'mère!*"

"*Mon enfant.*" She held him off and put up her lorgnettes. "*Tu es fatigué?*"

"*Moi? Non. Pas du tout.*"

"*Mais, elle est ennuyante, cette Venable, n'est-ce-pas?*"

He laughed. She liked the trick he had of keeping his short square teeth tight together when he laughed.

"*Mademoiselle Sally? Jamais. Elle est drôle!*"

"*Drôle?*" She nodded. "*Ah, oui, c'est bien possible.*" There was a shade of malice in her smile. "*Oui, c'est bien possible!*" Then, in English, "You are hungry?"

"Of course."

Madame called, "Anna!"

A short fat maid appeared so quickly that one suspected that she had been waiting at the door.

"*Anna, dass Kind hat Hunger.*"

The maid smiled broadly. "*Was willst du—Milch, Brot—eine Pastete?*"

"*Was für Pastete gibt es, Anna?*"

"*Kirsch—ganz frisch.*"

The trilingual discussion continued without anyone being aware of the shifts from one tongue to another. Parris decided on the cherry pie, and Anna left the room with a loud rustle of starched petticoats.

Madame turned to her desk again. "Go with Anna, please, Parris. I have more work."

He started to speak, checked the words, and went softly out.

Madame von Eln's house was as individual as she was herself. The plastered walls of the big square rooms were whitewashed. Bright rag carpets covered the floors and gay prints hung at the windows. There were rows of potted plants in all of the deep windows. The furniture was nearly all of sycamore, made in the cabinet shops of the asylum for the insane. All of the pieces were massive and plain. There were patchwork quilts on the beds and some rather garish religious prints. There were none of the knickknacks common to most houses. People exclaimed when they saw it, "Quaint! Charming!"

Madame always shrugged indifferently. "Peasant style," she said. "It is comfortable and convenient."

Lately Parris had realized the difference between his home and other houses. Home was comfortable and he loved it, but he thought red velvet curtains and flowery Brussels carpets very elegant. Sometimes he wondered if his grandmother was less rich than he had supposed.

One thing he was self-conscious about. His grandmother

smoked cigarettes. He had seen country women smoke pipes, and it seemed quite the same. Once he had asked her not to smoke when he had visitors. He had been disconcerted and mystified beyond measure by her laughter. But she respected his wishes, and he never mentioned it again.

After the cherry pie he went directly to his piano practice. The square rosewood piano was old, and the keys were yellow, but it was in good tune. Very slowly, very carefully, counting aloud as he practiced, he attacked the Bach piece "in four flats." Fifteen minutes passed—half an hour. He began again at the beginning for the tenth time when his grandmother came to the door.

"What is this that you play?"

"It is an *Invention.*"

"Indeed. Is that something important?"

"Herr Berdorff says so."

"It is extremely ugly. It must be frightful to learn such a thing! Come with me—it is enough of this—this *Invention* as you call it—and it is your birthday. I have a present for you."

Parris lay in bed listening to the little sounds of the night. He was very happy. It had been a beautiful evening, and his present —all those books! His *"belle, belle, belle grand'mère!"* It would be nice when vacation came and he could stay at home. But in thinking of that he felt a tightening in his chest. He had heard Anna say that Madame was growing old. Anna said he should never wish time away. Old! Someday his grandmother would die—sooner than other boys' mothers who were much younger. He had had another grandmother, but she had died a long time ago. Terror seized him. He took the edge of the quilt between his teeth so he wouldn't cry, but it was no use—he was already crying. His throat felt like stone.

No, no, no! *Le bon Dieu* would never permit that. He remembered once that his grandmother had shrugged her shoulders contemptuously at something Anna said about trusting the good God. Was it—was it possible that his grandmother knew something she had never told him—that perhaps—perhaps there wasn't a *bon Dieu* at all, just as he had found out when he was a very little boy that there was no Santa Claus and no real giants?

He turned his face down into the pillow and pulled the covering over his head.

# SAMUEL HOPKINS ADAMS

※ ※

*A terrifying patriarch is discovered to be human after all in* The Grandfather Stories.

## "Two Grandfathers"

. . . GRANDFATHER ADAMS lived in a simple cottage on unfashionable South Union Street in Rochester, New York. Before any of us grandchildren were born, he had sold a once prosperous farm and retired on an insufficient income. Retirement did not mean idleness for him. The name, Myron Adams, frequently appeared in signature to communications to the newspapers, severe in style and often richly archaic in expression. Upon invitation he would address public meetings, his favorite topics being the evil of strong drink, the degeneracy of the times, and the conspiratorial activities of the Democratic party. He also wrote papers on subjects as diverse as the influence of sunspots on the weather and the domestic tomato as a causative factor in cancer.

The South Union Street household was made up of Grandfather, his second wife, and a man-of-all-work who was earning his way through the Baptist Theological Seminary. To this day I do not know our step-grandmother's given name. Grandfather addressed her as "Mrs. Adams" and would have been shocked at any such unwarranted familiarity as "Myron" on her part. Placidity and good humor were her memorable characteristics. Conversation between her and her husband was restricted to household economics and the old gentleman's health, which was more rugged than he believed it to be. She fussed indulgently over his ills, real or imaginary, and encouraged his self-dosing with the popular crypto-alcoholic nostrum, Hop Bitters, which was always at hand.

He pretended annoyance at her solicitude. Actually he enjoyed and depended upon it. Most of her time was spent in the kitchen with the door open a crack to listen for symptomatic coughs or sneezes. Though formal, their relations were not unfriendly. He respected her particularity as a housekeeper and her frugality at the market, and had been known to extol her cooking to outsiders.

The third member of the household was the meek, bespectacled, fledgling theologian to whom Grandfather always referred as "my man, Geordis." Why, we never knew, his name being Howard Holder. "Geordis" he remained, notwithstanding, in family usage. He was small, quiet, earnest and much concerned with his studies, which he repeated as he went about his chores, in a rapid mumble. Geordis was a conscientious worker. He did all the heavy work of house and garden and took good care of Horace G. (for Greeley), the family horse. In recompense he received lodging in the barn, two meals a day in the house, and two dollars a week wage. Apparently the arrangement suited; Geordis was never heard to complain.

Horace G. was the apple of Grandfather's eye. The horse was of indeterminate ancestry, uncertain age, and lethargic habit. Family tradition held that before any of us was born, Grandfather had outswapped the chief of a band of gyppos, somewhere out beyond Spencerport, for him. His conformation was lumpy, his disposition aloof, and his appearance unbelievably shaggy, shabby and moth-eaten. But he could maintain a steady jog of five miles an hour indefinitely, which is all that his owner exacted of him. Daily he was exercised, hitched to a rattletrap buggy in summer, an ancient sidebar cutter in winter, and driven through Rochester's busiest thoroughfares, in calm disregard of the sensation which the venerable rig occasioned on fashionable East Avenue or crowded Main Street. When we young Adamses reached the age of social self-consciousness we used to shrink from the conspicuousness of riding behind Horace G. Grandfather was immune to any such embarrassment.

"Horace G. may not be as pompous as Dan Patch," he admitted, "but no horse has a more respectable character." In Grandfather's mouth the word, respectable, reverted to its primal meaning, worthy of all respect, estimable in a high degree. Pompous, of course, meant of fine and impressive appearance.

Family piety ran strong in the Adams line. At least once a week we grandchildren were required to pay our formal respects at South Union Street. There were five of us in regular attendance. The age-span from Jenny, the eldest, to Charlie, the youngest, was ten years. In between were John, Sireno and myself, all born at the beginning of the 1870's.

It took years for us to become at all well acquainted with Grandfather. In the early days of our duty visits there was a romantic halo about his person, due to a misconception. Up to the time when I was ten years old, I cherished, in common with my cousins, the proud illusion that he was a retired horse-thief. The ground for our faith was a framed certificate, hanging in the sitting room. It was the one wordly touch on walls otherwise given over to the pious aridity of crewel-work texts and the mortuary reminders of Currier & Ives. In clear and elegant script it set forth that Mr. Myron Adams of East Bloomfield, New York, was a member in good and regular standing of the Wayne County Horse-thief Society, witness the sign and seal of the secretary, Anno Domini, 1821. There was, of course, no way of our knowing that the Society was formed for the purpose of discouraging raids on farm stock, and was also a social and festal organization comprising the young bloods or "Corinthians" of the county.

John, Reno and I bragged unconsciously to our envious play-mates of the strain of criminality in our blood. Only Jenny was of another mind. For some reason incomprehensible to the rest of us, she pretended to regard the record as faintly discreditable. Jenny was precociously ladylike.

It was difficult to reconcile the old gentleman's personality with the glamorous past which we attributed to him. Certainly there was nothing rakish about him as an octogenerian. My early recollection is of a partriarchally bearded and imposing figure in a Boston rocker beside a Franklin stove. From the ample expanse of beard issued a calm and preceptorial voice, dispensing admonition, instruction, exhortation to good and warning against evil conduct, sage advice and stern reproof; seldom praise and never levity. I was in my tenth year before I ever heard him laugh.

It was that occasion which broke the ice between the generations. The five of us had been bidden to breakfast at the cottage, a harsh ordeal, involving, as it did, a seven o'clock arrival, and family prayers in the heatless parlor. It was on a raw March morning that John innocently precipitated the event.

Fifteen minutes was the scanty time allotted for breakfast on our step-grandmother's toothsome battercakes, after which we were herded into the devastating chill of the parlor. Grandfather read from the Scriptures. We sat, shivering and stiffening. Grandfather led in prayer. We knelt on the stone-cold floor with quaking knees. Grandfather lifted up his voice in sacred song. We joined in, doing our conscientious best to control our tremulous jaws.

> Broad is the p-p-p-path
> That leads to d-death,
> And thousands w-w-walk
> Together ther-r-r-re.

Then a protracted benediction, after which we were free to make for the warmth and comfort of Benjamin Franklin's patent stove. All but one. This time John cringed in his chair, immobilized by a cramping chill. He was hustled out to the sitting room where Grandma swathed him in a blanket, Geordis fetched a hot brick for his feet, and Grandfather reached for the ever-handy Hop Bitters bottle.

A tablespoonful of a forty percent alcohol solution is calculated to produce effects upon the ten-year-old human organism. John, normally the most decorous of our generation, reacted atypically to the stimulus. Fixing the framed certificate with a glittering eye, he said loudly, "Grandpa!"

"Yes, John."

"I gotta question to ask you."

A galvanic shock went through the rest of us. Interrogate our grandfather? Except for a polite inquiry as to his health, none of us would have dared such a thing. What alcoholic temerity was John about to perpetrate?

"Ask it." The tone was not encouraging.

"Where did you get Horace G.?"

"Hah!" Grandfather ejaculated, the memory of that equine transaction still warm within him.

"I know," John asserted with profound conviction.

"Do you, indeed!" said Grandfather ominously.

"You stole him."

Grandma uttered a faint shriek.

"Didn't you? Didn't you steal Horace G.?"

Grandfather turned to his wife. "The boy is exalted in the head. Send for Dr. Ely."

"Horse-thieves steal horses, don't they?" his grandson insisted. "And you used to be a horse-thief, didn't you? That paper"—he pointed a wavering finger at the wall—"says so. I read it, myself, and I got Jenny to read it after me so's to be sure I was right. How can you be a member of a horse-thief society unless you're a horse-thief? Wasn't he a horse-thief, Jenny?" he appealed to his cousin.

"No, you ninkum!" she snapped.

John looked searchingly at her and then at his grandfather. He read blank denial in their faces. Confidence oozed out of him. "I told all the fellas you were," he said brokenly. "And n-n-now . . ." He choked up.

We listeners sat, sunk in despondency. Our dreams of ancestral derring-do were dissolved. Gone was the vision of a young and dashing Grandpa, riding at the head of his Wayne County cohorts upon some predatory and perilous mission. What a disillusionment! The old gentleman turned his slow regard upon the stricken faces around him.

"So you all consider your grandfather a malefactor," he said.

"I never!" cried Jenny.

"No, sir," Reno and I said. It was a hollow disclaimer. Young Charlie simply raised a wail of disappointment.

A strange alteration took place in the aged visage before us. Something was happening to Grandpa. His face worked. His beard quivered. From it issued a rumble which presently became a roar. We were appalled. It did not at first occur to us that this convulsion in one so mirthless could be laughter. Grandma was the first to recognize it. She began to giggle. Jenny joined in. One after another, we boys, our alarms dissipated, timorously ventured participation; then, as nobody rebuked us, gave ourselves up to whole-hearted glee. The little room rang to Grandpa's deep boom, Jenny's soprano peals, and a pandemonium of gurgles, shrieks and whoops from us boys.

Only Geordis refrained. With an expression of pain upon his meek countenance, he went out to look after Horace G.

Things were never the same again in the South Union Street home. The solvent of shared laughter melted the glacial barriers which Grandfather had unwittingly set up between age and youth. We never became actually chummy with him, it is true, but a cautiously progressive companionship did develop, respectful on our part, condescending on his. To our gratified surprise we discovered that we and he had interests in common. His enlightenment was even more revolutionary; we were revealed to his astonished recognition as human beings.

The visits to the little cottage ceased to be uniformly penitential. Instead of long, unrelieved, impersonal discourses, the old gentleman now developed for our edification and discomfiture, a playful device. He would interlard his conversation with obsolete terms and feign surprise and mortification when his hearers manifested a lack of understanding. We never knew when to expect these pitfalls. In the midst of some reminiscence of his youth he might let fall a casual mention of "the October improvement party at the minister's house," and then pause expectantly.

One or another of his hearers would repeat, "Improvement party?"

"Certes. Surely you know what an improvement party is."

Dubiously shaken heads.

"What ignorami! Why, the veriest abecedarian of my school-days would exhibit more docity."

Groping for a clue, Jenny would venture, "I'm going to join the Self-Improvement Class next term."

"Self-improvement, indeed! Hunca-munca."

It was now John's turn. He was our scholar. "Was it to improve the minister, sir?"

"No parson who needed improvement from his congregation would have lasted long in East Bloomfield."

After several other feeble essays, which he properly rebuked, Grandfather would vouchsafe to enlighten our ignorance: every October, in the olden time, the church folk gathered at the parsonage with axe, saw and wedge, and moved on to the nearest woodlot to improve—i.e., augment—the parson's woodpile for the impending winter.

As time went on our range of communication broadened. One could never tell what the day's visit might bring forth. It might be a scientific dissertation on snails, a horde of which invaded the cellars of South Union Street one August. It might be a reading from the almanac, with historical commentary. It might be a narrative brought out by reference to the old gentleman's "ort-book," a massive, leather-bound volume of heterogeneous memorabilia, kept under lock and key in his secretary-desk. This was a never-failing source.

After the label-prescribed dosage of his favorite Hop Bitters, he was likely to lapse into light and brief slumber, emerging with some old-time aphorism on his lips, usually of didactic or economic purport.

"Let young Loosetongue hire a turnip cart and preach the end of the world from its tailpiece."

"A pig on credit makes a good winter and a long spring."

"Blow high, blow low, hired money passes with the wind."

"Why pay a malkin to skin a cooked eel?"

And once he scandalized our childish sensibilities by coming out of a doze and announcing briskly, "Only a waste-thrift would plane the under side of a privy seat."

It was the only indelicacy that we ever heard him utter, and the only occasion on which he ever showed embarrassment.

A drunken man who staggered by in the street one Saturday served as text for a temperance sermon, with a distant, obscure and deceased cousin as horrible example. This relative, it appeared, after having "bowed his manly head to the killing cup," had wandered away into the forest and been eaten by bears. As epitaph, Grandfather recited with solemn fervor a favorite poem, of which the opening stanza is indelibly if perhaps not quite accurately imprinted on my memory.

> Ah, see where the red-glowing grogshop appears,
> As the waves of adversity swell.
> How it burns on the verge of tempestuous years,
> The horrible lighthouse of Hell!

Next to drunkenness he reprehended gambling, with one exception. He stoutly deplored the abolition of lotteries. Consider the good accomplished by them in the past, he argued. Libraries built, cultural institutions established, colleges and seminaries endowed, churches supported, charities enriched, all through the beneficent operations of these temples of chance.

"How," he inquired rhetorically, "would my own alma mater, Hamilton College, have won through its early vicissitudes without the funds allotted to it by that praiseworthy enterprise, the Literary Lottery? If I win a wager from a friend, I profit by the mulct of his money. But who is the worse for the luck of the draw in a properly conducted House of Fortune? Nobody!"

He was exceedingly proud of having attended Hamilton, though he did not finish his course. His name appears in the 1816 Catalogue as a member of the Sophomore class. Owing to some breach in the then rigid tenets of academic discipline ("I did a barney in Spring term" he once revealed to us), he was rusticated under the surveillance of that same East Bloomfield clergyman whose woodpile he helped to improve. Annoyed at the dereliction, his canal-contractor-father, Deacon Abner Adams, withdrew him from "those classic shades" and set him to work as a surveyor.

That he harbored no grudge is proven by his having sent two of his sons to Hamilton. When I entered, he signalized the event by giving me a dollar. On my return to Rochester for my first college vacation, he greeted me as "Fellow Alumnus." Secretly tickled at having caught him in a slip, I pointed out that a freshman could hardly lay claim to that title. He turned a chilling eye upon me.

"Do not play the callow dawplucker with me, Samuel," he said sternly.

I hastened to apologize.

"Consult the dictionary," he directed, pointing to the bookshelf. I did so and learned what I should have known from past experiences, the inadvisability of challenging the old gentleman on a point of verbal usage. Any member of a collegiate body, I found, graduate, undergraduate, or non-graduate, is an alumnus.

Why Grandfather left unmentioned for so long the most glorious (to our appreciation) phase of his career is a puzzle. He must have known that the Erie Canal which threaded the center of the city, was an integral part of daily life to Rochester youth. In summer we swam and fished in it. In winter we played shinny-on-your-own-side at the Wide Waters. Between seasons we extended respectful landsmen's greetings to the lordly mariners on its surface, and, on rare and beatific occasions, dropped by invitation from an arched bridge to the deckhouse roof of some hospitable, time-grizzled captain.

Our juvenile ambitions centered upon the canal. Let others aspire to become locomotive engineers, Indian scouts, or baseball captains with whiskers; for us the grassy berm, the toiling mules and the smooth-gliding craft were the ultimate in ambition. Reno, the practical, business-minded member of the group, was for steam. He would be master of a profitable stern-propeller, make a pile of money towing, and sign on Charlie as cabin boy if that young hopeful would learn to salute and call him "sir." John and I were willing to start at the bottom as mule-drivers and work up from the dust of the towpath. Jenny had decided to become mistress of the mahogany-fitted tugboat, *Annie Laurie,* even though it involved marrying the captain, a design which would have considerably surprised him, his wife, and their five children. We had nothing but pity in our hearts for those unfortunate children who lived in canal-less regions.

Yet we might never have learned from Grandfather of our vested interest in the great waterway, had it not been for a chance encounter. On a June day of 1881 the old gentleman gave evidence of expanding fellowship by inviting us to go driving with him. Only three of us were available that day: John, Reno and I. Jenny had to do some church sewing, and Charlie had the earache. While Geordis was harnessing Horace G., Grandfather unlocked his private repository and got out from his ort-book a document which he carefully inserted in the breast pocket of his rusty Prince Albert coat. Having buttoned it in, he led the way to the rig and we were off at a reliable five-miles-per-hour.

Out through Brighton we jogged to Pittsford, where our driver turned left. A moment later, John gave apprehensive warning.

"You can't drive there, Grandpa."

"Why not?"

"That's the towpath."

"I am aware of the fact."

"But, Grandpa! Nobody's allowed on the towpath but the canallers."

Reno and I added our protests. Too many times had we been chased from that forbidden territory with horrid imprecations and whizzing rocks not to have a fearful respect for it. Grandpa, it appeared, did not share our alarms.

"Giddap, Horace," he said placidly as he turned right upon the mule's highway.

A span of mules appeared, with a hulking lout at the lines. Fifty yards back of him loomed the freighter, light and riding high. Grandfather pulled to the offside to give the team passage room. The muleteer stared hard at our rig, scowled formidably, and, as we boys shrank into the smallest possible compass, threw up his hand, grinned, and passed on. From his lofty stance at the tiller the captain, as the boat drew level, saluted. Grandfather civilly lifted his whip. We marveled.

"Grandpa," Reno said in a small voice, "do you *know* those canallers?"

"Hah!" said Grandfather noncommittally.

Several other craft passed. The phenomenon was repeated; nobody interfered with our progress. Presently we came in sight of a man fishing from the towpath. He carried a staff and wore a badge. Our companion scrutinized him.

"That must be a new bankwatcher," he said. "I do not recognize his face."

"What's a bankwatcher, sir?" I asked.

"The degenerate successor to the old-time pathmaster."

"What's a pathmaster?" John inquired.

Before there was time for a reply, the fisherman spied us. He jumped to his feet, lumbered out into the middle of the right of way, and brandished the staff.

"Whoa!" he shouted loudly in Horace G.'s face.

Surprised and shocked, Horace G., who was unaccustomed to such discourtesy, stopped. The bankwatcher addressed Grandfather.

"Where do you think *you're* goin'?"

"Down to the lock," Grandfather said mildly.

"Not on this towpath. You're trespassin'. Mizzle!"

With a confident smile Grandfather unbuttoned his Prince Albert, took out the document from the inner pocket, unfolded it tenderly, and presented it. The official glared at it suspiciously.

"What's that?"

"A permit from the Honorables, the Erie Canal Commissioners, certifying my right to use the towpath, ad libitum, and signed by Gov. Clinton. (Obit 1828)"

"Who?"

"Governor Clinton. The Honorable De Witt Clinton."

"Never heard of him."

Hot color flushed into the old gentleman's cheeks. "You are a disgrace to the Grand Erie Canal which you serve, sir," he declared.

The bankwatcher grabbed Horace G.'s bridle and attempted to swing him around.

"Drop that bridle," said Grandfather sharply.

"Who says so?"

Grandfather half stood up and glanced east and west. Boats were coming from each direction. He put two fingers between his lips and whistled in astonishing volume. It was an accomplishment which we would never have expected in him. The bankwatcher jerked at Horace G.'s head. The wagon wheels cramped. The body tipped. There was a fair chance of our all being shunted into the water when the diversion came. Five runners on the towpath were converging upon us from the boats, which had veered in. The official hailed them.

"This old fool . . ."

He got no further. The first canaller to reach the spot, a burly, old steam captain, swept the official's feet out from under him.

Two others rolled him over the bank, while the remaining pair straightened out Horace G. The assaulted man beat the water bellowing for help, but there was no help. Menacing faces loomed over him. He swam across to the berm opposite, where he crawled out, spluttering and snarling threats of arrest. The steamer captain addressed him.

"Why, you crawfish-catching, turtle-chasing mudchunker, you! Do you know who this old gentleman is?"

The man gaped and gurgled.

"This is Squire Adams, this is. Ever hear of Adams Basin, you gillychick? Why, the Adamses *built* the Erie. You'd run *him* off the towpath, would you? Skedaddle before I come over there and drown you."

The dejected bankwatcher dribbled a trail into the underbrush and vanished. Grandfather warmly thanked the rescue squad for their "officiousness," by which he meant—and correctly, by the old usage—helpfulness. They returned to their boats, and the old gentleman turned Horace G. around for the trip back.

Sheer awe held us passengers silent for several miles. Our grandfather was suddenly revealed as a tradition, a fellow-canaller held in honor by these tough inland mariners. And we had never suspected any such glory. Reno made the break.

"Grandpa?"

"Yes, Sireno."

"Did you really build the canal?"

"I had a hand in it."

"Did you help run it after it was built?"

"As a young man, I held a quasi-official position."

"Is that why they all came running when you whistled?"

Grandfather smiled. "There's an old saying canalside: Once an Erie man, always an Erie man."

John now took his turn. "Is Adams Basin us Adamses?"

"You may so put it."

"Named after you?"

"After my father, the Deacon, and his brother."

"Is it in the geography?"

"Certes."

John drew a long breath. "Wait till I get back to school!" he said.

It was a gala day thereafter when we could get the old gentleman on the subject of the canal. Through his sly trickeries of speech we became steeped in canal lore. We maintained a conscious verbal superiority over our less erudite contemporaries. In casual conversation we would toss off references to hoodledashers, hoggees, occupation bridges, water-hire, and mudlarking. We could have told a ballhead from a needleboat a mile away. We were precise as to the authority of a pathmaster, the rates exacted at a toll lock, and the broad piscatorial scope of a mackerel inspector, though these offices had been obsolete for generations.

The designation of the vagrant bands that had formerly ranged canalside was familiar to us: gyppos, pikies, tenkers, swingkettles, blanketeers, anatomists, redemptioners, and ashbucket apprentices, and, in the towns, the tough soaplocks and roadrunners. Where a juvenile inlander on occasion of peril would have hissed, "Cheese it, the cops!" we warned, "Low bridge! Everybody down!" And we would never have been so conventional as to suggest a let-up in operations by such a term as, "Let's lay off," or, "Enough's enough." Our word was, "Look for a post," the hoggee's signal for a night's rest.

Grandfather's attitude toward the canal was almost reverential. He would brook no frivolity on the subject. Withering, indeed, was the wrath which Reno brought down upon himself by jocosely referring to the far bank of the waterway as the "heelpath."

"A paltry jest," Grandfather exploded. "A cheap and witless play upon words. Berm! Berm! Berm! Fix that sound American word in your pudding head and never again let me hear that other vulgarism from your lips."

He would pronounce with lingering affection the titles of boats long rotted into canal-bed slime: *The Stormy Lass, The Young Lion of the West, The Golden Flash, The Try-and-Catch-Me, The Two Faithful Brothers,* and *The Merry Fiddler,* successor to *The Mary Fiddler* which was struck by an electron and burned while mudlarked in the thunderstorm that caused the Gerundigut breach of 1831. Equally memorable if less poetic was the nomenclature of waterside taverns, The Hungry Pike, Hoggee's Rest, Death to Chinches (bedbugs), Welcome All, and The Well-

Stuffed Gut of brief existence before the name was suppressed by those upholders of the proprieties, the Canal Commissioners.

In the ort-book could be found places which had vanished from the official maps years before: Pilgrimsport, Gasport, Joppa Basin, Poverty's Pinch, Ratcatcher's Wharf, and Cholera Hitch.

"The canal authorities of today," Grandfather would observe, "are devoid of geographical imagination."

Once again Grandfather became a proud boast on our lips. His new distinction compensated for the loss of face we had suffered when compelled to abandon our claim of having a horse-thief in our immediate ancestry. After all, that was in the past. This was in the present. There was Grandfather's name—our name—on the map for all to see. It gave us precedence—at least, in our own consideration—over Craig Powers who had a mere building named after his father, Powers Block at the Four Corners; over George Pond whose local fame depended upon the larger-than-life statue of Mercury, visible from all parts of the city, on the tower of his uncle's tobacco factory; over Norman Mumford who could prove that his grandfather's pasture lot was the playing field of Rochester's pioneer baseball team, perhaps the first in the state, possibly in the whole United States since it dated from 1827.

All these were shining honors. But they lacked the indelible testimony of the printed word. They were not of general record. We were. Adams Basin might be an inconsiderable canalside hamlet. But there it stood, indelible, in every geography book of our school system. That was an unforgettable day for us when John was called upon in Number Three Geography class to answer the proposition, "Name four important communities in New York State west of Albany."

"Utica, Syracuse, Rochester and Adams Basin," said John in crescendo.

Frequently Grandfather had to admonish us against snobbishness. He was not wholly free from it, himself, however. A visiting New England lady to whom he was presented at a church festival, said, "Adams? Adams? Do you claim kinship with the Boston Adamses?"

"There is a Boston branch, I believe," he answered cautiously.

"I refer to the Presidential Adamses," the lady said haughtily.

"Ah! I was personally acquainted with the Honorable John Quincy Adams. A very respectable gentleman. He may well have been a connection of our line, though, being no brag-hard, he would naturally not press the claim. . . . May I fetch you a glass of water, madam?"

Privately he considered the Boston Adamses rather an effete and unenterprising lot. They clung to an easeful existence in Massachusetts while the hardier pioneers of the breed were risking the perils and hardships of the wilderness that made up Western New York in 1791.

# CLAUDE BROWN

禁 禁

*Manchild in the Promised Land* tells of a visit made by a Harlem boy to his grandparents in the South and of his reactions to the discovery that his grandmother cares for him.

SOMETIMES Grandpa used to hum some of the church songs when he was sitting in his rocking chair out on the porch patting his foot and watching the sun go down behind Mr. Hayward's tobacco barn. He would close his eyes and just start humming away. Maybe he was thinking about a funeral where he sang a song real good for somebody. Or maybe he was thinking about a funeral that didn't happen yet, a funeral where he wouldn't hear the songs, wouldn't know who was singing them, and wouldn't hear the preacher talking . . . talking about him . . . real loud. Maybe he was thinking about who would sing his favorite song for him and hoping that Mr. Charlie Jackson would live long enough to do the singing for him.

I couldn't understand why they sang nothing but those sad old church songs. They sure seemed to be some dumb country people to me. They didn't know any boogie songs or jump songs—they didn't even know any good blues songs. Nobody had a record player, and nobody had records. All the songs they sang, they'd been singing for years and years.

Somebody would sing real good at Grandpa's funeral, and a lot of people would be there. It would have to be a big funeral, because Grandpa was a real bad and evil nigger when he was a young man. He had the devil in him, and everybody knew it, even people who didn't know him. When Grandma took me to town or to church, people would come up to me and stare at me for a while, then ask, "Boy, is Mr. Son Brown yo' grandaddy?" And after a while, I knew why they were looking at me so hard; they were trying to see if I had the devil in me too.

For a long time, I used to be scared of Grandpa. He used to go walking in the woods in the evening, and when I asked Grandma where Grandpa was always going, she said he was hunting the devil. I only asked one time. I started to follow him once, but I got scared and changed my mind.

People used to say I was going to be just like Grandpa, since I had the devil in me too. I never paid attention to what people said about being like Grandpa until one day. That day, my cousin McKinley Wilson and me were out in the yard seeing who could pick up the biggest and heaviest sack of corn. While I was straining to pick up a sack, I heard Grandma scream and felt a stinging feeling on my neck that made me drop the sack, jump up and down, and grab my neck. When I turned around to see what had happened to me, I saw Grandma standing there with a switch in her hand. She was screaming and hollering a whole lot of things at me, but all I could make out was that she was going to kill me if I ever did that again. I didn't know what to think except that maybe she was going crazy. She had never said anything when I messed with the wasps' nests and got stung and cried and kept on messing with them. I couldn't understand why she had hit me, and Grandma didn't talk much. I knew she had mistreated me, and I had to do something about it, so I started walking, walking back to New York.

When Grandma caught up with me on the highway, she had a bigger switch, and she was real mad. After she finished beating me for running away, she said she had hit me because she didn't want me to be walking like Grandpa. I asked her if Grandpa had gotten his stroke from lifting corn.

She said, "It wasn' no stroke that makes Grandpa walk the way he do. The stroke just stiffened up his right side. But you see the way he gotta swing his left leg way out every time he take a step?"

I said, "Yeah, I seen him do that."

Grandma said that Grandpa walked that way because he was toting corn one day. I didn't understand, but I kept on listening. Then Grandma started telling me about the things I saw Grandpa cut out of the pig to keep the bacon from getting rank when they killed the pig. And she told me that right above the things that make the bacon rank are the chitterlings and that chitterlings press against a thin window in pigs and boys and men. I never knew I had chitterlings in me until that day. Grandma said if somebody lifted something too heavy for him, the chitterlings would press right through that window and the man would have a hard time walking and doing a lot of other things for the rest of his life. She said one time Grandpa was in the woods making liquor, and his dog started barking. Grandpa picked up his still and started running with it. The still was too heavy—the window broke, and now Grandpa had to walk real slow. She was saying that she didn't mean to hit me. She just didn't want me to break my window.

We walked back home up the highway. Grandma had her arm around my shoulder, and I had my arm around her waist. That was the only time I ever touched Grandma—and the only time I recall wanting her to touch me and liking her touch. When I saw the house coming at us up the road, I was kind of sad. I looked at Grandma's wrinkled face and liked it. I knew I had fallen in love with that mean old wrinkled lady who, I used to think, had a mouth like a monkey. I had fallen in love with a mean old lady because she hit me across the neck for trying to lift a sack of corn.

# Parents and Children

# THE HOLY BIBLE

(Authorized King James Version)

## ✠ ✠

*Through the ages parents have been shaken when the
child over whom they have had authority suddenly as-
serts himself as an individual. The Gospel According
to St. Luke records the bewilderment the young
Jesus caused his parents with his first gesture of inde-
pendence.*

## From the Gospel According to Saint Luke,
## Chapter 2, Verses 41–50

Now his parents went to Jerusalem every year at the feast
of the passover.

And when he was twelve years old, they went up to Jerusalem
after the custom of the feast.

And when they had fulfilled the days, as they returned, the
child Jesus tarried behind in Jerusalem; and Joseph and his
mother knew not of it.

But they, supposing him to have been in the company, went a
day's journey; and they sought him among their kinsfolk and
acquaintance.

And when they found him not, they turned back again to
Jerusalem, seeking him.

And it came to pass, that after three days they found him in the
temple, sitting in the midst of the doctors, both hearing them, and
asking them questions.

And all that heard him were astonished at his understanding
and answers.

And when they saw him, they were amazed; and his mother
said unto him, Son, why hast thou thus dealt with us? behold thy
father and I have sought thee sorrowing.

And he said unto them, How is it that ye sought me? wist ye not that I must be about my Father's business?

And they understood not the saying which he spake unto them.

# MOTHER GOOSE

*A lullaby takes account of the fact that every baby is born into a busy and generally aggressive family.*

### "Bye, Baby Bunting"

BYE, baby bunting,
Father's gone a-hunting,
Mother's gone a-milking,
Sister's gone a-silking,
And brother's gone to buy a skin
To wrap the baby bunting in.

# JOHN FORSTER

*Dickens, ultimately the father of ten, was a doting parent, but even the most devoted father has moments when the life he knew before parenthood has its appeal, as witness this letter from* The Life of Charles Dickens.

. . . EIGHTEEN HUNDRED AND FORTY-FOUR was but fifteen days old when a third son (his fifth child, which received the name of its godfather Francis Jeffrey) was born; and here is an answer sent by him, two days later, to an invitation from Maclise, Stanfield, and myself to dine with us at Richmond.

DEVONSHIRE LODGE,
*Seventeenth of January*, 1844.

Fellow Countrymen!

The appeal with which you have honoured me, awakens within my breast emotions that are more easily to be imagined than described. Heaven bless you. I shall indeed be proud, my friends, to respond to such a requisition. I had withdrawn from Public Life—I fondly thought forever—to pass the evening of my days in hydropathical pursuits, and the contemplation of virtue. For which latter purpose, I had bought a looking-glass.— But, my friends, private feeling must ever yield to a stern sense of public duty. The Man is lost in the Invited Guest, and I comply. Nurses, wet and dry; apothecaries; mothers-in-law; babbies; with all the sweet (and chaste) delights of private life; these, my countrymen, are hard to leave. But you have called me forth, and I will come.

Fellow countrymen, your friend and faithful servant,

CHARLES DICKENS.

# DOROTHY CANFIELD

꽃 꽃

*In* The Bent Twig *a couple seek strength from each other as they face what seems like disastrous behavior in their daughter.*

. . . JUDITH AND LAWRENCE had gone upstairs to do their lessons, and Professor Marshall at once broached the subject by saying with considerable hesitation, "Sylvia—well—how about this house-party at the Fiskes'?"

Sylvia was on the defense in a moment. "Well, how about it?" she repeated.

"I hope you don't feel like going."

"But I do, very much!" returned Sylvia, tingling at the first clear striking of the note of disapproval she had felt for so many weeks like an undertone in her life. As her father said nothing more, biting his nails and looking at her uncertainly, she added in the accent which fitted the words, "Why shouldn't I?"

He took a turn about the room and glanced at his wife, who was hemming a napkin very rapidly, her hands trembling a little. She looked up at him warningly, and he waited an instant before speaking. Finally he brought out with the guarded tone of one forcing himself to moderation of speech, "Well, the Colonel is an abominable old blackguard in public life, and his private reputation is no better."

Sylvia flushed. "I don't see what that has to do with his son. It's not fair to judge a young man by his father—or by anything but what he is himself—you yourself are always saying that, if the trouble is that the father is poor or ignorant or something else tiresome."

Professor Marshall said cautiously, "From what I hear, I gather that the son in this case is a good deal like his father."

"No, he *isn't!*" cried Sylvia quickly. "He may have been wild when he first came up to the University, but he's all right now!" She spoke as with authoritative and intimate knowledge of all the details of Fiske, Jr.'s, life. "And anyhow, I don't see what difference it makes, *what* the Colonel's reputation is. I'm just going up there with a lot of other young people to have a good time. Eleanor Hubert's invited, and three or four other society girls. I don't see why we need to be such a lot more particular than other people. We never are when it's a question of people being dirty, or horrid, other ways! How about Cousin Parnelia and Mr. Reinhardt? I guess the Fiskes would laugh at the idea of people who have as many queer folks around as we do, thinking *they* aren't good enough."

Professor Marshall sat down across the table from his daughter and looked at her. His face was rather ruddier than usual and he swallowed hard. "Why, Sylvia, the point is this. It's evident, from what your mother tells me of Mrs. Fiske's visit, that going to this house party means more in your case than with the other girls. Mrs. Fiske came all the way to La Chance to invite you, and from what she said about you and her stepson, it was evident that she and the Colonel—" He stopped, opening his hands nervously.

"I don't know how they think they know anything about it," returned Sylvia with dignity, though she felt an inward qualm at this news. "Jerry's been ever so nice to me and given me a splendid time, but that's all there is to it. Lots of fellows do that for lots of girls, and nobody makes such a fuss about it."

Mrs. Marshall laid down her work and went to the heart of the matter. "Sylvia, you don't *like* Mr. Fiske?"

"Yes, I do!" said Sylvia defiantly, qualifying this statement an instant later by, "Quite well, anyhow. Why *shouldn't* I?"

Her mother assumed this rhetorical question to be a genuine one and answered it accordingly. "Why, he doesn't seem at all like the type of young man who would be liked by a girl with your tastes and training. I shouldn't think you'd find him interesting or—"

Sylvia broke out: "Oh, you don't know how sick I get of being so everlastingly high-brow! What's the *use* of it? People don't think any more of you! They think less! You don't have any better time—nor so good! And why should you and Father always be so down on anybody that's rich, or dresses decently? *Jerry's* all right—if his clothes *do* fit!"

"Do you really *know* him at all?" asked her father pointedly.

"Of course I do—I know he's very handsome, and awfully good-natured, and he's given me the only good time I've had at the University. You just don't know how ghastly last year was to me! I'm awfully grateful to Jerry, and that's all there is to it!"

Before this second disclaimer, her parents were silent again, Sylvia looking down at her lap, picking at her fingers. Her expression was that of a naughty child—that is, with a considerable admixture of unhappiness in her wilfulness.

By this time Professor Marshall's expression was clearly one of downright anger, controlled by violent effort. Mrs. Marshall was the first one to speak. She went over to Sylvia and laid her hand on her shoulder. "Well, Sylvia dear, I'm sorry about—" She stopped and began again. "You know, dear, that we always believed in letting our children, as far as possible, make their own decisions, and we won't go back on that now. But I want you to understand that that puts a bigger responsibility on you than on most girls to make the *right* decisions. We trust you—your good sense and right feeling—to keep you from being carried away by unworthy motives into a false position. And, what's just as important, we trust to your being clearheaded enough to see what your motives really are."

"I don't see," began Sylvia, half crying, "why something horrid should come up just because I want a good time—other girls don't have to be all the time so solemn, and thinking about things!"

"There'd be more happy women if they did," remarked Mrs. Marshall, adding: "I don't believe we'd better talk any more about this now. You know how we feel, and you must take that into consideration. You think it over."

She spoke apparently with her usual calmness, but as she finished she put her arms about the girl's neck and kissed the flushed cheeks. Caresses from Mrs. Marshall were unusual, and, even through her tense effort to resist, Sylvia was touched. "You're just worrying about nothing at all, Mother," she said, trying to speak lightly, but escaped from a possible rejoinder by hurriedly gathering up her textbooks and following Judith and Lawrence upstairs.

Her father and mother confronted each other. *"Well!"* said Professor Marshall hotly, "of all the weak, inconclusive, modern parents—is *this* what we've come to?"

Mrs. Marshall took up her sewing and said in the tone which always quelled her husband, "Yes, this is what we've come to."

His heat abated at once, though he went on combatively, "Oh, I know what you mean, reasonable authority and not tyranny and all that—yes, I believe in it—of course—but this goes beyond—" he ended. "Is there or is there not such a thing as parental authority?"

Mrs. Marshall answered with apparent irrelevance, "You remember what Cavour said?"

"Good Heaven! No, I don't remember!" cried Professor Marshall, with an impatience which might have been Sylvia's.

"He said, 'Any idiot can rule by martial law.'"

"Yes, of course, that theory is all right, but—"

"If a theory is all right, it ought to be acted upon."

Professor Marshall cried out in exasperation, "But see here, Barbara—here is a concrete fact—our daughter—our precious Sylvia—is making a horrible mistake—and because of a theory we mustn't reach out a hand to pull her back."

"We *can't* pull her back by force," said his wife. "She's eighteen years old, and she has the habit of independent thought. We can't go back on that now."

"We don't seem to be pulling her back by force or in any other way! We seem to be just weakly sitting back and letting her do exactly as she pleases."

"If during all these years we've had her under our influence we haven't given her standards that—" began the mother.

"You heard how utterly she repudiated our influence and our standards and—"

"Oh, what she *says*—it's what she's made of that'll count—that's the *only* thing that'll count when a crisis comes—"

Professor Marshall interrupted hastily: "When a crisis! What do you call *this* but a crisis—she's like a child about to put her hand into the fire."

"I trust in the training she's had to give her firm enough nerves to pull it out again when she feels the heat," said her mother steadily.

Professor Marshall sprang up, with clenched hands, tall, powerful, helpless. "It's outrageous, Barbara, for all your talk! We're responsible! We ought to shut her up under lock and key—"

"So *many* girls have been deterred from a mistake by being shut up under lock and key!" commented Mrs. Marshall, with an ironical accent.

"But, good Heavens! Think of her going to that old scoundrel's —how can I look people in the face, when they all know my opinion of him—how I've opposed his being a Trustee and—"

"*Ah,*—!" remarked his wife significantly, "that's the trouble, is it?"

Professor Marshall flushed, and for a moment made no rejoinder. Then, shifting his ground, he said bitterly: "I think you're forgetting that I've had a disillusionizing experience in this sort of thing which you were spared. You forget that Sylvia is closely related to my sister."

"I don't forget that—but I don't forget either that Sylvia has had a very different sort of early life from poor Victoria's. She has breathed pure air always—I trust her to recognize its opposite."

He made an impatient gesture of exasperation. "But she'll be *in* it—it'll be too late—"

"It's never too late." She spoke quickly, but her unwavering opposition began to have in it a note of tension.

"She'll be caught—she'll have to go on because it'll be too hard to get out—"

"The same vigor that makes her resist us now will give her strength then—she's not Eleanor Hubert."

Her husband burst out upon her in a frightened, angry rush of reproach: "Barbara—how *can* you! You make me turn cold! This isn't a matter of talk—of theories—we're confronted with—"

She faced him down with unflinching, unhappy eyes. "Oh, of course if we are to believe in liberty only so long as everything goes smoothly—" She tried to add something to this, but her voice broke and she was silent. Her husband looked at her, startled at her pallor and her trembling lips, immensely moved by the rare discomposure of that countenance. She said in a whisper, her voice shaking, "Our little Sylvia—my first baby—"

He flung himself down in the chair beside her and took her hand. "It's damnable!" he said.

His wife answered slowly, with long pauses. "No—it's all right—it's part of the whole thing—of life. When you bring children into the world—when you live at all—you must accept the whole. It's not fair to rebel—to rebel at the pain—when—"

"Good God, it's not *our* pain I'm shrinking from—!" he broke

"No—oh no—that would be easy—"

With an impulse of yearning, and protection, and need, he leaned to put his arms around her, his graying beard against her pale cheek. They sat silent for a long time.

# DANIEL FUCHS

亚 亚

*The unconscious arrogance of approaching maturity often leads children to see their parents as people whose lives are over. The world the parents have created for the children has its power even so, as evoked in* Summer in Williamsburg.

ON FRIDAY NIGHTS the yellow stars on top of the three candles shed their soft light through the dim room with the gentleness of enchanted fingers. The tablecloth still showed the fresh creases, and on it, in a long oval dish, rested the knotted challee shining from egg yolk Mrs. Hayman's palms had patted on the dough. Philip's family was not very orthodox, but on Friday night a special air of quiet and peace pervaded the rooms, and it was in this atmosphere on these nights that Philip enjoyed lulling his mind into a kind of warm sleepiness.

Earlier, when the dark had first come, over his book he watched, without seeming to watch, his mother light one candle with a match and use this as a taper for the other two. This was, perhaps, a simple thing, but he always observed the ritual, and it affected him. She would soften the heels of the other candles with the flame, press them into the sockets of the candlesticks, and light them one after the other. Then she covered her head with a napkin, placed her fingertips to her eyelids, and moving her lips in a murmur, withdrawn for a moment and apart from the world, she recited the ancient prayer. There was always something strange, a little awesome, in the spectacle.

At eight o'clock Philip's father came home from the shop. He walked with the tired tread of a worker, and the expression on his face was as if glazed, the lips were dry and cracked. But he greeted

Mrs. Hayman warmly, to her "Good Sabbath," he answered, "Good year."

"Home already?" he asked as he noticed Philip. He was pleased, and smiled, but there was little ceremony. At the broom closet, where he kept his coat and slippers, he changed his shoes. This was one of his customs, performed regularly as he entered the house every night. It was the first thing he did, but it no longer attracted notice. Then Philip had to leave the chair he was sitting in, for it happened to be "Poppa's Chair." When he was home he sat only in this chair and it was given up to him, as a matter of course, whenever he appeared. Now he sat down for his evening meal. He dipped a piece of the white bread into the salty sauce on his fish plate, wetting his throat as he ate. Then slowly, chatting with Philip's mother as she served him, he ate the Friday dinner—the chopped fish, noodle soup, chicken and applesauce.

"That man, Coblenz, he was here again today," he said. "I don't know why he's looking for trouble."

"Well," asked Philip's mother, "are you going to let him buy the business?" She was upon him at once.

"It's ridiculous. He wants to give five thousand dollars. The place isn't worth it. If I let him have it, it would be a swindle pure and simple." He rustled his newspaper. "Besides," he added, "what would I do with myself?"

"Sell it," she said. "Don't be silly. See, Philip, it's just like I told you."

His father read, and his mother, with the marvelous serenity of older people, cleared the table and washed the dishes. She was finished with the week's work, had bathed, and her long, black hair, washed and combed, hung on her nape in a neat shining knot. Philip too was reading, but the pages remained unturned. Philip supposed it often happened that children had no intimate knowledge of their parents. His also were distant. That was because he did not understand them; they were strange to him and often even unreal. What had they been when they were my age? he speculated. Was it possible that they had been once boy and girl? What had their courtship been when they were young? And what would happen when the time came for them to die? It was difficult to imagine that they had been young once, or indeed that they had ever been other than as he saw them now. He was, of course, young himself and had no vivid understanding of the remarkable phenomenon of growth, but especially with his father and mother it was not easily possible for him to think of them as young, lively and fresh.

And yet there was an old picture of his mother, taken over thirty years ago. It was a large picture with a heavy, ornate old-fashioned frame, and his mother kept it hidden in the cellar because at a certain age not only is there no affectation but honest sentiment becomes a little pretentious. Often Philip gazed at his mother as she was years ago, deeply impressed and wondering at the young, fine face with the sad innocent eyes. He could never picture his mother as a girl, and here she was, soft, feminine, and really very lovely. At those times too, Philip thought of earlier days when he himself had been younger and watched his mother in her bedroom brush her hair or powder her face. Even then the performance affected him strangely. Once he examined her box of face powder. The cover was printed in soft, gray-blue colors, the design was of blossoms and leaves delicately intermingled, and the French words held a mysterious charm. Pussy-willow, the box said, and, fascinated, he used to say to himself, pussy-willow, pussy-willow, hardly knowing what exactly those silky syllables meant. Later, as often happens in such cases, walking, or at a theater, thinking of other matters, the chance scent of powder would bring back in a sudden nostalgic wave the memory of his mother in those days and his wondering about her.

On the other hand, even this much could not be said for his father. He had always been, as Philip remembered him, old, and this was something his mother confirmed. Even when she married him, she said, his hair had been white and he had had the appearance of an old man. He was bent now, drier and skinnier, shriveling with age, but except for those changes Philip supposed he was the same. The old pictures sustained this impression. There was one of his father and mother at the tombstone of his older brother. This had been twenty years before, when Philip was born, for while his mother was in bed with him his brother George was pushed off a roof. The picture, rusty-yellow from time, showed his mother still young and slender, but his father with his big mustaches was almost exactly as he was now. He might have been her father.

However, just as Philip remembered his mother's box of face powder and its effect on him, so he could recall his father ten years back. In the summer months he wore a Palm Beach suit, a Panama hat, and he carried a cane, walking with the jaunty step of a young man. And when Philip walked with him, accompanying him along Grand Street where he shopped on Sundays, it was Philip's practice to walk, not along side of him, but some paces to the rear. Mr. Hayman would enter a shop, pick his article and lay the money on the counter, point at Philip with the stick to indicate that he was to be given the package, and walk out, leaving him to follow. In the warm sun Philip would come after him down the street, holding his purchases, waiting until his father felt ready to return home and never thinking of questioning this odd little custom. At that time Philip held great respect for his father because of his dignity, his years, and his noble presence.

While Philip might have had difficulty in visualizing his parent's younger days, they had had them, of course, and it was this realization, as he contemplated them over his book on that Friday evening, that saddened him. For their youth was gone, they were old now, and when something was gone it made no difference whether you had ever had it in the first place or not. It was truly as though it had never been. A memory was unsatisfying solace. His mother, in speaking of herself, would often say with wry humor, "Down hill. We're going down hill now." They had been young, they would soon come to die, and it would all be finished, a drop of water losing its identity in the sea.

# JESSAMYN WEST

漢 漢

*Sometimes a father is best at understanding the needs of an adolescent daughter, sometimes a mother is. In* Cress Delahanty, *a lovelorn teenager benefits from both.*

## "Summer II"

It was a hot August morning, Saturday, six-thirty o'clock, and Mr. and Mrs. Delahanty still lingered at the breakfast table. Six-thirty is midmorning for a rancher in summer; but Mrs. Delahanty hadn't finished talking about the hat.

"It's perfectly clear why she wants it," she said.

It wasn't perfectly clear to Mr. Delahanty. Besides, he thought it would be interesting to know what one woman thinks of another's reasons for buying a hat, even though the second is only thirteen and her daughter.

"Why?" he asked.

"Edwin," said Mrs. Delahanty.

Mr. Delahanty put down his coffee which was too hot, anyway, for a hot morning.

"Edwin!" he exclaimed.

"Oh yes," Mrs. Delahanty assured him.

Mr. Delahanty decided to drink his coffee. After drinking, he asked, "How does the hat figure in it?"

"I think Cress thinks this hat would make Edwin see her in a new light. Frail and feminine."

"Better let her have it, hadn't you?" asked Mr. Delahanty. "Not that I like the idea of encouraging Edwin in any way."

"This hat," Mrs. Delahanty said, "wouldn't encourage anyone. This hat . . . Oh, Cress," she cried, "don't slip around that way. You gave me a start. What are you doing up this hour of the day anyway?"

During summer vacation Cress, unless she had projects of her own afoot, had to be routed from bed.

"I couldn't sleep," she said. She could tell from their faces that they had been talking about her. "And I wanted to ask Father something before he went out to work." She sat down at the table and turned toward her father as if they were two together, though seated unfortunately at a table with a stranger. "Can I call the store and tell them that if they'll hold the hat, you'll come in and look at it with me when we go to town tonight?"

"I've looked at it, Cress," said her mother.

"Mother," said Cress very sweetly, "I was speaking to Father. May I?"

"You don't have to ask permission of me, Cress, to speak to your father."

"Thank you, Mother," said Cress. "May I, Father?"

"Well," said Mr. Delahanty, "I don't suppose there'd be any harm in taking a look. Would there, Gertrude? Though you mustn't count on me for any expert advice about a hat, Cress."

Cress leaned toward her father. "Daddy," she said—she hadn't called her father Daddy for years but somehow the word seemed right and natural to her this morning—"Daddy, if you thought a hat was beautiful and becoming, I'd know it was beautiful and becoming. Or if you thought it was ugly and unsuitable, I'd know it was ugly and unsuitable. Do you know what, Daddy," Cress said and leaned toward her father, admiring the philosophic lines which ran, not from his nose to his mouth and which she thought made people look sour, but from his cheek bone to his jaw bone. "Do you know what?"

"No, Cress," said Mr. Delahanty, "I don't. But I'm waiting to be told."

"I think you probably have instinctive taste."

Mrs. Delahanty laughed, quite loud and long for so early in the morning.

Cress looked at her mother with a mingling of shock and disapproval on her face.

"Were you laughing at me or Daddy, Mother?" she asked politely.

"The two of you," said Mrs. Delahanty. "You and your daddy. Your daddy, Cress, can't tell a bonnet from a bushel basket. Not if the basket has a flower on it, anyway."

"Well, Gertrude," said Mr. Delahanty, "I may not be an expert on hats. I grant you that. But I think I know a pretty hat when I see one."

"That's why I want you to see this hat, Daddy," cried Cress. "It's so downright beautiful."

"That hat, Cress," said her mother, "is the most unsuitable object for a girl of thirteen years to put on her head I ever laid my eyes on."

"Just what do you mean by unsuitable, Gertrude?" asked Mr. Delahanty.

"I mean that hat was never intended for a thirteen-year-old girl. It's for an older—woman," concluded Mrs. Delahanty, wasting irony.

Mr. Delahanty poured himself a glass of milk. "You mean it ties under the chin?" he asked. "Or has . . ." he took a drink of milk, visibly running out of what suggested to him the hat of an older woman.

"Or has a black veil?" Cress helped him.

"No," said Mrs. Delahanty, "it hasn't got a black veil and it doesn't tie under the chin. But every single other thing on this earth that hat has got."

"Now, Gertrude," said Mr. Delahanty, "maybe you'd just better tell me what this hat is really like."

Mrs. Delahanty had a musing look in her eyes. "John, do you remember the chamber of commerce dinner last fall? In Santa Ana?"

"I remember we were there."

"Do you remember the table decorations?"

"No," said Mr. Delahanty, "I can't say I remember the table decorations."

"Well, it's a pity you can't, because then you would know what this hat looks like."

Cress did not like the way her mother had of being funny about serious matters. It was objectionable in anyone, in any mature person that is, and particularly so in a mother. When I have a child, Cress thought, I'll be serious and understanding the rest of my days.

"The table decorations," said Mrs. Delahanty reminiscently, "were horns of plenty, made out of straw mats. And out of them came spilling every fruit, grain, and flower ever grown in Orange County. Cress's hat would look right at home on that table."

"Oh Mother!" cried Cress.

"Except," said Mrs. Delahanty, "that those horns of plenty were of natural-colored straw, while this hat . . ." she paused, searching the room for some object with which to compare it, "while this hat," she concluded, "is an indescribable color."

"Oh Mother," cried Cress again. "It isn't. It's flamingo red."

"I've always considered red a nice warm color," said Mr. Delahanty.

"This is the warmest red, if it *is* red," agreed Mrs. Delahanty, "you ever laid eyes on. And its size!" Once again Mrs. Delahanty's eyes searched the kitchen without finding a comparable object. "It's just unbelievable," she said, shaking her head.

"Which all adds up to saying, I gather," said Mr. Delahanty, "that this hat Cress wants is large and flowered. Is that right, Cress? Is that the way it strikes you?"

The way the hat struck Cress was so overwhelming that she felt she might search the whole world over and still not find any word, any comparison which would explain it or the way she felt about it. The hat was summer time. It was deep and broad like summer. It caused soft scallops of shadow, like summer shadows under the densest trees, to fall across her face. It was like a poem; it was as much, "The rose is in full bloom, the riches of Flora are lavishly strown," as though Keats when he wrote had been thinking of it. The person wearing it would be languorous, gentle, and delicate. Looking at herself in the store mirror with that hat on, she had heard herself saying to Edwin, "If you'll be kind enough to give me your arm I think I'd like to stroll a little before the dew comes out." And she had seen how she would look, saying that, glancing appealingly upward at Edwin from under the brim of the shadow-casting, summery, flower-laden hat.

"Well, Cress?" asked her father.

"Oh, yes!" said Cress. "That's how it strikes me. May I call the store and say you'll come in tonight to look at it?"

"There's no rush, is there?" asked Mr. Delahanty. "Could look Monday as well as tonight, couldn't we?"

"The rush," said Cress, "is because I want it to wear to the beach tomorrow. That is, if you approve of it, Daddy."

"What's the idea, Cress?" asked her father. "A hat to the beach? You usually put on your bathing cap before we leave the house."

"Tomorrow," said Cress, "I'm not going to go thrashing about in the water. I'm going to walk about and observe."

"You're not going to be able to observe much, Cress," said her mother, "with that hat hanging down over your eyes."

Cress ignored this. "Father, may or may not I call the S.Q.R.? You don't have to promise to buy it or like it. Only to look at it."

"I guess looking never did any harm," said Mr. Delahanty.

"Now you've gone and done it," said Mrs. Delahanty, when Cress had gone.

"Done what?" asked Mr. Delahanty, innocently.

"Promised her that monstrosity. And all in the world she wants it for is to parade around Balboa in it tomorrow hoping Edwin will catch sight of her."

"Is Edwin at Balboa?"

"His family is. And as far as I know they haven't abandoned him."

"I didn't promise to buy the hat," protested Mr. Delahanty. "All I said I'd do was look at it."

Wearing the hat, Cress felt just as she had known she would: gentle and fragile and drooping. Beautiful, too. Running, with it on, would be utterly out of the question. Even sitting with it on had its difficulties, for the hat with its burden of fruits and flowers had to be balanced just so.

"Father," she called from the back seat, "will you please roll up your window? It's blowing my hat."

"Cress," said Mr. Delahanty, "it's at least ninety in here now and I'm not going to roll this window up another inch. We're barely getting enough fresh air to keep us alive as it is."

"It's blowing the flowers off my hat," cried Cress.

"A few will never be missed," said Mr. Delahanty.

Mrs. Delahanty leaned across her husband and rolled up his window.

"How I could signal, if the need suddenly arose, I don't know," Mr. Delahanty told her, "apart from the fact that I'm suffocating right now."

"Nonsense," said Mrs. Delahanty. "Besides we'll be there in a few minutes."

"Steer for me for a minute, will you, Gertrude?" asked Mr. Delahanty. "I want to get out of this coat before I have a heat stroke."

How ridiculous! Cress felt just right. Warm, summery warm, of course, but though the car windows were tightly closed she could feel the freshness of the sea breeze which was bending the brown grass by the roadside, shaking the palm fronds, ruffling the white leghorns' tails up over their backs like untidy skirts. She could smell the strange salt freshness of the sea, the far, non-land scent of its never-quiet water; and suddenly, in a little gap between two brown hills, she saw the sea itself, blue in the hot air, rippling and glinting under the sun like the scales of big silver-blue fish. Cress sighed so deeply with pleasure that her hat rocked unsteadily and she righted it, holding it for a minute with both hands at just the angle which she hoped it would have when Edwin saw her.

Because Edwin would see her, of course. It was impossible to believe that she, having become the owner of the most beautiful hat, should be in the same town with Edwin, without his seeing it and her.

After her father parked the car, he got out his own and her mother's bathing suits; then the two of them stood for a time looking at her.

"Well, times change," said Mr. Delahanty. "Times change. I never thought I'd live to see the day, Cress, when you'd elect to tramp up and down the boardwalk on a hot day instead of going swimming with us."

"I'm going to walk and observe," said Cress holding onto her hat which was hard to control in the stiff sea breeze which was blowing. "I'm getting a little old for just sporting around in the water."

"Observe," said Mr. Delahanty, seriously regarding her. "I can only hope, Cress, the shoe won't be too decidedly on the other foot."

"Now, John," said Mrs. Delahanty, and though she wasn't ordinarily a mother much given to kissing, she managed to get sufficiently under the brim of Cress's hat to give her a loving kiss.

"You're all right, Crescent," she said. "That hat's a little unusual, but I don't know that I'd want a daughter of mine trigged out like everyone else. Have a good time. And I hope you see Edwin."

"Oh Mother," said Cress earnestly, for the knowledge of her mother's understanding was as comforting to her as confession after sin.

"Run on now," said Mrs. Delahanty.

"We'll meeet you at Tiny's at four," said her father, "and have some ice cream before we go home."

At first, Cress was so certain of seeing Edwin that she walked along the boardwalk, really observing and truly, except for the difficulties she had keeping her hat righted, enjoying the sights and smells of the town and the sea. Now and then in front of a plate glass window which served her as mirror she stopped to admire her hat, to get it on straight again and to poke up the stray hairs which kept dangling down from her not very solid kid-curler curls. Her mother had tried to persuade her not to wear a middy and skirt, saying they didn't go well with her hat. She was glad she hadn't listened to her. A middy was a nautical costume, and what, unless you actually went to sea, was more nautical than the shore? And her hat was the heart of summer, and where was the heart of summer to be found if not in August at the beach? No, looking at herself in the plate glass windows she passed, she was very content with what she saw: under the large hat her neck looked slender and reed-like, a blossom's stem; her eyes were shadowed, her entire aspect gentle, and even, she thought, mysterious. She was glad she had worn her high-heeled patent leather pumps, too. They made her teeter a little, but a swaying gait, she thought, suited the day, the hat, and her own personality; besides denying in the sharpest way possible the tomboy she was afraid

Edwin thought her, and who would, no doubt, have worn sneakers.

What with observing, keeping her hat on straight, and practicing on occasional strangers the look of melting surprise with which she planned to greet Edwin, the first hour went by quickly. After the quietness of the ranch, where a whole day often passed with no other sounds than her own and her father's and mother's voices, and where the chief diversions, perhaps, were those of digging up a trap-door spider, or freeing a butcher-bird's victim, the sights and sounds of a beach town on a Sunday afternoon were almost too exciting to be borne.

First, there was the strange light touch of the penetrating wind off the sea on her warm inland body. Then there was the constant, half-heard beat of the surf, hissing as it ran smoothly up the sand, thundering as it crashed against the rocks of the breakwater. There were all the smells of salt and seaweed, of fish and water and wind. There were all the human smells too of the hundreds of people who filled the boardwalk: ladies in print dresses smelling like passing gardens; swimmers with their scents of sun-tan oils and skin lotions; there were the smells of the eating places: of mustard and onions, of hamburgers frying; and the sudden sharp smell of stacks of dill pickles, as brisk in the nose as a sudden unintended inhalation of sea water. There was the smell of frying fish from the many fish grottos. And outside these places, in the middle of the boardwalk like miniature, land-locked seas, the glass tanks, where passers-by might admire the grace and color of their dinners before eating them. It was hard to say who did the most looking; fish outward from these sidewalk aquariums, at the strange pale gill-less pedestrians, or pedestrians inward at the finny swimmers.

Cress liked them both. Solemn fish and passers-by, some also solemn, with problems sun and water had not made them forget. For the first hour this was enough for Cress: being a part of this abundance and knowing that at any minute she would see Edwin. For in a town of one street how could she miss him?

Then suddenly the first hour was gone by; it was past three and already the wind seemed a little sharper, the sun less bright, the boardwalk less crowded. More of her hair had come uncurled; her hat took more righting to keep it straight; her neck ached from holding her head high enough to see out from under the hat's brim; occasional stabs of pain shot up the calves of legs unaccustomed to the pull of high heels. A thought, with the swiftness of a stone dropping through water, settled in her mind: he isn't coming. It was a possibility she had not even thought about before. She had thought he would *have* to come. The hat was *for* him. The day was *for* him. How could she possibly, without seeing him, meet her father and mother, say yes, say no, eat ice cream, get in the car, go home, take off her hat, go to bed, sleep?

It was fifteen after three. At first she had been willing that Edwin see her first. Now, she searched every figure, every slight, short man or boy's figure, for as great a distance as she could make them out, saying, "Be Edwin." So strongly did she will it that she thought she might, by determination alone, transform a stranger into Edwin.

It was three-thirty. It was fifteen of four. Her hat was on one side, her mouth weary from practicing her smile on strangers, the pleat out of her freshly starched skirt, her feet mere stumps of pain. Still, she would not give up. "Edwin, appear, Edwin appear," she willed.

Edwin did appear, crossing the street a block away, small and neat and thin in white duck pants and a white shirt. He crossed and turned toward Cress, walking steadily toward her. In two minutes or three he would see her, and see the hat and notice her new gentleness. All tiredness and pain left Cress. She could very easily have flown, or played a piece she had never seen before on the piano, or kissed a mad dog and not been bitten. She had just time to arrange herself, resettle her hat, give her now completely uncurled hair a quick comb upward. To do this she took her hat off, stood on tiptoe, and with fingers which trembled with excitement managed to get it up onto the top of one of the rectangular glass aquariums which by chance stood conveniently before her in the middle of the sidewalk.

Before she, herself, understood what had happened someone was jovially yelling, "Hey, sis, bread crumbs is what you feed them," and there was her hat, slowly, gracefully settling among the startled fish of the aquarium.

The man who had yelled was a short fat man, wearing pants, but no shirt or undershirt. He had sand in the hair on his chest; like dandruff, Cress thought wildly, unable for shame to raise her eyes to his face. "What's the idea, sis?" he asked.

Forcing her eyes away from the sandy dandruff, Cress saw that her hat, still gradually, gracefully floundering, was bleeding flamingo red into the aquarium, so that the amazed fish now swam in sunset waters.

"I thought it had a top," she whispered to no one in particular.

"The hat, sis?" asked the shirtless man.

"The glass place for the fish," Cress whispered. "I thought it had a top."

"It didn't, sis."

"I was resting my hat on it," Cress whispered, "while I fixed my hair."

"You was resting your hat on air, sis."

"It dropped," said Cress. "It fell right out of my hands."

"Gravity, sis," said the fat man. "It was gravity."

"Will it make the fish sick?" asked Cress.

"Make 'em die, sis, in my opinion. Make 'em all puke and throw up their shoestrings I should think."

"What'll I do?" asked Cress.

"Watch 'em die," said the fat man comfortably. "That big one's a goner already."

Cress wanted to die herself. She willed it very hard, but she couldn't. She couldn't even faint, though she held her breath and willed her heart to stop beating. But a sort of numbness did come over her, making all the voices blurred and indistinct, making all the people, and there were dozens, hundreds it seemed to Cress, now pressed about the aquarium, distant and hazy.

It was a field day for fish and humans. It was a great occasion for fish, who had had nothing more exciting to look forward to than death in the frying pan: a big blunt-nosed fish swam at the hat as if to ram it; smaller fish circled it curiously; nervous fish parted the darkening waters in a fishy frenzy. It was a glorious moment for humans, too, a sight they had never expected to see. Someone, a worthy man dedicated to service, brought out the fish grotto proprietor. He came in his white apron and tall chef's hat, brandishing a long-handled ladle and happy at first to see his fish arousing so much interest. He shouldered his way through the crowd, his blood-shot eyes bright with pleasure, until he caught sight of vermilion waters, frantic fish, and the heart of summer, still partially afloat among them. He had had a long hard day frying fish. This was the last straw, fish dying without frying.

"In God's name," he cried, sadly, "who is murdering my fish?"

Cress was too frightened to reply.

"She is," said the fat man, pointing. "Sis, here, done it."

"What does she mean?" the fish grotto proprietor cried. Cress opened her mouth, but not a sound came out. She was as speechless as the fish.

"Sis here was resting her hat on the top of the aquarium," explained the fat man.

"There ain't no top," said the fish grotto owner. "Is she blind?"

"More or less, I reckon," said the fat man. "You kind of blind, sis?" he asked kindly.

Cress was able only to moan a little. With a long shudder, like a capsized ship coming to rest, her hat settled to the bottom of the aquarium. It lay there at a crazy angle, one side held up by a small castle with which the fish grotto proprietor had attempted to give his aquarium a romantic, gothic air. Out of a castle window one frightened fish eye peered, trying to penetrate the murky waters, make out if this was the end of the world for fish. It looked to be. Flowers and fruits were now adding their colors to that of the flamingo red straw. Streaks of purple from pansies and violets, puffs of sulphurous yellow from the daisies, veins of green from stems and flowers richly marbled the general red of the water. And the hat, in form as well as color, was suffering a sea change. It was softening up, flattening out. Each minute it looked less and less like a hat.

Cress finally found her voice. "Save my hat," she whispered.

"It's too late," the fish grotto proprietor said, "to speak of saving anything. Hat or fishes. They are all goners. Let 'em die together."

"Die?" asked Cress.

"Poisoned," said the fish proprietor, pointing to his frantic fish, the vari-colored water. "What've you got agin fish, kid?"

"I like fish," Cress whispered.

"She likes fish," said the fat man. "Hate to consider what she might do if she didn't." Those who had gathered about the aquarium laughed. Somewhere among them must be Edwin, Cress thought: seeing her, seeing her face trembling with the effort not to cry, seeing her beautiful hat, its colors fading out amongst an aquarium full of fish. The laughter was not malicious; it was lazy Sunday afternoon laughter; lazy Sunday afternoon laughers, watching, as if at play, to see what the fish proprietor would do, if he were villain or hero, straight man or clown. But it might as well have been malicious; it shamed Cress to the bone. It was unthinkable that anyone after such public humiliation could live. She would do nothing wild nor dramatic, simply refuse food, fade quietly away, die.

"Poisoned," declared the fish proprietor again, gloomily, "deliberately poisoned."

"I think you're mistaken about their being poisoned."

It was impossible, Cress thought, that anyone should be defending her: let alone Edwin—Edwin, who was always a victim himself.

"I think that color is probably from pure vegetable dyes," said Edwin. Edwin's face was as white as his shirt and Cress could see that his upper lip trembled. But he was defending her, defying the fish grotto proprietor, not ashamed to be on the side of a person who had been publicly laughed at.

"It might even be good for the fish," suggested Edwin, "that pure vegetable dye."

"Good for them!" cried the fish proprietor. "Them fish have been scared to death at the very least, poison or no poison. Hats descending on them! I wouldn't feed them fish to a cat now. Their nervous systems have been shook up. You related to this girl?"

"No," said Edwin.

"Well, someone," said the fish proprietor, coming to the crux of the matter, "has got to pay for my ruined fish."

"That'll be me, I reckon," said Mr. Delahanty who, without enthusiasm, was pushing his way through the crowd. He took the ladle from the fish owner's hand, and being a tall man was able, by stretching a little, to fetch up the hat, heavy and dripping from the bottom of the aquarium. He held the hat toward Cress, who without a word took it. Then Mr. Dalahanty handed the ladle back to its owner.

"I'll pay ten dollars," he said.

"Twenty-five," said the fish grotto proprietor. "Not a cent less. Those were fancy fish and not to be picked up every day in the week."

"Eleven," said Mr. Delahanty.

"I was fond of those fish," said their owner. "They were pets, so to speak."

"Eleven fifty," said Mr. Delahanty.

"It was cruelty to animals putting that hat in with them. I could turn you in to the S.P.C.A."

"Twelve," said Mr. Delahanty.

They settled for fifteen, Mr. Delahanty getting the fish.

Cress, the hat, and the fish, in an oversized kettle loaned by the fish man, occupied the back of the car on the trip home. It was a slow trip because speed tended to slosh the water in the kettle, together with a fish or two, out on the floor. It was a silent trip because Cress was thinking, and because up in the front seat, while Mr. and Mrs. Delahanty had plenty to say, they didn't want to be overheard by Cress.

They were nearly home before Mrs. Delahanty said, very low, "What a terrible thing to happen! It might mark her emotionally for life."

Mr. Delahanty agreed. "It wouldn't have been so bad though if that Edwin hadn't had to turn up in time to see it all."

"I know. She wanted to be such a lady—for him. That hat . . . and the curls . . . and then the hat in with the fish, the curls gone, and all those people laughing. I'm a grown person, John, but I just don't think I could live down such a thing. I think I might just stick my head in that bucket of fish and end everything."

As if her own words had put an idea into her mind, Mrs. Delahanty looked quickly around.

"Cress," she cried, "what have you got that hat on your head for?"

"It'll shrink if I don't," said Cress very calmly.

"Well, let it. Let it shrink. And you've got all those colors dribbling down your face and neck."

"I'm trying to keep them mopped up," said Cress, mopping some more.

"Throw that hat away," ordered Mrs. Delahanty. "Toss it out the window, Cress. You don't ever have to wear it again. We'll get you a new one."

"Oh no," cried Cress, "I love it. I'm going to keep it all my life."

"Keep it all your life?" Mrs. Delahanty asked, feeling rather dazed. "Cress, that hat didn't look too good in the first place. I can't begin to tell you what it looks like now. Throw it away!"

"No," said Cress stubbornly. "I want to keep it to remember today by."

"Remember today," repeated Mrs. Delahanty, who was beginning to feel increasingly that she and her daughter were not speaking of the same day at all. "Why in the world do you want to remember today?"

"Because of the brave way Edwin defended me," said Cress.

"Oh," said Mrs. Delahanty faintly.

"He was really wonderful, Mother. He defied that man."

"I'm afraid we missed that, Cress."

"And I was stricken, Mother, really stricken. It was the first time Edwin ever saw me stricken. He didn't even know I could be. He's always been the stricken one so far. The most I'd dared hope for was to be gentle. Then," said Cress with great satisfaction, "stricken."

There was complete silence in the car for some time. "Don't you think I was, Mother?" Cress asked anxiously.

"Yes," said Mrs. Delahanty with conviction, "I think that's about the word for it."

"And whenever I wear this hat, he'll remember."

Mrs. Delahanty took her husband's handkerchief from his pocket and handed it back to her daughter. "Tuck this around your neck, Cress. It'll keep those colors from staining your middy."

With one hand Cress tucked the handkerchief about her neck, with the other she kept her hat in place.

## MARIA AUGUSTA TRAPP

The Story of the Trapp Family Singers *includes a portrayal of a whole family—a young mother-to-be, her husband, and her seven stepchildren—happily awaiting the birth of a baby.*

ONE DAY after the guests had left, and the children were playing on the lawn, Hedwig said quite indignantly: "Now, Mother, this is the third time that you haven't played volley ball with us. That's no fun. Come on; here's the ball."

I took them all along with me, and sitting in front of the log cabin in the park, I told them that some time after Christmas God would send them a little sister or brother.

"Oh, Mother, let it be a boy," sighed Werner. "We have five girls already!"

And Martina said: "If it is only coming after Christmas, how do you know now?"

So I told them.

This was one of those rare hours where heaven seems to touch earth, where a firm bond is woven between hearts.

Advent had come again, the most beautiful Advent of all; that life of real expectation. When the long evenings set in and we met around the fireplace, there was the same atmosphere, which can only be characterized by that untranslatable word, *gemütlich.* There was something new, which one could feel but not put into words. That mood of cheerful anticipation had taken hold of the whole family. The knitting needles in busy young hands did not bring forth lengthy men's socks any more, but the cutest little sweaters and caps and playsuits and panties, all in blue, of course, because "we already had five girls." Georg and the boys were working noisily on a beautiful cradle; and when I read aloud the passage of a fairy tale where it says: "And after a year the young queen gave birth to a little son, and they lived happily ever after," Martina looked at her toy dwarfs and nodded gravely.

The Christmas story about the Holy Mother with her Holy Child blooms all anew in your heart when you are living through the great mystery of becoming a mother yourself, a bearer of life.

After Christmas I called on Frau Vogl to make arrangements. She was the youngish widow of a doctor, and had been recommended to me as the best midwife in town. Together we did some figuring, and then it was decided that the baby was due by the middle of February.

"Do you have everything ready for the baby?" Frau Vogl asked me.

"I don't know," I said, rather nervously. "I'll tell you what I have: ten dozen diapers; three dozen shirts, size one; and three dozen, size two; six dozen diaper-panties, sixteen jackets, a cradle, a crib, a basket, and a carriage."

"For heaven's sake, stop!" cried Frau Vogl. "You don't expect triplets, do you?"

Very few of these things had been newly acquired. Most of them were still there from the older children. I only had to get them down from the attic, have them washed, ironed, and pleated, because these cute little things were full of ruffles and tiny pleats.

By the middle of February Frau Vogl came to stay, and two days later it was obvious: this was the day.

As it hadn't occurred to anyone to bring a doctor into the picture during those past nine months, so it also didn't occur to anybody that I should take even so much as an aspirin. Frau Vogl's presence radiated confidence. Everything was just fine, the pain simply belonged to it; thus it was ordained by God Almighty ever since Eve ate the apple.

Georg was sitting at my bedside, and that was very necessary. He knew so much more about it all than I; he had gone through it seven times. He assured me that I was not going to die, and the less I moaned now, the more strength I would have later, and this was only the beginning. He said it so casually that it took the edge off my anxiety. I went through the entirely new sensation that this was not a pain like a toothache, which at times seems to screw itself into your very bones. These pains seemed to come in regular intervals like breakers at the seashore. The moment they stopped, you felt perfectly wonderful and ready to dance, only to change your mind rather quickly when the next breaker came.

"Will it take longer than half an hour?" I whispered to Frau Vogl, who didn't seem to understand, because she only said: "Breathe deeply."

That was early in the afternoon. When Frau Vogl came back after supper, the uninterested expression on her face changed suddenly. She became all concentration.

Through the open door I could hear the children. They were saying the rosary now. After every decade they sang a song—softly and only in two parts, as the tenor and the bass were missing. It sounded to me like angels. What a wonderful prayer the rosary is! For eight hundred years it has carried the sorrows and troubles, the joys and happiness through the hands of the Heavenly Mother to the Throne of God. When we repeat over and over: "Holy Mary, Mother of God, pray for us . . ." it is like the begging of little children who want something with all their heart: "Please, Mother, please! Oh, Mother, please, please!"

With all my heart I joined the chorus silently. Georg hadn't left the room during those long hours. His strong hand was like an anchor to which I clung when the hurricane of pain tossed about the little boat of a frail human body.

During the first weeks of the nine months, we had been rather choosy. It should be a boy—blond-haired, blue-eyed, tall and thin. Georg wanted him to look like his mother, whereas I definitely wanted him to be the image of my hero. The closer the time came, the less fussy we were. If he is only healthy with straight arms and legs, even the color of eyes and hair wouldn't matter any more. And right now it was just the same whether it was a boy or a girl. All the strength of the whole being was concentrated on the one thing necessary:

"Oh God, help, help that this Thy child be born healthy in body and soul."

When a piercing little shriek cut through the solemn silence, I heard the children downstairs jump from their seats and jubilantly break into the hymn of thanksgiving by the old master Bach: "Now Thank We All Our God," while Georg was bending over me, kissing me on the forehead. In these precious moments the human being feels itself lifted up into the heights of God, partaking of His power, a co-worker of God, the Father, Creator of heaven and earth.

Then Georg stepped over to Frau Vogl and looked at his sixth daughter.

"Looks like every other newborn baby," he said in the tone of one who knows what he is talking about—"like a little monkey." The spell was broken. Under my feeble protest he left the room "to tell the children."

Had he seen a tear welling up in the hurt young mother's eye? He was right back and with a warm glow in his fine eyes, he whispered earnestly:

"But little monkeys are the loveliest, sweetest creatures, and I wouldn't want her to look any other way!"

What could I do but laugh through tears? Then he left me to Frau Vogl's professional hands. Later, after the children had tiptoed in to admire the baby and to kiss me good night, I suddenly felt very tired. It had been a full day. Right in the beginning of my evening prayer: "I thank Thee, oh God, for these and all Thy gifts," I fell asleep. My last thought was:

"It—was—wonderful!"

# PHYLLIS McGINLEY

🐜 🐜

*From* On the Contrary.
"The Children's Hour"

THE melancholy days are come
That annually deposit

Beetles in the bureau drawers
And rocks in the closet;

Sprawling garments everywhere,
And all to take a stitch in;
Warnings from the janitor;
Complaints from the kitchen;

Salamanders in the sink,
From which the life's departed.
The camps are closed, the camps are closed,
And school hasn't started!

# SHIRLEY JACKSON

🦋 🦋

*The larger the family, the more complicated can be
the exact placement of blame for untoward incidents.
One such situation is explored in* Life Among the
Savages.

. . . I HAVE NEVER really believed that my husband is the
Kit Carson type, but it is remotely possible that occasionally a
feeling for the life romantic overcomes him; this air gun was
large and menacing and he told me, in that terribly responsible
voice men get to using when they are telling their wives about
machinery, or guns, or politics, that he got it for target practice.

There had been a rat in the cellar, he said; he was sure he had
seen a rat when he went down to start the furnace. So, of course,
he was going to shoot it. Not trap it or poison it—that was for boys
and terriers; *he* was going to shoot it.

For the better part of a Sunday morning he crouched dangerously at the open cellar door, waiting for the rat to show his
whiskers, which the rat was kind enough not to do. Our two

excellent cats were also staying inside, sitting complacently and with some professional interest directly behind my husband. The rat hunt was broken up when the kitchen door banged open and Laurie crashed in with three friends to see how his father shot the rat. Eventually, I suppose, the rat wandered off, although I do not see how he could conceivably have been frightened by the prospect of being shot. Probably he had never realized until then that he had strayed into a house with cats *and* children. At any rate, my husband and the cats, hunting in a pack, managed to bring down even better game; it must have been about the Tuesday after the rat hunt that our female cat, Ninki, who is something of a hunter, caught a chipmunk. She has done this before and will do it again, although I am sure she will never again ask my husband to sit in with her. The chipmunk she caught that morning—it was about nine-thirty—was not co-operative, and when Ninki brought him into the kitchen, where she usually brings chipmunks with some odd conviction that she must eat them in her own dish, the chipmunk ducked under her paw and raced madly to a rather tall plant on the window sill. The plant was just strong enough to bear the weight of one chipmunk, and Ninki, in a sort of frenzy, hurried into the dining room where my husband was just finishing his coffee and talked him into going into the kitchen to see her chipmunk in the plant. My husband took one look and went for his air gun.

Ninki was able to get onto the window sill, but the plant was tall enough and the pot it stood in shaky enough so that she could not quite reach the chipmunk, who was standing precariously on the very top of the plant. My husband drew a careful bead with the air gun and then found that unless he stepped up and held his weapon against the chipmunk's head, he stood a very good chance of missing the chipmunk, if not actually hitting the cat, who was a large and intrusive target.

By this time, of course, I had put down my coffee cup and was standing in the doorway between the kitchen and the dining room, safely out of range as women should be when men are hunting, and saying things like "Dear, why don't you put a paper bag over it or something and take it outside?" and "Dear, don't you think it would be easier if—"

Ninki was by this time irritated beyond belief by the general air of incompetence exhibited in the kitchen, and she went into the living room and got Shax, who is extraordinarily lazy and never catches his own chipmunks, but who is, at least, a cat, and preferable, Ninki saw clearly, to a man with a gun. Shax sized up the situation with a cynical eye, gave my husband and his gun the coldest look I have ever seen a cat permit himself, and then leaped onto the window sill and sat on the other side of the flowerpot. It made a pretty little tableau: Ninki and Shax sitting on either side of the flowerpot and the chipmunk sitting on top of the plant.

After a minute the chipmunk—feeling rightly that all eyes were upon him—fidgeted nervously, and the plant began to sway. As the chipmunk was very nervous and the top of the plant very supple, soon the top of the plant began to swing from side to side, like a pendulum, so that the chipmunk, going faster and faster, rocked over to one cat and then to the other, grazing a nose of each, while they backed away dubiously. My husband still had his aim on the chipmunk and *he* began to rock back and forth. When the cats finally realized what was happening, they took turns batting the chipmunk as he swung between them.

All of this happened so quickly that I believe—unless I prefer to move out I have no choice *but* to believe—that my husband pressed the trigger of the air gun without really meaning to, because it is certain that he missed the chipmunk and the cats, and hit the window. The crash sent cats, chipmunk, and Nimrod in all directions—the cats under the table, the chipmunk, with rare presence of mind, out the broken window, and my husband, with even rarer presence of mind, back to the dining room and to his seat at the table. I advanced from my post in the kitchen doorway and picked up the air gun from the floor; then, with what I regard as unique forbearance, I went for the broom and dustpan. All I permitted myself, spoken gently and without undue emphasis, was "Thank heaven Laurie is in school."

I was indulgent enough to return the air gun to my husband after a few days, but I would have thought that Ninki had more sense. Perhaps she never dreamed I would give the air gun back, or perhaps she just thought target practice around the house had been given up as impractical; perhaps, with some kind of feline optimism I cannot share, she believed that the chipmunk episode had been a freak, the sort of thing that might happen to any man confronting an oscillant chipmunk.

So it was not more than a week later that Ninki gave the air gun another chance. It was a cool evening, and I was lying on the couch with a blanket over me, reading a mystery story; my husband was sitting quietly in his chair reading the newspaper. We had just congratulated one another on the fact that it was now too late for casual guests to drop in, and my husband had mentioned three or four times that he thought he might like some of that pot roast in a sandwich before he went to bed. Then we heard Ninki's unmistakably triumphant mighty-hunter howl from the dining room.

"Look," I said apprehensively, "Ninki's got something, a mouse or something. *Make* her take it outside."

"She'll get it out by herself."

"But she'll chase it around and around and around the dining room and kill it there and—" I gulped unhappily "—eat it. Get it out *now* while it's still alive."

"She won't—" my husband began, when Ninki's triumphant wail broke off with a muffled oath and Ninki herself came hurriedly to the dining room door and stared compellingly at my husband.

"Do you *always* need help?" he asked her crossly. "Seems to me a great big cat like you—"

I shrieked. Ninki lifted her head resignedly, as one whose bitterest views of fate have been confirmed; my husband gasped. Ninki's supper, a full-grown and horribly active bat, was sweeping magnificently down the length of the living room. For a minute I watched it with my mouth open and then, still yelling, buried my head under the blanket.

"My gun," I heard my husband shouting at Ninki, "where is my gun?"

Even under the blanket I could hear the flap of the bat's wings as it raced up and down the living room; I put my knees under my chin and my arms over my head and huddled under the blanket. Outside, they were stalking the bat; I could hear my husband tiptoeing warily down the room, with Ninki apparently right behind him, because he was saying, "Don't *hurry*, for heaven's sake, give me a chance to *aim*."

A hideous thought came to me. "Is it on me?" I said through my teeth, "just tell me once is it on me, on the blanket? Ninki, *is it?* Is it?"

"Now you just stay perfectly still," my husband said reassuringly. "These things never stay in one place for very long. Why, only the other day I was reading in the paper about a woman who—"

"Is it on the *blanket?*" I insisted hysterically, "on *me?*"

"Listen," my husband said crossly, "if you keep on shaking like that, I'll *never* be able to hit it. Hold still, and I'm sure to miss you."

I do not know what the official world's record might be for getting out from under a blanket, flying across a room, opening a door and a screen door, and getting outside onto a porch with both doors closed behind you, but if it is more than about four seconds I broke it. I thought the bat was chasing me, for one thing. And I knew that, if the bat was chasing me, my husband was aiming that gun at it, wherever it was. Outside on the porch, I leaned my head against the middle pillar and breathed hard.

Inside, there was a series of crashes. I recognized the first as the report of the air gun. The second sounded irresistibly like a lamp going over, which is what it turned out to be. The third I could not identify from the porch, but my husband said later that it was Ninki trying to get out of the way of the air gun and knocking over the andirons. Then my husband spoke angrily to Ninki, and Ninki snarled. Each of them, it seemed, thought the other one had frightened the bat, which had left the blanket when I did, although not half so fast, and was now circling gaily around the chandelier.

"Come on in," my husband said through the door; he tried to open it but I was hanging on from the outside. "Come on in, it won't hurt you. I promise it won't."

"I'll stay out here," I said.

"It's just as frightened as you are," he said.

"It is *not*," I said.

Then he apparently spoke to Ninki again, because he said excitedly, "It's landing; keep away now, you'll be hurt."

There was a great noise of rushing and snarling and shooting, then a long silence. Finally I asked softly, "Are you all right?"

Another silence. "Are you all *right?*" I said.

Another silence. I opened the door a crack and peered in cautiously. My husband was sitting on the couch, beating his hands on his knees. The air gun was on the floor. Ninki and the bat were gone.

"Is it all right to come in?" I asked.

"I don't know," my husband said, looking at me bitterly, "have you got a ticket?"

"I mean," I said, "where's the bat?"

"She's taken it into the dining room," my husband said.

There was a nick in the wallpaper over the couch. In the dining room Ninki was growling pleasurably, deep in her throat. "She went faster than the pellet, is all," my husband said reasonably. "I was just getting ready to aim and she passed me and passed the pellet and hit the bat just as the pellet hit the wall."

"Hadn't you better get it out of the dining room?" I asked.

He began to beat his knees again. I went back to the couch, shook the blanket thoroughly to make sure there had been only one bat on it and that one was gone, and settled down in my chair with my mystery story. After a while Ninki came out of the dining room, nodded contemptuously at my husband, glanced at me and, with a grin at the air gun, got onto my husband's chair and went to sleep on his paper.

I took the air gun and put it on the top shelf of the pantry, where I believe it still is. Now and then it occurs to me that in case of burglars I can take it down to protect the house, but I really think one of the kitchen knives would be safer, if Ninki is not around to take care of me.

It was only the next morning that the man came to fix the glass in the kitchen window, and when Laurie, who was on his reluctant way to school, told the man his father had shot it out with a gun, I laughed cheerily and remarked that boys always had such good stories to cover their own misdeeds. Laurie looked at me in honest indignation, and I told him that he could take a package of gum from the pantry. Although I do not believe in actually encouraging children to tell lies, and do not in any case suppose that one pack of gum can cover up a flagrance like that one, Laurie gave every impression of being satisfied to share a joke about his father. It never occurred to me that the foundations of our parental authority were being slowly shattered until he came home from school some three or four days later with his jacket torn and an air of great innocent suffering. He was half an hour late, and he was accompanied by two of his friends, both of unsavory character; they strode manfully into the house and on into the study where my husband was peacefully doing research for an article on extinct fishes. I heard part of the conversation from upstairs where I was trying to dress Jannie after her nap. With my mind almost unoccupied, I listened without any real attention. "And they threw stones," one of Laurie's friends said in a thin, excited voice; he is somewhat older than Laurie, and he usually tells Laurie's stories for him when Laurie is too modest to tell them for himself, "and they said *terrible* language, and they *hit* Laurie, and *everything.*"

"Where were *you* all this time?" my husband asked. I could feel through the floor the righteous indignation mounting in the study. "Where were you two while these boys were hitting Laurie?"

There was a moment of quiet, and then Laurie's voice: "George was behind the tree, and William was running up here to tell you." Laurie apparently stopped to think for a minute. "I didn't run," he added finally, "because I *can't* very well, in these snow pants."

The enemy—I could see them from the upstairs front window—were still lingering outside, backing down the hill slowly, prepared to do further battle. Then I heard the front door slam. My husband issued forth, supported valiantly on either side by Laurie's two friends, while Laurie, with commendable discretion, stayed just inside the front door, yelling, "Here comes my *father!*"

Halfway up the hill, the enemy waited for my husband, and, although I could not hear, I could see them—my husband speaking fiercely and the enemy looking at him with wide, honest eyes. Presently the battle was resolved; my husband turned and stamped back to the house and the enemy went on down the hill, turning at a safe distance to call inaudible insults.

When my husband came inside, I went downstairs to meet him. "Well?" I said.

All of them began talking at once. "And they *hit* Laurie and *every*thing," his talkative friend said; "They even chased *me*," his other friend added.

"And these darn old snow pants," Laurie said at the same time, while over all of them rose the voice of my husband saying, "Ought to be taught better manners. Boy like that deserves a good whipping."

Jannie came down the stairs behind me, asking hopefully, "Was Laurie bad? I'm good, aren't I? Did Laurie do something *new* bad?"

When I had isolated the various political maneuvers into offense and defense, the story went something like this: Laurie and his two friends were walking home from school, entirely without malice, not hurting anybody and minding their own business. As a matter of fact, they stopped quite of their own accord to pick up the books of a little girl who had dropped them into a mud puddle. Furthermore, they were not even thinking any harm, because they were all three most unpleasantly surprised when the largest of the enemy, a boy named David Howell, came up behind them and pulled on the hood of Laurie's jacket. When Laurie said "Hey!"—and we all agreed he was perfectly justified—David spat at him, pronounced half a dozen forbidden epithets, and finally struck him. Laurie's two friends took no active part in the battle, partly because David was bigger than any of them and partly because, as they explained at great length, they felt strongly that it was Laurie's fight and interference would not be sporting. They had come home with Laurie, however, to be his witnesses and to see that justice was done.

"What did you do to David?" I asked my husband.

"I said you'd tell his mother," he said virtuously.

I have seen David's mother, have even spoken to her at P.-T.A. meetings. She is one of those impressive women who usually head committees on supervising movies, taking the entire sixth grade on a tour of one of our local factories, or outlawing slingshots, and I daresay she would be the first person everyone would think of if there should arise an occasion for the mothers to lift the school building and carry it bodily to another location. I felt very strongly, as a matter of fact, that bringing David's mother into this incident was a grave tactical error.

But there were the four of them looking at me trustingly—five, if you count Jannie, who was saying "Poor, poor Laurie," and rubbing his head violently.

"I'll phone her right away," I said, trying to make it sound resolute and threatening. After some unavoidable fumbling with the telephone book I found the Howells' number and finally, with everyone sitting around the phone expectantly, cleared my throat, straightened my shoulders, and briskly gave the number to the operator. After a minute, a strong, no-nonsense voice said "Hello?"

"Hello," I said faintly, "is this Mrs. Howell?"

"Yes," she said. She sounded quite civil, so I changed my mind and said as politely as I could, "Mrs. Howell, I don't know if your boy David has told you about attacking my son Laurie on his way home from school today, but I thought I'd better call you anyway and see if we can't do something about it." Realizing that I had ended a little weakly, I added, "Laurie is *quite* badly hurt."

Laurie looked up, gratified, and nodded. "Tell her I'm dead," he said.

"Mrs. Howell," I said into the phone, scowling at Laurie, "I *do* think that a boy so much bigger than Laurie—a boy so much bigger, as David is—I mean, David is so much bigger than Laurie that I *do* think—"

All this time Mrs. Howell had been silent. Now she said amiably, "I quite agree with you, of course. But I can't quite believe this of David; David is such a *quiet* boy. Is your little boy sure it wasn't David Williams or David Martin?"

"Are you sure it wasn't David Williams or David Martin?" I asked hopefully of the audience beyond the telephone. They all shook their heads violently, and one of Laurie's friends—the one who ran—said enthusiastically, "I know David Howell, and it was him all right. Anyway, he's always doing things like this. Two, three times now, he's hit Laurie. And me, too. He hits everybody."

"It was certainly your David," I said to Mrs. Howell. "They all agree on that. He picked a fight with Laurie on the way home from school and really hurt Laurie *quite* badly."

"Well," she said. "I'll certainly speak to David," she added after a minute.

"Thank you," I said, perfectly content to depart with this empty triumph, but my husband said, "Tell her he was fresh to me, too."

"He was fresh to my husband, too," I said obediently into the phone.

"Really?" Mrs. Howell said, as though David were fresh to her husband all the time and this was no surprise. "Well," she said again, "I'll certainly speak to him."

"Tell her he's hit me lots of times," Laurie said.

"Don't forget the bad words," one of Laurie's friends prompted.

"Make it really forceful," my husband said. "Why should he get away with a thing like this?"

"Will you see that this is stopped once and for all?" I demanded emphatically into the phone.

Her voice sharpened. "I *said* I'd speak to David," she repeated ominously.

We were congratulating one another on our victory when the phone rang. "This is Mrs. Howell," she said when I answered, and her voice had lost much of its civility. "I spoke to David," she went on. "I told you I would. And it seems that David was not entirely at fault." She dwelt on the last few words as though they gave her some fierce pleasure.

"I don't understand," I said. "Laurie was just walking along the—"

"I beg your pardon," she said, still with great relish. "What about the rock he threw at David?"

I looked at Laurie over the top of the phone, and he returned my glance with sober earnestness. "What rock?" I said, and Laurie's gaze did not waver, but an odd sort of reminiscent pleasure crept into his eye.

"Laurie," said Mrs. Howell plainly, "threw a rock and hit David in the head. There's a big big bump. David hadn't done *anything* up to then. But if your little boy throws rocks, I can hardly blame—"

I retreated abruptly to safer ground. "Surely," I said, "you are not going to say that there is *any* excuse for a bigger boy hitting a smaller boy?"

"I shall certainly speak to David about that," she said stiffly. "But then, when Laurie's father called David a little sneak and said he ought to be horsewhipped—"

"What about what David called Laurie?" I countered tellingly. "It was so bad that Laurie wouldn't dream of repeating it."

Laurie and his two friends immediately said loudly what it was.

"Your husband said David ought to be horsewhipped," she said, not shaken, and almost, I thought, as though he were not actually the first person who had suggested major punishment for David, "and poor little David tried to tell him that Laurie had been throwing rocks. You really *ought* to do something about a child throwing rocks. None of *my* children throw rocks; it's something I can't stand. But poor little David—"

"David did so throw rocks," I said. "And if my husband said—"

"I did not say it," my husband said.

"Surely there is no excuse," she said, "for a grown man to pick on a poor little boy."

I backed up again. "What about poor little Laurie?" I asked. "He was *quite* badly hurt. Surely there is no excuse—"

"Poor little David—" she began.

"And my poor little—" I said, and then started again. "My husband, I mean. What about the names they yelled at *him?*"

I was suddenly reminded of the time Mrs. Howell had taken part in a local debate, holding and maintaining with absolute conviction the position that our state should secede from the United States to avoid having its natural resources completely depleted. "Furthermore—" she was saying.

"What a way to bring up a child," I said gently. "What kind of a mother are you?"

My audience, I perceived, was growing restless. Laurie's two friends were putting on their overshoes; Laurie himself had entered into an elaborately casual game with Jannie that had taken them almost to the kitchen doorway, and my husband was sauntering almost noiselessly back to the study.

"Now you listen to me," Mrs. Howell began, her voice rising, "now you listen to me—"

I hung up gracefully and followed Laurie into the kitchen.

"Laurie," I said sternly, "did you throw a rock at David?"

Laurie pondered, frowning, his head on one side and one finger thoughtfully tapping his cheek. "I forget," he said at last.

"Try to remember," I said threateningly. Laurie shook his head in despair.

"I just forget," he said.

I went to the study door. "Did you call David a little sneak?" I demanded.

My husband looked up from his article on extinct fishes. "A little what?" he said.

"A little sneak."

"Don't be ridiculous," my husband said. "Why would I call what's-his-name a little sneak?" He turned back to his article. "Are you still worrying about *that?*" he asked.

The phone rang. I strode over and slammed it out of the receiver. "Well?" I said.

"If you think you can just hang up on people just because your son is a little bully and goes around throwing rocks and—"

"If you think you and your half-witted David can get away with picking on every child in the neighborhood just because he's overgrown and stupid—"

"If you would care to—"

"Perhaps *you* would like to—"

We hung up simultaneously. My husband opened the study door and looked out. "Who were you talking to?" he asked.

"Look," I said, "if you'd just take care of your own affairs and let Laurie fight his own battles and not come to me to—"

"I'm good, aren't I?" Jannie said. She came over and pulled at my hand. "I'm *good,* aren't I?"

My husband said loudly, "Let's box for a while, son. Get the gloves." Without looking at me he added, "We'll box out in the woodshed. Then," he said thoughtfully, "the noise won't bother Mother when she's on the phone."

"Aren't I?" said Jannie urgently. "*Aren't* I?"

I reached for the phone, and then hesitated. It was time to start the potatoes for dinner; I had a quick picture of Mrs. Howell peeling potatoes with one hand while she held a phone with the other, and I heard Laurie yelp as he walked into what was almost certainly a right cross.

"Want to help Mommy make dinner?" I asked Jannie.

Mrs. Howell and I met at the meat counter in the grocery the next morning; she smiled and I smiled and then she said, "How is Laurie today?"

"He seems much better, thanks," I said solemnly. "And David?"

"Fairly well," she said without turning a hair.

"Horrible little beasts," I said.

"Liars, all of them," she said. "*I* never believe a word they say."

We both laughed and turned to regard the meat. "They certainly do eat, though," she said mournfully. "I suppose it's hamburger again today."

"I was thinking about liver," I said.

"Will Laurie eat liver?" she asked with interest. "David won't touch it; do you cook it any special way?"


# ERNEST JONES

꿋 꿋

*When Sigmund Freud's studies of family relationships began to filter into the public consciousness, there were those who thought he meant to destroy the family. That this was untrue is attested by Freud's autobiographical writings. And in* Free Associations, Memories of a Psycho-analyst, *Ernest Jones, one of Freud's chief disciples and biographers, recalls his own family in quiet and loving detail.*


THE STOCK from which I sprang is, I fancy, characteristic for those Welshmen who have managed to play a part outside their native land, so I will say something of it; what I have to narrate is based only on immediate knowledge, assisted, it is true, by several family Bibles in my possession, since I have never been concerned to institute any genealogical researches. Probably most readers will do well to skip these dry details. So far as I can judge, the direct influence of my parents seems to me more important mentally than what I can trace of hereditary agencies.

Of the patronymic sources I know little. My father's paternal grandfather, Thomas Jones, was in charge of a colliery's pit ponies, and migrated from Merthyr Tydfil to Swansea, where he worked in a livery stable, but, unlike Keats's father in a similar situation, omitted to marry his master's daughter; he was illiterate, as I know from the cross he affixed to his son's indenture of apprenticeship. His son, John Jones, whom I just remember, was a self-employed carpenter. I am told that he had the habit of taking refuge from his wife's tongue by immersing himself in the light literature, the counterpart of our detective stories, of the day, though, even so, she was apt to remove his "farthing dip" as an unnecessary extravagance, leaving the poor man in the dark. More complete, though temporary, escapes were afforded by embarking on long voyages, even round the world, as a ship's carpenter, and I recall my fondness for the souvenirs of those voyages, huge tortoise-shells and the like. My grandmother certainly had a vivid personality. I saw nothing of her reputed shrewishness—though my mother told me she was a thorn in her flesh in the early days of her son's marriage—partly because by then time had softened that aspect of her nature and partly because she allowed herself to show an affection for me which apparently she had been wont to check with her own children. The impression she left on me was that of an intelligent, kindly woman with a caustic turn to her speech and a devastatingly disillusioning vision of reality. She was given to expressing her views on life in proverbial sayings, a habit I seem to have acquired from her. She would, for instance, usually diminish the proportions of any family dispute with the words: "It will be all the same in a hundred years."

Her father, Joseph Beddoe, belonged to a branch of the Shropshire Beddoe family who had settled in Gorseinon (midway between Swansea and Llanelly) in the seventeenth century. At the end of the eighteenth century, one of them was drowned with his son when ferrying across the River Llwchwr; it always struck me as a particularly unmerited fate, since they were on their way to a chapel service to which they had piously walked several miles. Her mother, Ann Rees by name, came from Old Walls in the Welsh part of Gower. I well remember this old lady and the sponge cakes I used to buy for her as a delicacy in her toothless old age. She had been married to a weaver from Penmaen, also in Gower, but he had died at the age of forty-nine, so that she had to spend thirty-seven years as a widow; her daughter was to pass forty-three years in that state. Undeterred by her fate, she migrated to Swansea to be near her only daughter, whom my grandfather married in the same year, and took over the brewing department of the Red Cow in the High Street. Her mother, Margaret David of Llanrhidian, lived to be eighty-four, she herself lived to be eighty-one, and her daughter to be ninety-one. She was born in 1808, and so could relate to me memories of the Napoleonic wars. She of course never saw the great man herself but, incidentally, many years later I met another old lady who had—in Torbay.

Some of the Beddoe attributes appear to belong to dominant genes, for they have faithfully manifested themselves down the generations, and I have felt justified in giving the name to each of my sons. I did so in a vain endeavour to lessen the handicap my patronymic ancestry had laid on me. It is statistically demonstrable that the odds are heavy against anyone achieving distinction in life if he has to share his surname with hundreds of thousands of his contemporaries. Among the many handicaps that the Welsh share with the Jews, such as their outworn attachment to the Old Testament, not the least was the acquisition of surnames in unfortunate circumstances; and one can foresee a time when, if these attributes are to fulfil their proper function, an extensive re-naming will have to take place. To get back to the immediate theme: I have always fancied that if my father and I inherited an I.Q. higher than that of our relatives it probably came, via his mother, from the Beddoe stock. At one time I even toyed with the idea of hyphenating the name with my surname, but Freud dissuaded me on the ground of its being confusing.

My maternal heredity was almost as uninspiring. My mother's paternal grandfather, John Lewis, was a mason at Llandilo—the scene now shifts to the county of Caermarthen; he had come there from Llangefelach, once famous for its animal fair and now the site of an enormous steel works. Her father, Benjamin Lewis, who died when I was nine years old, had moved to Swansea. He was a competent architect and contractor, building railway stations, docks, and other constructions, and he tried to get me to follow in his footsteps by presenting me with his tomes on architecture. His biblical first name, so common in Wales, led to a curious contretemps in the time of the Nazi regime. His niece was married to a German in Berlin, the Herr Schmidt who managed the Adlon Hotel. The Nazis insisted that her maiden name, Lewis (like Louis, a corruption of the very Teutonic Ludwig), must be a corruption of Levi, and the fact of her grandfather being called David and her uncle Benjamin seemed to clinch the matter of her supposed Jewish origin. She had to appeal to me to verify her descent.

My grandfather was an attractive but eccentric person, with an all-or-nothing attitude towards life. He had a deep suspicion of doctors and their ways, and on the rare occasions when he was persuaded to listen to one he would say with a sigh of irritation: "Well, I'll give them another chance," and drink down the whole bottle of medicine at one gulp; the results at times confirmed his worst suspicions. Fifty years after his death his daughter, my mother's only sister, followed his example with a lethal result. She had been given some anti-thrombotic medicine for purpura in the skin, swallowed the whole of it, and promptly died of a pontine haemorrhage. Once my grandfather's wife commissioned him to buy some wallpaper for a bedroom that wanted repapering. In the course of the morning a van appeared and to her great dismay the unloading continued until one of their two living-rooms was chock-full of the material her obedient, or contumacious, husband had requisitioned—my earliest experience of sabotage. In his later years he took to drinking more than was good for him, and it became one of my duties—for I often stayed with these grandparents in their home in Swansea—to fetch him home from his haunts of revelry in the local pub—a summons he never failed to obey. This conduct saddened my saintly mother and, pursued by the fear, which had been increased by injudicious reading on the subject of heredity, that this trait would reappear in her son, she tried hard to bind me to total abstinence. Never having perceived in myself any sign of this dreaded inheritance, I saw no necessity for such an extreme measure. My grandfather and I were greatly attached to each other and my father must have thought he spoiled me. At all events, I recall his strongly disapproving what he considered the precocious proceeding of my grandfather replacing my petticoats by a pair of knickerbockers at the early age of four. My grandfather had a long stride and I evidently imitated him in this as well as no doubt in other ways, for I was much surprised in my early teens at being stopped by a stranger in a street in Swansea with the remark: "You must be a grandson of Benjamin Lewis, for you walk just like him."

My maternal grandmother was a Miss Jones, who married a Mr. Lewis, whilst my mother reversed the proceeding—not a difficult feat in Wales. She was gentle, refined, and had some aesthetic appreciation, but with a softer type of intellect than my paternal grandmother; she tried to instil into me various medical supersititions of the herbalist variety which my more robust Beddoe blood promptly rejected. She used to tell me tales of the Rebecca riots of the eighteen-forties and of the alarm felt when the rioting approached Swansea. Her family came from Llandybie, near Llandilo, and her mother, Ann Morris by name, was the only member of my immediate ancestry with some pretension to being "wellborn"; the town of Morriston is named after her family. I was told that she had eloped with my great-grandfather, who was merely an employee on the estate. I possess a photograph of her in her fifties with her granddaughter, my mother, standing at her knee.

My maternal grandmother's father and brother, together with a friend called Davies, were drawn by the Australian gold rush of the 'fifties. On the way there they were wrecked on the coast of Ireland, and Davies, having had enough, went home and made a fortune in the tin-plate trade. His son became a fashionable London doctor and his grandson a distinguished surgeon, Morriston Davies, and a close friend of mine. We were entertained on discovering our ancestral friendship. The more pertinacious couple, however, proceeded on their way and apparently achieved their object, for a year or so later a cheque for £300 turned up as a first instalment of their gains. Then silence fell and no more was ever heard of them; presumably they were murdered or perished in some epidemic. My poor grandmother, not over-endowed with worldly wisdom, hoarded the cheque for a rainy day and was much distressed on discovering, more than fifty years later, that it was no longer valid. These were far from being the only adventurous members of my family: as a boy I used to exchange Christmas greetings with others in Canada, India, Italy, Natal, Australia, and the United States. But that particular family contributed its full share to the *wanderlust* that had led to their father's destruction. The eldest, Morris, became a farmer at Nelson, Ontario. The next, Richard, was the one who perished with his father in Australia. Then came my Uncle Tom, the only one to stay at home, whose son Herbert was in school with me. The next brother, Herbert, spent his life at sea, and the youngest, Henry, settled in Ohio.

I come now to much more important people in my life—my parents. My father was twenty-five years old when I was born, and my mother twenty-three. My father, Thomas Jones (1853–1920), was tall, blond, handsome—evidently a Celt. My mother, on the other hand, was rather short, quite dark, and very pale—the "Iberian" type of Welsh. Theirs must have been a wonderful love-match, as I gathered from many hints my mother dropped about love-letters and the poetry they shared, and the marriage was a completely happy one. I never heard a cross or even impatient word pass between them. My mother was the more openly affectionate of the two, and had little of my father's noteworthy restraint of emotion. Save for some deep inner reserve, which probably no one ever penetrated, I should say he was as mentally "normal" as one could reasonably expect, and for a psycho-analyst to say this means a great deal.

My father had a good grasp of the fundamentals of science, and was also pretty well read in the main English classics of prose and poetry.

He underwent a notable change in character after his three children were born, one of which my mother by no means fully approved. As a youth he had been very serious and rather stern, with unusually high aspirations of a moral order. The eldest of a family of six, he had psychologically replaced his father as the responsible head of the family at an early age. I may quote an example of this attitude. His next brother, John, had enlisted in the cavalry, but complained bitterly at having to regroom his mount whenever the officer found a stain on his white gloves when stroking it. So my father, at the cost of postponing his wedding for a year, bought him out—a dubious piece of kind-heartedness. The week after, John enlisted in the infantry, where he served for many years in Egypt and India. I know, particularly from the time of his last illness, that there was a deep bond between my father and his mother, who survived him, but I imagine it never found expression on either side. She certainly brought him up severely, with no "nonsense," as she would no doubt have termed any sign of sentiment, and what she expected of him he expected of himself. He early became converted to Baptism—also my mother's faith, hence their meeting—by the great preacher of the same name as himself, Thomas Jones, the father of three famous sons, one of whom was Principal of the University College of South Wales in my student days there. Furthermore he insisted on having the rest of the family baptised, except the youngest who escaped on the score of age. Like most Welshmen of that generation he was Radical in politics and entertained lofty hopes of social brotherhood in the future. The first of the many later discussions in which I have had to partici-pate on the old theme of relative importance of the inner and the outer world, of environment versus heredity, nurture versus nature—there are many variations of it—was between my parents, since my father believed in progress by means of material better-ment while my mother pinned her faith to internal regeneration, of course in religious terms. My father was the more convincing at the time, but on looking back I wonder whether my mother was not the nearer to the truth; I will not, however, embark on this theme, which would demand a book to itself.

Well, such was my father at the time of my birth. Shortly before this they had removed from Swansea to Gowerton, as it is now called, and that meant trudging six miles each way—there being then no Sunday trains in Wales—to attend the Sabbath service. In the village there were at least four chapels, among them a Baptist one, but the services were all in Welsh, a language in which my father was far from proficient. (My mother knew it well, and thereby hangs another tale. She had been sent for a year or two to a remote farm in Brecon to perfect it. And when, more than seventy years later, I engaged a teacher in London to gratify my little daughter's wish to learn Welsh, what was my amazement to find that she came from that very same farm!) Admittedly this was a severe strain in wintry weather, and my father fell from grace. Perhaps marriage, providing a solution of the sexual problem, had something to do with the relieving of his rigid principles, as may have also the "hardshell" intolerance of the local Baptists. Be that as it may, fortunately for us he took to attending the Church of England service and we children were brought up under that aegis.

I remember, however, being somewhat shocked when, at about the age of nine, I learnt of this apostasy of my father's. I had been delving into some of his Baptist literature and had been persuaded of the propriety of their two main contentions. One of them turns on the Protestant view that the moral responsibility of the individual cannot with advantage be shifted. Put anthropologically, it is plain that baptism, like circumcision, tattooing, and other similar rites, is an initiation ceremony that belongs to puberty, not to infancy. Or, in more modern language, sin is a personal matter that must be dealt with at a suitable age and cannot be dispelled at birth on the plea of its being inherited. A friend of mine, wishing to visit Sweden, bought a conversational manual in the hope of being able to deal with porters. The first sentence in it was the unexpectedly mandatory one: "Do not implant a prejudice in the mind of a child," and I do not fancy he ever had the opportunity of using it in his capacity as a tourist. Now the ceremony of christening, with all it implies, decidedly contravenes the Swedish exhortation, and some people think that it takes an unfair advantage of the plastic mind of the child. The second Baptist contention is less interesting, though it seems logical enough, if somewhat pedantic: it is simply that, if one holds with following the actual teaching and example of Jesus, one can hardly deny that he believed in the efficacy of total immersion of the body in sanctified water as the best means of purifying it of its sins.

Though it never occurred to me to be baptised, I exploited the idea when in school to avoid being confirmed in Church, alleging that my parents were Baptists and wouldn't like it; it greatly annoyed the headmaster, who in the most materialistic fashion was roping into the "confirmation class" all the boys he could with the obvious aim of making a good impression on the ecclesiastical authorities; he became a bishop not long after. As a result of all this I have never passed through any religious ceremony, at birth, puberty, or marriage, and it is certain there will not be one when I die.

To return to my father. His backsliding proved a turning-point in his life, since it was followed by a notable change in character. He began with being strict in his attendance, and ours, at Sunday morning service, but it took me only a couple of years' pleading before I got at least let off the Sunday school in the afternoons. He was never a member of the Congregation, and so never communicated, but that did not prevent his being made a church-warden. The previous one, an apparently very pious old gentleman, had purloined the church funds, and the authorities apparently came to the conclusion that honesty possessed certain advantages over orthodoxy. Whether this piece of cynicism finished my father or not, he evidently felt that strict attendance to his new financial duties absolved him from the need for further Sabbatarian obligations, much to the relief of all of us except perhaps my mother. His religious beliefs faded and he must have been a complete atheist after the age of forty.

Two modes of expression remained for what was left of his former ideals and principles. One was the faithful pursuit of social activities: School Board, Parish and District Councils, and the like. He took charge of the higher education of the neighbour-hood, and I remember a series of examiners dining with us on their way to the South Kensington Science and Art examinations that were then the vogue; I attended some of the courses myself on steam, electricity, and other technical subjects. The other expression was the highest level of integrity in business matters. On one occasion he and a friend spent four long evenings in chasing through numerous ledgers in pursuit of an elusive two-pence whose absence marred the perfection of the annual balance sheet, nor were they to be deflected by the bribes offered by their distracted wives. I was brought up to believe not merely that "business is business" and must come first before all other human considerations, but that such dictates of the Manchester school were the only sound basis for civilisation, chaos being the alternative. I remember at the age of eight being disturbed at hearing that the great firm of the neighbourhood, of which more anon, made a present of a turkey to each employee at Christmas. It seemed an irrelevant intrusion into what ought to have been a definite "business" relationship: what would happen to a clear-cut scheme of the universe if that sort of thing were allowed to go on? I need scarcely say that my father was highly amused at finding me adopt his business principles so literally.

The change in character to which I have alluded consisted essentially in an all-round relaxing and softening of various previously rigid attitudes. He became more tolerant, less strict, and in general more easy-going. On the other hand, and this was the aspect my mother regretted, he became less idealistic, less serious, more mundane, and perhaps more commonplace—more bourgeois. This tendency increased with the years as he rose in the world until at the end he could be distinguished from the average industrialist only by a certain air of distinction, a specially high standard of integrity and general trustworthiness, and a rare tender-heartedness. The change in question clashed with the idealism that naturally accompanied my own adolescence, so that I found his conversation less and less interesting, whereas in my childhood it had been inspiring. It was he who gave me my respect for science, and my devotion to its ideals.

I have said nothing so far about my father's career. Although he was a man at ease in every social *milieu*, his beginnings were humble enough and he was throughout a self-made man. He began life as a clerk in the well-known coal firm of Messrs. Cory; at the end of his life he took over the estate where his former chief had lived. He studied hard—I still possess his books from those days on astronomy, navigation, and other scientific or technical subjects—qualified as a colliery engineer, and was at the time of his early marriage the manager of a colliery near Gowerton. Soon after my birth he took the post of accountant at a large steel works, Messrs. Wright, Butler & Co., where he was before long made the general secretary. The firm, which is now an important constituent of the Baldwin amalgamation, had many ramifications; it possessed collieries, and also iron-ore mines in Spain and Italy, which my father had often to visit, so that his work was far from monotonous. In the late forties, in pique at not being granted the partnership he had been promised, he retired, but before long immersed himself in fresh undertakings, chiefly in his first love— coal; his last years seemed to be spent passing from one meeting to another of various Boards of Directors in Cardiff and London. Altogether a typical Samuel Smiles hero, and one of the better products of the "liberal" industrial era of good Queen Victoria.

Two of his failings were specially destined to deepen the inevitable rift between son and father. They were a difficulty in admitting that he could ever not be in the right—which of course gave me no chance of ever being so myself unless I accepted his every opinion—and the belief that young people should be kept very much in their place—a decidedly subordinate one; I was far from being the only youth to suffer from this latter characteristic, his younger brother being another. In fact, my father's retirement from the firm was induced by his resentment at being passed over by a callow youth, Charlie Wright, who, however, possessed the advantage of being the son of the senior partner. Being a specially argumentative youngster myself, I was in for trouble; and it came to a head when I was about thirteen. It began with an acrimonious argument about the theory of the siphon pump, and to this day I do not know which of us was in the right. I am afraid my sharp and perhaps impertinent retorts caused my poor father much pain; he had no recourse but to withdraw somewhat from me for a time, though he always retained a deep affection for me. His own characteristics did not change much, but I could afford to be amused when at the age of forty I was informed that I had travelled to Paris by the "wrong" route.

Of my mother, Mary Ann (May), *née* Lewis (1855-1909), I shall say less. A mother's influence, though more profound, is less tangible. My mother's influence over me did not continue much beyond the age of eight, and it made no direct contribution to my intellectual development, whereas my father's certainly did— between the ages of eight and thirteen. She was a most tender and affectionate mother, and completely devoted to me. Yet she did not spoil me; indeed, she often enough remonstrated with my shortcomings, particularly my argumentativeness, and I can still see her warning me by pointing at my tongue, which she maintained was "sharp as a needle." Its quickness of response has often got me into trouble, but I nevertheless sympathised when later on I read T. H. Huxley's remark in the same connection that in spite of its disadvantages he would part more readily with most of his gifts sooner than his mother-wit. I knew well enough, however, as she explicitly told me, that nothing I could do would ever forfeit her affection and sympathy. An early relationship of this kind, as Freud has truly remarked, provides an unshakable basis for self-confidence in later life, and that I have never lacked. The only difference of opinion that ever arose between us—and it was doubtless a grave one—did so involuntarily on both sides. When I was three months old she was taken with rheumatic fever and that of course disturbed our intimacy. Anxious to do what she could to remedy the situation, she obtained various patent and well-advertised milk foods, which effectively deprived me of all vitamins. In consequence I was a puny and ailing infant, with pronounced rickets and a not very happy disposition. She was the most thoroughly and yet unostentatiously self-effacing woman I have known, devoted to the interests of her husband, her children, relatives, neighbours, house, and garden. She was thought highly of in the neighbourhood for her good works and unfailing kindness. She worked hard and unceasingly, and was extremely competent. She had a shrewd judgment, and my father constantly sought her advice in his affairs; he also found her useful in the check she gently imposed on his somewhat impulsive tendencies.

On looking back I think my mother must have had a slightly snobbish outlook—though I am not using the term in Thackeray's sense of "meanly admiring mean things." She did, however, think it seemly to aspire to a higher social status. When I rejected, and quite decisively, her suggestion that I enter the Church and announced my intention of becoming a doctor, she reflected that those were the two people who had an *entrée* everywhere. My wish was certainly unaffected by any such consideration; it had far deeper roots. Nevertheless, in my youth I can recall having a somewhat similar attitude to my mother's, and I still find it hard to understand those of the younger generation whose aim is to ape the manners and speech of classes below their own in the hierarchy. Fortunately, belonging to a profession obviates the question of one's "class," and makes it easy to be on instinctively natural terms with all varieties of one's fellow-beings.

Living in the country in those days was a very different matter from what it is now. For light the poor had candles, the others oil lamps. One cooked meat on a spit before an open fire and the basting was an interesting ceremony. All bread was made at home and it was my task to fetch the "barm" or yeast. The barm came from a shop belonging to a grocer who had spent some time in America, so we always spoke of the "American shop." We acquired also in this way a familiarity with American slang terms, such as "gosh," which in the early 'eighties could hardly have been widespread in this country. Laundries were unheard of, so that washing, mangling, and ironing took up a great part of two days a week. We had a cask of rain water, but the rest had to be fetched from a well a mile and a half away. I commonly accompanied this expedition through the woods; the servants of several houses would join together for the opportunity of gossip and to heave the heavy jars on to each other's shoulders after climbing stiles. Later on my grandfather was called in to build a reservoir in the hills and supply the village with water—a great event. I have retained a distinct memory of the prices of certain provisions my mother used to buy from vendors who brought them to her house. Eggs, for instance, were sixpence a dozen and would no longer be bought at the time of year when they reached the exorbitant price of tenpence. Butter, brought on cool cabbage leaves, was ninepence or tenpence a pound.

To complete my description of the domestic life I should say that the house consisted of eight rooms. The downstairs ones were in my early childhood labelled in order kitchen, dining-room, back parlour, front parlour. When I was about six or seven, however, my parents invested in a modern enclosed cooking stove, and that altered the nomenclature to scullery, kitchen, dining- and sitting-room, drawing-room.

My mother retained her piety longer than my father, and we

would occasionally discover her rather shamefacedly reading the Bible. She was a faithful reader of the *Christian World*, though I suspect it was more for the weekly epitome of current events than for truly religious reasons. She would dole out to us items of stale news from this source for days afterwards. She was so easily shocked that when one spoke to her she at once put on a shocked expression in preparation for what might come. This reaction, though habitual, was fairly superficial, for it was seldom followed by any condemnation: she did not sit in judgment on her fellows. She had a very anxious temperament, and in my later boyhood it became related to constant illness and pain. She suffered from a gynaecological affection. This was finally cured, at a time when I was in my hospital studies, by an operation performed by Sir John Williams. It was an occasion for my having an interview with the famous man who brought two kings of England into the world; I had heard him lecture from time to time at the hospital, although he had by then retired to the consulting staff. He did not make any great impression on me, but I revere his memory, since few men have done more for their native land than John Williams did in his years of assiduous collecting of priceless historical manuscripts, the basis of the National Library of Wales which he subsequently founded. I had one more interview with him, in an agreeable *viva voce* examination, after which he awarded me the M.B. Gold Medal and Scholarship in Midwifery.

After this operation my mother enjoyed good health, and more affluent circumstances, combined with release from the upbringing of children, enabled her to devote herself more to the pleasures of gardening, a taste which all her three children have inherited from her. She died suddenly of cerebral haemorrhage at the early age of fifty-four, when I was thirty, and my father survived her for thirteen years.

# HAROLD WITT

*There are moments when every parent feels himself a link in a chain of the generations.*

## "Now in November"

Now in November, ten years
　　　after then,
fragility grows to bigness,
　　　Emily runs
homeward from fractions with
　　　her violin,
her hair as brilliant as the turn-
　　　ing oaks,
followed by Eric vivid in his
　　　shirt.
Flitting behind them, sparrows
　　　tip with sun
and peck the pyracanthas' ber-
　　　ried arcs.
I didn't guess this autumn lesson
　　　when
I heard them, dimly, cry in early
　　　darks—
meanings of time we learn only
　　　from children,
how they come in from the
　　　arrowy sun,
leaves falling behind them, as I
　　　ran once,
and the glad dog does a delicate
　　　dance,

their "Oh, O.K.," when asked
      how school was,
then off to try their balance on
      a fence.
I hear, as evening deepens,
      acorns thud
from the darkening tree they're
      climbing in
against a glow that slowly
      streaks with blood,
and on that golden bough I am
      the one
who hears my vanished father
      call me home.

# Family Gatherings

# MOTHER GOOSE

茨 茨

*As always,* Mother Goose *sums up a situation in plain folk talk.*

## "There Was An Old Woman"

THERE WAS an old woman who lived in a shoe.
She had so many children she didn't know what to do.
She gave them some broth without any bread.
She whipped them all soundly and put them to bed.

# H. G. WELLS

茨 茨

*It is common knowledge that a funeral, however saddening, is a prime cause of large family gatherings. The* History of Mr. Polly *reports on such a family congregation.*

## I

THEN A GREAT CHANGE was brought about in the life of Mr. Polly by the death of his father. His father had died suddenly—the local practitioner still clung to his theory that it was imagination he suffered from, but compromised in the certificate with the appendicitis that was then so fashionable—and Mr. Polly found himself heir to a debateable number of pieces of furniture in the house of his cousin near Easewood Junction, a family Bible, an engraved portrait of Garibaldi and a bust of Mr. Gladstone, an invalid gold watch, a gold locket formerly belonging to his mother, some minor jewelry and bric-a-brac, a quantity of nearly valueless old clothes and an insurance policy and money in the bank amounting altogether to the sum of three hundred and ninety-five pounds.

Mr. Polly had always regarded his father as an immortal, as an eternal fact, and his father being of a reserved nature in his declining years had said nothing about the insurance policy. Both wealth and bereavement therefore took Mr. Polly by surprise and found him a little inadequate. His mother's death had been a childish grief and long forgotten, and the strongest affection in his life had been for Parsons. An only child of sociable tendencies necessarily turns his back a good deal upon home, and the aunt who had succeeded his mother was an economist and furniture polisher, a knuckle rapper and sharp silencer, no friend for a slovenly little boy. He had loved other little boys and girls transitorily, none had been frequent and familiar enough to strike deep roots in his heart, and he had grown up with a tattered and dissipated affectionateness that was becoming wildly shy. His father had always been a stranger, an irritable stranger with exceptional powers of intervention and comment, and an air of being disappointed about his offspring. It was shocking to lose him; it was like an unexpected hole in the universe, and the writing of "Death" upon the sky, but it did not tear Mr. Polly's heartstrings at first so much as rouse him to a pitch of vivid attention.

He came down to the cottage at Easewood in response to an urgent telegram, and found his father already dead. His cousin Johnson received him with much solemnity and ushered him upstairs, to look at a stiff, straight, shrouded form, with a face unwontedly quiet and, as it seemed, with its pinched nostrils, scornful.

"Looks peaceful," said Mr. Polly, disregarding the scorn to the best of his ability.

"It was a merciful relief," said Mr. Johnson.

There was a pause.

"Second—Second Departed I've ever seen. Not counting mummies," said Mr. Polly, feeling it necessary to say something.

"We did all we could."

"No doubt of it, O' Man," said Mr. Polly.

A second long pause followed, and then, much to Mr. Polly's great relief, Johnson moved towards the door.

Afterwards Mr. Polly went for a solitary walk in the evening light, and as he walked, suddenly his dead father became real to him. He thought of things far away down the perspective of memory, of jolly moments when his father had skylarked with a wildly excited little boy, of a certain annual visit to the Crystal Palace pantomime, full of trivial glittering incidents and wonders, of his father's dread back while customers were in the old, minutely known shop. It is curious that the memory which seemed to link him nearest to the dead man was the memory of a fit of passion. His father had wanted to get a small sofa up the narrow winding staircase from the little room behind the shop to the bedroom above, and it had jammed. For a time his father had coaxed, and then groaned like a soul in torment and given way to blind fury, had sworn, kicked and struck at the offending piece of furniture and finally wrenched it upstairs, with considerable incidental damage to lath and plaster and one of the castors. That moment when self-control was altogether torn aside, the shocked discovery of his father's perfect humanity, had left a singular impression on Mr. Polly's queer mind. It was as if something extravagantly vital had come out of his father and laid a warmly passionate hand upon his heart. He remembered that now very vividly, and it became a clue to endless other memories that had else been dispersed and confusing.

A weakly wilful being struggling to get obdurate things round impossible corners—in that symbol Mr. Polly could recognise himself and all the trouble of humanity.

He hadn't had a particularly good time, poor old chap, and now it was all over. Finished. . . .

Johnson was the sort of man who derives great satisfaction from a funeral, a melancholy, serious, practical-minded man of five and thirty, with great powers of advice. He was the up-line ticket clerk at Easewood Junction, and felt the responsibilities of his position. He was naturally thoughtful and reserved, and greatly sustained in that by an innate rectitude of body and an overhanging and forward inclination of the upper part of his face and head. He was pale but freckled, and his dark grey eyes were deeply set. His lightest interest was cricket, but he did not take that lightly. His chief holiday was to go to a cricket match, which he did as if he was going to church, and he watched critically, applauded sparingly, and was darkly offended by any unorthodox play. His convictions upon all subjects were taciturnly inflexible. He was an obstinate player of draughts and chess, and an earnest and persistent reader of the *British Weekly*. His wife was a pink, short, wilfully smiling, managing, ingratiating, talkative woman, who was determined to be pleasant, and take a bright hopeful view of everything, even when it was not really bright and hopeful. She had large blue expressive eyes and a round face, and she always spoke of her husband as Harold. She addressed sympathetic and considerate remarks about the deceased to Mr. Polly in notes of brisk encouragement. "He was really quite cheerful at the end," she said several times, with congratulatory gusto, "quite cheerful."

She made dying seem almost agreeable.

Both these people were resolved to treat Mr. Polly very well, and to help his exceptional incompetence in every possible way, and after a simple supper of ham and bread and cheese and pickles and cold apple tart and small beer had been cleared away, they put him into the armchair almost as though he was an invalid, and sat on chairs that made them look down on him, and opened a directive discussion of the arrangements for the funeral. After all a funeral is a distinct social opportunity, and rare when you have no family and few relations, and they did not want to see it spoilt and wasted.

"You'll have a hearse of course," said Mr. Johnson. "Not one of them combinations with the driver sitting on the coffin. Disrespectful I think they are. I can't fancy how people can bring themselves to be buried in combinations." She flattened her voice in a manner she used to intimate aesthetic feeling. "I *do* like them glass hearses," she said. "So refined and nice they are."

"Podger's hearse you'll have," said Johnson conclusively. "It's the best in Easewood."

"Everything that's right and proper," said Mr. Polly.

"Podger's ready to come and measure at any time," said Johnson.

"Then you'll want a mourner's carriage or two, according as to whom you're going to invite," said Mr. Johnson.

"Didn't think of inviting any one," said Polly.

"Oh! you'll *have* to ask a few friends," said Mr. Johnson. "You can't let your father go to his grave without asking a few friends."

"Funerial baked meats like," said Mr. Polly.

"Not baked, but of course you'll have to give them something. Ham and chicken's very suitable. You don't want a lot of cooking with the ceremony coming into the middle of it. I wonder who Alfred ought to invite, Harold. Just the immediate relations; one doesn't want a great crowd of people and one doesn't want not to show respect."

"But he hated our relations—most of them."

"He's not hating them *now*," said Mrs. Johnson, "you may be sure of that. It's just because of that I think they ought to come— all of them—even your Aunt Mildred."

"Bit vulturial, isn't it?" said Mr. Polly unheeded.

"Wouldn't be more than twelve or thirteen people if they *all* came," said Mr. Johnson.

"We could have everything put out ready in the back room and the gloves and whiskey in the front room, and while we were all at the ceremony, Bessie could bring it all into the front room on a tray and put it out nice and proper. There'd have to be whiskey and sherry or port for the ladies. . . ."

"Where'll you get your mourning?" asked Johnson abruptly.

Mr. Polly had not yet considered this by-product of sorrow. "Haven't thought of it yet, O' Man."

A disagreeable feeling spread over his body as though he was blackening as he sat. He hated black garments.

"I suppose I must *have* mourning," he said.

"*Well!*" said Johnson with a solemn smile.

"Got to see it through," said Mr. Polly indistinctly.

"If I were you," said Johnson, "I should get ready-made trousers. That's all you really want. And a black satin tie and a top hat with a deep mourning band. And gloves."

"Jet cuff links he ought to have—as chief mourner," said Mrs. Johnson.

"Not obligatory," said Johnson.

"It shows respect," said Mrs. Johnson.

"It shows respect of course," said Johnson.

And then Mrs. Johnson went on with the utmost gusto to the details of the "casket," while Mr. Polly sat more and more deeply and droopingly into the armchair, assenting with a note of protest to all they said. After he had retired for the night he remained for a long time perched on the edge of the sofa which was his bed, staring at the prospect before him. "Chasing the O' Man about up to the last," he said.

He hated the thought and elaboration of death as a healthy animal must hate it. His mind struggled with unwonted social problems.

"Got to put 'em away somehow, I suppose," said Mr. Polly.

"Wish I'd looked him up a bit more while he was alive," said Mr. Polly.

## II

Bereavement came to Mr. Polly before the realization of opulence and its anxieties and responsibilities. That only dawned upon him on the morrow—which chanced to be Sunday—as he walked with Johnson before church time about the tangle of struggling building enterprise that constituted the rising urban district of Easewood. Johnson was off duty that morning, and devoted the time very generously to the admonitory discussion of Mr. Polly's worldly outlook.

"Don't seem to get the hang of the business somehow," said Mr. Polly. "Too much blooming humbug in it for my way of thinking."

"If I were you," said Mr. Johnson, "I should push for a first-class place in London—take almost nothing and live on my reserves. That's what I should do."

"Come the Heavy," said Mr. Polly.

"Get a better class reference."

There was a pause. "Think of investing your money?" asked Johnson.

"Hardly got used to the idea of having it yet, O' Man."

"You'll have to do something with it. Give you nearly twenty pounds a year if you invest it properly."

"Haven't seen it yet in that light," said Mr. Polly defensively.

"There's no end of things you could put it into."

"It's getting it out again I shouldn't feel sure of. I'm no sort of Fiancianier. Sooner back horses."

"I wouldn't do that if I were you."

"Not my style, O' Man."

"It's a nest egg," said Johnson.

Mr. Polly made an indeterminate noise.

"There's building societies," Johnson threw out in a speculative tone. Mr. Polly, with detached brevity, admitted there were.

"You might lend it on mortgage," said Johnson. "Very safe form of investment."

"Shan't think anything about it—not till the O' Man's underground," said Mr. Polly with an inspiration.

They turned a corner that led towards the junction.

"Might do worse," said Johnson, "than put it into a small shop."

At the moment this remark made very little appeal to Mr. Polly. But afterwards it developed. It fell into his mind like some small obscure seed, and germinated.

"These shops aren't in a bad position," said Johnson.

The row he referred to gaped in the late painful stage in building before the healing touch of the plasterer assuages the roughness of the brickwork. The space for the shop yawned an oblong gap below, framed above by an iron girder; "windows and fittings to suit tenant," a board at the end of the row promised; and behind was the door space and a glimpse of stairs going up to the living rooms above. "Not a bad position," said Johnson, and led the way into the establishment. "Room for fixtures there," he said, pointing to the blank wall.

The two men went upstairs to the little sitting-room or best bedroom (it would have to be) above the shop. Then they descended to the kitchen below.

"Rooms in a new house always look a bit small," said Johnson.

They came out of the house again by the prospective back door, and picked their way through builder's litter across the yard space to the road again. They drew nearer the junction to where a pavement and shops already open and active formed the commercial centre of Easewood. On the opposite side of the way the side door of a flourishing little establishment opened, and a man and his wife and a little boy in a sailor suit came into the street. The wife was a pretty woman in brown with a floriferous straw hat, and the group was altogether very Sundayfied and shiny and spick and span. The shop itself had a large plate-glass window whose contents were now veiled by a buff blind on which was inscribed in scrolly letters: "Rymer, Pork Butcher and Provision Merchant," and then with voluptuous elaboration: "The World-Famed Ease-wood Sausage."

Greetings were exchanged between Mr. Johnson and this distinguished comestible.

"Off to church already?" said Johnson.

"Walking across the fields to Little Dorington," said Mr. Rymer.

"Very pleasant walk," said Johnson.

"Very," said Mr. Rymer.

"Hope you'll enjoy it," said Mr. Johnson.

"That chap's done well," said Johnson *sotto voce* as they went on. "Came here with nothing—practically, four years ago. And as thin as a lath. Look at him now!"

"He's worked hard of course," said Johnson, improving the occasion.

Thought fell between the cousins for a space.

"Some men can do one thing," said Johnson, "and some another. . . . For a man who sticks to it there's a lot to be done in a shop."

### III

All the preparations for the funeral ran easily and happily under Mrs. Johnson's skilful hands. On the eve of the sad event she produced a reserve of black sateen, the kitchen steps and a box of tin-tacks, and decorated the house with festoons and bows of black in the best possible taste. She tied up the knocker with black crape, and put a large bow over the corner of the steel engraving of Garibaldi, and swathed the bust of Mr. Gladstone, that had belonged to the deceased, with inky swathings. She turned the two vases that had views of Tivoli and the Bay of Naples round, so that these rather brilliant landscapes were hidden and only the plain blue enamel showed, and she anticipated the long-contemplated purchase of a tablecloth for the front room, and substituted a violet purple cover for the now very worn and faded raptures and roses in plushette that had hitherto done duty there. Everything that loving consideration could do to impart dignified solemnity to her little home was done.

She had released Mr. Polly from the irksome duty of issuing invitations, and as the moments of assembly drew near she sent him and Mr. Johnson out into the narrow long strip of garden at the back of the house, to be free to put a finishing touch or so to her preparations. She sent them out together because she had a queer little persuasion at the back of her mind that Mr. Polly wanted to bolt from his sacred duties, and there was no way out of the garden except through the house.

Mr. Johnson was a steady, successful gardener, and particularly good with celery and peas. He walked slowly along the narrow path down the centre pointing out to Mr. Polly a number of interesting points in the management of peas, wrinkles neatly applied and difficulties wisely overcome, and all that he did for the comfort and propitiation of that fitful but rewarding vegetable. Presently a sound of nervous laughter and raised voices from the house proclaimed the arrival of the earlier guests, and the worst of that anticipatory tension was over.

When Mr. Polly re-entered the house he found three entirely strange young women with pink faces, demonstrative manners and emphatic mourning, engaged in an incoherent conversation with Mrs. Johnson. All three kissed him with great gusto after the ancient English fashion. "These are your cousins Larkins," said Mrs. Johnson; "that's Annie (unexpected hug and smack), that's Miriam (resolute hug and smack), and that's Minnie (prolonged hug and smack)."

"Right-O," said Mr. Polly, emerging a little crumpled and breathless from this hearty introduction. "I see."

"Here's Aunt Larkins," said Mrs. Johnson, as an elderly and stouter edition of the three young women appeared in the doorway.

Mr. Polly backed rather faint-heartedly, but Aunt Larkins was not to be denied. Having hugged and kissed her nephew resoundingly she gripped him by the wrists and scanned his features. She had a round, sentimental, freckled face. "I should 'ave known 'im anywhere," she said with fervour.

"Hark at mother!" said the cousin called Annie. "Why, she's never set eyes on him before!"

"I should 'ave known 'im anywhere," said Mrs. Larkins, "for Lizzie's child. You've got her eyes! It's a Resemblance! And as for never seeing 'im—I've *dandled* him, Miss Imperence. I've dandled him."

"You couldn't dandle him now, Ma!" Miss Annie remarked with a shriek of laughter.

All the sisters laughed at that. "The things you say, Annie!" said Miriam, and for a time the room was full of mirth.

Mr. Polly felt it incumbent upon him to say something. "*My* dandling days are over," he said.

The reception of this remark would have convinced a far more modest character than Mr. Polly that it was extremely witty.

Mr. Polly followed it up by another one almost equally good. "My turn to dandle," he said, with a sly look at his aunt, and convulsed everyone.

"Not me," said Mrs. Larkins, taking his point, "*thank* you," and achieved a climax.

It was queer, but they seemed to be easy people to get on with anyhow. They were still picking little ripples and giggles of mirth from the idea of Mr. Polly dandling Aunt Larkins when Mr. Johnson, who had answered the door, ushered in a stooping figure, who was at once hailed by Mrs. Johnson as "Why! Uncle Pentstemon!" Uncle Pentstemon was rather a shock. His was an aged rather than venerable figure; Time had removed the hair from the top of his head and distributed a small dividend of the plunder in little bunches carelessly and impartially over the rest of his features; he was dressed in a very big old frock coat and a long cylindrical top hat, which he had kept on; he was very much bent, and he carried a rush basket from which protruded coy intimations of the lettuces and onions he had brought to grace the occasion. He hobbled into the room, resisting the efforts of Johnson to divest him of his various encumbrances, halted and surveyed the company with an expression of profound hostility, breathing hard. Recognition quickened in his eyes.

"*You* here," he said to Aunt Larkins and then; "You *would* be. . . . These your gals?"

"They are," said Aunt Larkins, "and better gals—"

"That Annie?" asked Uncle Pentstemon, pointing a horny thumb-nail.

"Fancy your remembering her name!"

"She mucked up my mushroom bed, the baggage!" said Uncle Petstemon ungenially, "and I give it to her to rights. Trounced her I did—fairly. *I* remember her. Here's some green stuff for you, Grace. Fresh it is and wholesome. I shall be wanting the basket back and mind you let me have it. . . . Have you nailed him down yet? You always was a bit in front of what was needful."

His attention was drawn inward by a troublesome tooth, and he sucked at it spitefully. There was something potent about this old man that silenced everyone for a moment or so. He seemed a fragment from the ruder agricultural past of our race, like a lump of soil among things of paper. He put his basket of vegetables very deliberately on the new violet tablecloth, removed his hat carefully and dabbled his brow, and wiped out his hat brim with a crimson and yellow pocket handkerchief.

"I'm glad you were able to come, Uncle," said Mrs. Johnson.

"Oh, I *came*," said Uncle Pentstemon. "I *came*."

He turned on Mrs. Larkins. "Gals in service?" he asked.

"They aren't and they won't be," said Mrs. Larkins.

"No," he said with infinite meaning, and turned his eye on Mr. Polly.

"You Lizzie's boy?" he said.

Mr. Polly was spared much self-exposition by the tumult occasioned by further arrivals.

"Ah! here's May Punt!" said Mrs. Johnson, and a small woman dressed in the borrowed mourning of a large woman and leading a very small long-haired observant little boy—it was his first funeral —appeared, closely followed by several friends of Mrs. Johnson who had come to swell the display of respect and made only vague, confused impressions upon Mr. Polly's mind. (Aunt Mildred, who was an unexplained family scandal, had declined Mrs. Johnson's hospitality.)

Everybody was in profound mourning, of course, mourning in

the modern English style, with the dyer's handiwork only too apparent, and hats and jackets of the current cut. There was very little crape, and the costumes had none of the goodness and specialisation and genuine enjoyment of mourning for mourning's sake that a similar continental gathering would have displayed. Still that congestion of strangers in black sufficed to stun and confuse Mr. Polly's impressionable mind. It seemed to him much more extraordinary than anything he had expected.

"Now, gals," said Mrs. Larkins, "see if you can help," and the three daughters became confusingly active between the front room and the back.

"I hope everyone'll take a glass of sherry and a biscuit," said Mrs. Johnson. "We don't stand on ceremony," and a decanter appeared in the place of Uncle Pentstemon's vegetables.

Uncle Pentstemon had refused to be relieved of his hat; he sat stiffly down on a chair against the wall with that venerable head-dress between his feet, watching the approach of anyone jealously. "Don't you go squashing my hat," he said. Conversation became confused and general. Uncle Pentstemon addressed himself to Mr. Polly. "You're a little chap," he said, "a puny little chap. I never did agree to Lizzie marrying him, but I suppose bygones must be bygones now. I suppose they made you a clerk or something."

"Outfitter," said Mr. Polly.

"I remember. Them girls pretend to be dressmakers."

"They *are* dressmakers," said Mrs. Larkins across the room.

"I *will* take a glass of sherry. They 'old to it, you see."

He took the glass Mrs. Johnson handed him, and poised it critically between a horny finger and thumb. "You'll be paying for this," he said to Mr. Polly. Here's *to* you. . . . Don't you go treading on my hat, young woman. You brush your skirts against it and you take a shillin' off its value. It ain't the sort of 'at you see nowadays."

He drank noisily.

The sherry presently loosened everybody's tongue, and the early coldness passed.

"There ought to have been a *post-mortem*," Polly heard Mrs. Punt remarking to one of Mrs. Johnson's friends, and Miriam and another were lost in admiration of Mrs. Johnson's decorations. "So very nice and refined," they were both repeating at intervals.

The sherry and biscuits were still being discussed when Mr. Podger, the undertaker, arrived, a broad, cheerfully sorrowful, clean-shaven little man, accompanied by a melancholy-faced assistant. He conversed for a time with Johnson in the passage outside; the sense of his business stilled the rising waves of chatter and carried off everyone's attention in the wake of his heavy footsteps to the room above.

## IV

Things crowded upon Mr. Polly. Everyone, he noticed, took sherry with a solemn avidity, and a small portion even was administered sacramentally to the Punt boy. There followed a distribution of black kid gloves, and much trying on and humouring of fingers. "*Good* gloves," said one of Mrs. Johnson's friends. "There's a little pair there for Willie," said Mrs. Johnson triumphantly. Everyone seemed gravely content with the amazing procedure of the occasion. Presently Mr. Podger was picking Mr. Polly out as Chief Mourner to go with Mrs. Johnson, Mrs. Larkins and Annie in the first mourning carriage.

"Right O," said Mr. Polly, and repented instantly of the alacrity of the phrase.

"There'll have to be a walking party," said Mrs. Johnson cheerfully. "There's only two coaches. I daresay we can put in six in each, but that leaves three over."

There was a generous struggle to be pedestrian, and the two other Larkins girls, confessing coyly to tight new boots and displaying a certain eagerness, were added to the contents of the first carriage.

"It'll be a squeeze," said Annie.

"*I* don't mind a squeeze," said Mr. Polly.

He decided privately that the proper phrase for the result of that remark was "Hysterial catechunations."

Mr. Podger re-entered the room from a momentary supervision of the bumping business that was now proceeding down the staircase.

"Bearing up," he said cheerfully, rubbing his hands together. "Bearing up!"

That stuck very vividly in Mr. Polly's mind, and so did the close-wedged drive to the churchyard, bunched in between two young women in confused dull and shiny black, and the fact that the wind was bleak and that the officiating clergyman had a cold, and sniffed between his sentences. The wonder of life! The wonder of everything! What had he expected that this should all be so astoundingly different.

He found his attention converging more and more upon the Larkins cousins. The interest was reciprocal. They watched him with a kind of suppressed excitement and became risible with his every word and gesture. He was more and more aware of their personal quality. Annie had blue eyes and a red, attractive mouth, a harsh voice and a habit of extreme liveliness that even this occasion could not suppress; Minnie was fond, extremely free about the touching of hands and suchlike endearments; Miriam was quieter and regarded him earnestly. Mrs. Larkins was very happy in her daughters, and they had the naive affectionateness of those who see few people and find a strange cousin a wonderful outlet. Mr. Polly had never been very much kissed, and it made his mind swim. He did not know for the life of him whether he liked or disliked all or any of the Larkins cousins. It was rather attractive to make them laugh; they laughed at anything.

There they were tugging at his mind, and the funeral tugging at his mind, too, and the sense of himself as Chief Mourner in a brand new silk hat with a broad mourning band. He watched the ceremony and missed his responses, and strange feelings twisted at his heartstrings.

## V

Mr. Polly walked back to the house because he wanted to be alone. Miriam and Minnie would have accompanied him, but finding Uncle Pentstemon beside the Chief Mourner they went on in front.

"You're wise," said Uncle Pentstemon.

"Glad you think so," said Mr. Polly, rousing himself to talk.

"I likes a bit of walking before a meal," said Uncle Pentstemon, and made a kind of large hiccup. "That sherry rises," he remarked. "Grocer's stuff, I expect."

He went on to ask how much the funeral might be costing, and seemed pleased to find Mr. Polly didn't know.

"In that case," he said impressively, "it's pretty certain to cost more'n you expect, my boy."

He meditated for a time. "I've seen a mort of undertakers," he declared; "a mort of undertakers."

The Larkins girls attracted his attention.

"Let's lodgin's and chars," he commented. "Leastways she goes out to cook dinners. And look at 'em!

"Dressed up to the nines. If it ain't borryd clothes, that is. And they goes out to work at a factory!"

"Did you know my father much, Uncle Pentstemon?" asked Mr. Polly.

"Couldn't stand Lizzie throwin' herself away like that," said Uncle Pentstemon, and repeated his hiccup on a larger scale.

"That *weren't* good sherry," said Uncle Pentstemon with the first note of pathos Mr. Polly had detected in his quavering voice.

The funeral in the rather cold wind had proved wonderfully appetising, and every eye brightened at the sight of the cold collation that was now spread in the front room. Mrs. Johnson was very brisk, and Mr. Polly, when he re-entered the house found everybody sitting down. "Come along, Alfred," cried the hostess cheerfully. "We can't very well begin without you. Have you got the bottled beer ready to open, Betsy? Uncle, you'll have a drop of whiskey, I expect."

"Put it where I can mix for myself," said Uncle Pentstemon, placing his hat very carefully out of harm's way on the bookcase.

There were two cold boiled chickens, which Johnson carved with great care and justice, and a nice piece of ham, some brawn and a steak and kidney pie, a large bowl of salad and several sorts of pickles, and afterwards came cold apple tart, jam roll and a good piece of Stilton cheese, lots of bottled beer, some lemonade for the ladies and milk for Master Punt; a very bright and satisfying meal. Mr. Polly found himself seated between Mrs. Punt, who was much preoccupied with Master Punt's table manners, and one of Mrs. Johnson's school friends, who was exchanging reminiscences of school days and news of how various common friends had changed and married with Mrs. Johnson. Opposite him was Miriam and another of the Johnson circle, and also he had brawn to carve and there was hardly room for the helpful Betsy to pass behind his chair, so that altogether his mind would have been amply distracted from any mortuary broodings, even if a wordy warfare about the education of the modern young woman had not sprung up between Uncle Pentstemon and Mrs. Larkins and threatened for a time, in spite of a word or so in season from Johnson, to wreck all the harmony of the sad occasion.

The general effect was after this fashion:

First an impression of Mrs. Punt on the right speaking in a refined undertone: "You didn't, I suppose, Mr. Polly, think to 'ave your poor dear father post-mortemed—"

Lady on the left side breaking in: "I was just reminding Grace of the dear dead days beyond recall—"

Attempted reply to Mrs. Punt: "Didn't think of it for a moment. Can't give you a piece of this brawn, can I?"

Fragment from the left: "Grace and Beauty they used to call us and we used to sit at the same desk—"

Mrs. Punt, breaking out suddenly: "Don't *swaller* your fork, Willy. You see, Mr. Polly, I used to 'ave a young gentleman, a medical student, lodging with me—"

Voice from down the table: "'Am, Alfred? I didn't give you very much."

Bessie became evident at the back of Mr. Polly's chair, struggling wildly to get past. Mr. Polly did his best to be helpful. "Can you get past? Lemme sit forward a bit. Urr-oo! Right O."

Lady to the left going on valiantly and speaking to everyone who cares to listen, while Mrs. Johnson beams beside her: "There she used to sit as bold as brass, and the fun she used to make of things no one *could* believe—knowing her now. She used to make faces at the mistress through the—"

Mrs. Punt keeping steadily on: "The contents of the stummik at any rate *ought* to be examined."

Voice of Mr. Johnson. "Elfrid, pass the mustid down."

Miriam leaning across the table: "Elfrid!"

"Once she got us all kept in. The whole school!"

Miriam, more insistently: "Elfrid!"

Uncle Pentstemon, raising his voice defiantly: "Trounce 'er again I would if she did as much now. That I would! Dratted mischief!"

Miriam, catching Mr. Polly's eye: "Elfrid! This lady knows Canterbury. I been telling her you been there."

Mr. Polly: "Glad you know it."

The lady shouting: "I like it."

Mrs. Larkins, raising her voice: "I won't 'ave my girls spoken of, not by nobody, old *or* young."

Pop! imperfectly located.

Mr. Johnson at large: "*Ain't* the beer up! It's the 'eated room."

Bessie: "Scuse me, sir, passing so soon again, but—" Rest inaudible. Mr. Polly accommodating himself: "Urr-oo! Right? Right O."

The knives and forks, probably by some secret common agreement, clash and clatter together and drown every other sound.

"Nobody 'ad the least idea 'ow 'E died,—nobody. . . . Willie, don't *golp* so. You ain't in a 'urry, are you? You don't want to ketch a train or anything,—golping like that!"

"D'you remember, Grace, 'ow one day we 'ad writing lesson. . . ."

"Nicer girls no one ever 'ad—though I say it who shouldn't."

Mrs. Johnson in a shrill clear hospitable voice: "Harold, won't Mrs. Larkins 'ave a teeny bit more fowl?"

Mr. Polly rising to the situation. "Or some brawn, Mrs. Larkins?" Catching Uncle Pentstemon's eye: "Can't send *you* some brawn, sir?"

"Elfrid!"

Loud hiccup from Uncle Pentstemon, momentary consternation followed by giggle from Annie.

The narration at Mr. Polly's elbow pursued a quiet but relentless course. "Directly the new doctor came in he said: 'Everything must be took out and put in spirits—everything.' "

Willie,—audible ingurgitation.

The narration on the left was flourishing up to a climax. "Ladies," she sez, "dip their pens *in* their ink and keep their noses out of it!"

"Elfrid!"—persuasively.

"Certain people may cast snacks at other people's daughters, never having had any of their own, though two poor souls of wives dead and buried through their goings on—"

Johnson ruling the storm: "We don't want old scores dug up on such a day as this—"

"Old scores you may call them, but worth a dozen of them that put them to their rest, poor dears."

"Elfrid!"—with a note of remonstrance.

"If you choke yourself, my lord, not another mouthful do you 'ave. No nice puddin'! Nothing!"

"And kept us in, she did, every afternoon for a week!"

It seemed to be the end, and Mr. Polly replied with an air of being profoundly impressed: "Really!"

"Elfrid!"—a little disheartened.

"And then they 'ad it! They found he'd swallowed the very key to unlock the drawer—"

"Then don't let people go casting snacks!"

"*Who's* casting snacks!"

"Elfrid! This lady wants to know, 'ave the Prossers left Canterbury?"

"No wish to make myself disagreeable, not to God's 'umblest worm—"

"Alf, you aren't very busy with that brawn up there!"

And so on for the hour.

The general effect upon Mr. Polly at the time was at once confusing and exhilarating; but it led him to eat copiously and carelessly, and long before the end, when after an hour and a quarter a movement took the party, and it pushed away its cheese plates and rose sighing and stretching from the remains of the repast, little streaks and bands of dyspeptic irritation and melancholy were darkening the serenity of his mind.

He stood between the mantel shelf and the window—the blinds were up now—and the Larkins sisters clustered about him. He battled with the oncoming depression and forced himself to be extremely facetious about two noticeable rings on Annie's hand. "They ain't real," said Annie coquettishly. "Got 'em out of a prize packet."

"Prize packet in trousers, I expect," said Mr. Polly, and awakened inextinguishable laughter.

"Oh! the things you say!" said Minnie, slapping his shoulder.

Suddenly something he had quite extraordinarily forgotten came into his head.

"Bless my heart!" he cried, suddenly serious.

"What's the matter?" asked Johnson.

"Ought to have gone back to shop—three days ago. They'll make no end of a row!"

"Lor, you *are* a Treat!" said cousin Annie, and screamed with laughter at a delicious idea. "You'll get the chuck," she said.

Mr. Polly made a convulsing grimace at her.

"I'll die!" she said. "I don't believe you care a bit!"

Feeling a little disorganized by her hilarity and a shocked expression that had come to the face of cousin Miriam, he made some indistinct excuse and went out through the back room and scullery into the little garden. The cool air and a very slight drizzle of rain was a relief—anyhow. But the black mood of the replete dyspeptic had come upon him. His soul darkened hopelessly. He walked with his hands in his pockets down the path between the rows of exceptionally cultured peas and unreasonably, overwhelmingly, he was smitten by sorrow for his father. The heady noise and muddle and confused excitement of the feast passed from him like a curtain drawn away. He thought of that hot and angry and struggling creature who had tugged and sworn so foolishly at the sofa upon the twisted staircase, and who was now lying still and hidden, at the bottom of a wall-sided oblong pit beside the heaped gravel that would presently cover him. The stillness of it! the wonder of it! the infinite reproach! Hatred for all these people—all of them—possessed Mr. Polly's soul.

"Hen-witted gigglers," said Mr. Polly.

He went down to the fence, and stood with his hands on it staring away at nothing. He stayed there for what seemed a long time. From the house came a sound of raised voices that subsided, and then Mrs. Johnson calling for Bessie.

"Gowlish gusto," said Mr. Polly. "Jumping it in. Funererial Games. Don't hurt *him* of course. Doesn't matter to *him*. . . ."

Nobody missed Mr. Polly for a long time.

When at last he reappeared among them his eye was almost grim, but nobody noticed his eye. They were looking at watches, and Johnson was being omniscient about trains. They seemed to discover Mr. Polly afresh just at the moment of parting, and said a number of more or less appropriate things. But Uncle Pentstemon was far too worried about his rush basket, which had been carelessly mislaid, he seemed to think with larcenous intentions, to remember Mr. Polly at all. Mrs. Johnson had tried to fob him off with a similar but inferior basket,—his own had one handle mended with string according to a method of peculiar virtue and inimitable distinction known only to himself—and the old gentleman had taken her attempt as the gravest reflection upon his years and intelligence. Mr. Polly was left very largely to the Larkins trio. Cousin Minnie became shameless and kept kissing him goodby—and then finding out it wasn't time to go. Cousin Miriam seemed to think her silly, and caught Mr. Polly's eye sympathetically. Cousin Annie ceased to giggle and lapsed into a nearly sentimental state. She said with real feeling that she had enjoyed the funeral more than words could tell.

# RUTH McKENNY

*Cultural exhibitions by the young are practically compulsory at many family reunions. "Hun-Gah," from* My Sister Eileen *describes a dramatic presentation offered by two sisters to their assembled relatives.*

WHEN MY SISTER and I were ten and eleven, our six aunts on the lace-curtain-Irish, or Farrel, side of the family got up a little fund to make their nieces cultured.

In their dreams, they could see, these amiable ladies who loved us so dearly, Eileen at the piano bringing tears to the eyes of her relatives with a splendid performance of "Narcissus," the selection where you cross your hands on the keyboard. They could see me, too, in their affectionate musings, spreading a fluffy organdie skirt for a polite curtsy to a parlor full of admiring Farrels and Murphys and Flannigans, and then launching into a moving recitation of "Trees."

After all, our second cousins, the Murphy children, aged only eleven and twelve, could already recite "Trees" and play "The Rose of No Man's Land," not to speak of "Humoresque," on the piano. If the Murphys could be cultured, so, my aunts said grimly, could the McKenneys. If they had secret misgivings, they never said so. They started off the big culture program by getting Eileen a music teacher, a nervous, angular lady who wore her eyeglasses on a black ribbon and sniffled.

"One," she used to say, "two, three," and then a long sniffle, "four. One, two," then another short, ladylike sniffle, "three, four."

The sniffles and the black ribbon for the eyeglasses fascinated my sister. She used to keep time to the sniffles instead of the counting, and as a result her scales went from bad to worse. Eventually, though, she learned to read simple sheet music. She also learned a bass which consisted mostly of fearful thumping and a rolling sound like kettledrums, all in the lowest octave of the keyboard. With this equipment, she was able to play "Chloe," a popular song of the early nineteen-twenties. She was never able to play anything except "Chloe," but she certainly could play that.

She used to stalk to the piano and seat herself firmly, with quite a thump at the bench. Then, swaying largely from the waist, she picked up the melody, not without some difficulty. Finally, when the preliminaries were over, she burst into song, accompanying herself as she went along.

"Thr–ooo the bu-la-ck of NIGHT," Eileen used to intone in a deep bass growl, "I got tuh go wheah yew ARE."

The climax of the song, where the melody goes up, always used to baffle my poor sister, who, like myself, is absolutely tone-deaf and has never been able to carry a tune, even the simplest one, in her whole life. She solved the difficulty by simply pounding so hard in the bass that she drowned herself out. Her voice emerged triumphantly just at the end: "I GOT-TUH go wheah yew ARE."

While Eileen was learning to play a bayou chant, I, too, was busy with culture. I was taking what my aunts thought were elocution lessons. These thoughtful ladies, after a solemn family conclave, had decided I should study public speaking because I stuttered over the telephone. I still do. It is very humiliating.

How my conservative, respectable aunts fell afoul of Madame DuLak and her Studio of the Voice I cannot imagine. Certainly she was not the teacher they thought she was. They hoped that I would learn how to recite "Trees." Madame DuLak told me the first time I met her that Joyce Kilmer "stank." That was the word she used. I was eleven years old, and I certainly was surprised to hear that about Joyce Kilmer.

Madame DuLak had studied in Paris. She said so often. She had picked up a lot of fancy notions in gay old Paris, I gathered, not only about Joyce Kilmer but also about "recitations" and "elocution lessons."

"We are going," Madame DuLak intoned, in a rich, deep voice full of culture, that first morning our little class of six assembled, "to undertake the study of a litt-tul play which I rather" (she said "rawther," of course) "like. I shall assign and read the parts this morning. By next week you will have memorized your lines, and then we shall settle down for a winter's work."

I memorized my lines easily. My part consisted of the word "hunger." But do not imagine that I was a mere walk-on in this little play of Madame DuLak's. On the contrary, I was one of the leading characters. I was, in spite of my rotund figure, a hungry old beggar. I sat on the steps of what was supposed to be a cathedral. From the time the curtain went up until at last it went down, I sat on those steps, chanting the word "hunger" more or less at one-minute intervals. Sometimes I said it very loudly, drowning out the rest of the cast, and sometimes I was supposed to whisper it very softly, as background. It was a Greek-chorus idea.

The play was exceedingly symbolical. I was not supposed to be physically hungry, which was a good thing, considering my appearance; I was just supposed to be spiritually hungry. Madame DuLak used to urge me to put this difference into the reading of my lines, or, rather, line. I was a big girl for my eleven years, and I was often hungry in the good old-fashioned sense of wanting another piece of chocolate cake or second helping of chocolate pie. So when Madame DuLak would urge me on Saturday mornings to "Put some *feeling* into your part, Ruth," I would concentrate hard on something chocolate and howl, "Hun-gah!" with a fine frenzied note in my voice. Madame DuLak thought I was pretty good, on the whole. Of course sometimes I forgot and said, "Hunger," and then Madame DuLak used to denounce me as a boor.

The rest of the pupils were also symbolical. The only other girl in the class, Betty Chippendale, was Vice. I wanted to be Vice myself; I got pretty tired of being a dirty old beggar yelling, "Hun-gah!" all the time. Vice was a nice, rich part. There weren't any lines in the part, to be sure, not even a one-word chant like my "Hun-gah," but Vice got to stroll up and down the stage, wiggling her hips, brushing against other characters with lewd gestures, and such like. Of course Betty was only thirteen years old, and although she wanted to be an actress when she grew up, her life had been rather restricted so far. So she had some difficulty in making her character study of Vice symbolical enough to suit Madame DuLak.

"No, no, Betty," Madame DuLak would say in her cultured voice, "you represent the dregs of humanity, you are the symbol of lust and ugliness. You must make your audience feel that as you move across the stage, you must put that into every gesture of your little finger."

"Yes, Ma'am," Betty would say. She took her work very seriously, and never got tired of walking up and down and being the symbol of lust and ugliness.

The boys were, variously, Greed and Power and Truth and Loving Kindness. Since this was a pretty modern morality play, Loving Kindness and Truth got licked to a frazzle at the curtain. Greed and Power beat them up and dragged them off bodily every Saturday morning. Vice tagged along to get in on the kill, and that left me still sitting on the cathedral steps. I had the last lines. "Hun-gah!" I bellowed. "Hun-gah! Hun-gah!" Curtain.

I think now that Madame DuLak must have written that remarkable play herself. Of course it had certain resemblances to other dramas of its genre, but that smashing finish—that was pure DuLak.

After the first three weeks, Madame DuLak decided we must have costumes for our rehearsals. The costumes, she said, would help us get into the feeling of our roles. My costume was wonderful. I made it myself, and it certainly was realistic. I wore an old, ragged, burlap sack with holes cut out for the arms. My legs were bare, and I had a pair of Father's old bedroom slippers tied on my feet with rope. This was only the beginning, however. I took off my hair ribbon, unbraided my pigtails, and systematically, with a comb, snarled and matted my long hair. Then I covered my face, arms, and legs with artistic smatterings of coal dust. The first time Madame DuLak saw me emerge from my dressing room in her little studio, she gave me the highest praise a make-up artist can get.

"Awk!" she said, blasted out of her usual cultured calm.

With the first soft breezes of spring, with the first robin, my aunts began to question me rather sharply about my elocution lessons. I explained as well as I could about the play, but I could see that they rejected my story as the simple fantasy of an imaginative child. They urged me to recite my part for them, but some inner instinct warned me off.

Finally, though, one of the Farrel family reunions came along. The Farrels had family reunions at the drop of a hat, and the Murphys, the Flannigans, the McKenneys, Aunt Susan Maloney with her brood, and assorted other in-laws turned up, ate prodigiously, and argued about politics. Our aunts felt that it was practically certain that the Murphy girls would play "The Rose of No Man's Land" and recite "Trees."

"This time," Aunt Molly said, with a dangerous glitter in her eye, "we'll show them that the Murphy girls aren't the only ones in the family who take lessons."

Eileen and I turned up at the family reunion bearing our stage properties. I brought my costume in a box, with a neat bag of coal dust, and Eileen brought the sheet music of "Chloe." We weren't nervous in the least. After dinner we retired upstairs to prepare for what we felt would be our triumph Eileen gargled, and I repeated "Hun-gah, hungah" several times, to get in voice.

Downstairs we could hear Margaret Murphy playing "The Rose of No Man's Land," and very badly, too. She had to start over again several times. The applause, however, was generous.

When Cousin Rita Murphy began to recite "Trees," Uncle Wally went out to the kitchen, and we heard him say, "There is a limit to everything, Katie. Where do they keep the whiskey bottle around here?" Katie was the cook. We bridled. Uncle Wally would never walk out on *our* performances, we felt sure.

He didn't. Nobody did. They were frozen to their seats. We got, in fact, the most flattering kind of attention. Even Uncle Wally's jaws fell ajar.

Eileen played and sang first. Just as the final notes of her bass monotone chant, "I GOT-TUH go wheah yew ARE," and the final rumble of the piano died away, I burst dramatically through the door, shouting "Hun-gah! Hun-gah!" and shaking my matted and snarled locks at my assembled relatives. My grandmother Farrel, who always takes everything seriously, let out a piercing scream.

Ignoring the awed comments of the rest of the audience, I paced slowly over to the fireplace. "This," I said in stately tones, while my aunts stared at my coal-dust-streaked face, "is a cathedral. I am sitting on the cathedral steps." I sat down. There was a long pause. Then I put up my arms to the heavens.

"Hun-gah!" I shrieked. Grandma jumped and said audibly, "Mercy!"

I let another impressive silence fall. The Murphys, mother and father and the two accomplished child Murphys, breathed heavily. Suddenly I plopped down on the floor, my face turned to the horrified audience.

"Hun-gah," I barely breathed. Eileen struck a soft chord in the bass.

"God!" Uncle Wally said. In the silence, everybody heard him, but they were too engrossed in my performance to be shocked. I rolled over, one limp hand trailing on the carpet.

"Hun-gah!" I whined. I lay on the floor several seconds, letting it sink in. Then I began to drag myself to my feet. My knee joints always cracked, and in the silence you could hear them clearly all over the room. Nobody said anything. Finally I was all the way up, and panting. I was supposed to pant. I was supposed to have some kind of a terrible disease, like leprosy. I lowered my head, inch by inch. In those days I had a double chin, and I couldn't get my head down very far, unfortunately. I sighed, heavily.

Then in a flat, sad voice I said, "Hun-gah."

Eileen struck a minor chord. I bowed. I stalked toward the door. Eileen rose gravely and followed me. At the door we bowed together.

"Well, for God's sake!" my Uncle Wally said, quite loudly. We waited for the burst of applause, but our relatives sat glued to their seats, staring at us. Finally Aunt Molly pulled herself together and started to clap. Everybody else clapped too, dutifully, and we retired with the sweet sound of applause in our ears.

There never was another family reunion like that one. We knew perfectly well we had electrified our dear relatives. As Eileen put it, "It was about time somebody stuck a pin in them." Anyway, Uncle Wally told us afterward that he liked us better than "Trees." He thought that we had done it on purpose, and maybe, as I look back on it, we did. Our approach to life was somewhat confused at ten and eleven.

After that, the Murphy girls had the field of culture, in our family, to themselves. It never did them any good, either.

# FRANK B. GILBRETH, JR.,
## and ERNESTINE GILBRETH CAREY

※ ※

*Cross-country journeys* en famille *afford unique opportunities for family closeness, as* Cheaper by the Dozen *demonstrates.*

### "Kissing Kin"

THE DAY the United States entered the first World War, Dad sent President Wilson a telegram which read: "Arriving Washington 7:03 P.M. train. If you don't know how to use me, I'll tell you how."

Whether or not this heartening intelligence took some of the weight off Mr. Wilson's troubled shoulders, Dad never made entirely plain. But he was met at the train and taken over to the War Department. The next time we saw him, he was in uniform, assigned to motion study training in assembling and disassembling the Lewis machine gun and other automatic weapons. He had what probably was the most G.I. haircut in the entire armed forces, and when he walked into the parlor and shouted "Attention!" he wanted to hear our heels click.

Mother had been planning for several years to take all of us to California to visit her family. When Dad was ordered to Fort Sill, Oklahoma, the time seemed opportune.

Mother's family was genteel and well-to-do. She was the oldest of nine children, only three of whom were married. The other six, two brothers and four sisters, lived with their parents in a spacious house at 426 Twenty-Ninth Street, in Oakland. The house was fringed with palm trees, magnificent gardens, and concealed but nonetheless imposing outbuildings in which the family indulged its various hobbies. There were a billiard hall, radio shack, greenhouse, pigeon roost, and a place where prize-winning guinea pigs were raised.

The Mollers had three Packards, a French chauffeur named Henriette, a gardener, Chinese cook, first-story maid, and second-story maid. The Mollers managed, somehow, in spite of their wordly goods, to live fairly simply. They were quiet, introverted, and conservative. They seldom raised their voices and referred to each other as "Dear Elinor, Dear Mabel, Dear Gertrude," and so on. Mother was "Dear Lillie."

Mother was the only one in her family who had moved from California. Mother had left home after her marriage, as introverted and conservative, and possibly even more shy and bookish, than any of the others. In ten years, she had seven children. She was lecturing around the country. She was a career woman and her name kept bobbing up in the newspapers. Frankly, the Mollers didn't know exactly what to make of Dear Lillie. But they knew they loved her.

Even before we visited California, we knew all about the household at Oakland and its inhabitants, because Mother used to like to tell us about her girlhood. We knew the arrangement of the house, even down to the full-length mirror on the hall door, which Mother's younger sisters used to open at just the right angle so that they could watch Dad's courting technique.

Hearing Mother tell about the courtship, the sparking on the sofa, we used to wonder what Mother's parents had thought when Dad first came to call.

He had met Mother in Boston, about a year before, when she was on that well-chaperoned tour to Europe, with several other

Oakland girls. The chaperon, who was Dad's cousin, had introduced him to all the girls, but he had selected Miss Lillie as the
one on whom to shower his attention.

He took Mother for a ride in his first automobile, some early
ancestor of Foolish Carriage. As Dad and Mother, dressed in
dusters and wearing goggles, went scorching through the streets of
Boston, bystanders tossed insults and ridicule in their direction.

"Get a horse, get a horse."

Dad started to shout back an answer, but thought better of it.
He was already in love with Mother, and was anxious to make a
good impression. Mother's shyness and ladylike demeanor had a
quieting effect on him, and he was displaying his most genteel
behavior.

"Get a horse. Twenty-three skiddoo."

It was almost more than Dad could bear, but he didn't answer.

"Say, Noah, what are you doing with that Ark?"

That did it. Dad slowed the car and cocked his checkered cap
belligerently over one eye.

"Collecting animals like the good Lord told me," he screamed
back. "All I need now is a jackass. Hop in."

After that, Dad decided he might as well be himself, and his
breezy personality and quick laugh made Mother forget her
shyness and reserve. Soon she forgot herself laughing almost as
loud and as long at his jokes as he.

As was its custom, the automobile inevitably broke down, and
crowds of children gathered around. Mother stopped them from
breathing down Dad's neck by taking them aside and telling them
stories. When the car was fixed and they were on their way again,
Dad asked her how she had managed to hold the children's
attention.

"I told them some stories from *Alice in Wonderland*," Mother
said. "You see, I have eight younger brothers and sisters, and I
know what children like."

"*Alice in Wonderland*," Dad exclaimed. "You mean kids really
like that? They must be raising different kinds of kids than when
I was a boy. I never could get into it, myself."

"Of course they like it; they love it," Mother said. "You really
should read it. I think everybody should. It's a classic."

"If you say so, Miss Lillie," said Dad, who had already made up his mind she was going to be Mrs. Gilbreth, "I'll read it."

Mother went on to Europe. After her return, Dad followed her out to the West Coast.

When he arrived at Oakland, he telephoned the Mollers' house.

"Hello," he said, "who do you think this is?"

"Really, I have no idea."

"Well guess, can't you?"

"No, I'm sorry, I have no idea."

"Aw, you know who it is," said Dad, who now had read the book that Mother said everyone should read. "It's the White Rabbit from Boston."

"The who?"

"The White Rabbit from Boston."

"Oh, I see. I think you must want to talk with one of my daughters."

"My God," said Dad, who didn't stop swearing until after he was married. "Who's this?"

"This is Mrs. Moller. To whom did you wish to speak?"

"May I please speak with Miss Lillie?" Dad asked meekly.

"Who should I say is calling?"

"You might say Mr. Rabbit, please," said Dad. "Mr. W. Rabbit, of Boston."

A few days later, Dad was invited to Mother's house for tea, where he met her mother and father and most of her brothers and sisters. A workman was building a new fireplace in the living room, and as Dad was escorted through that room he stopped to watch the man laying bricks.

"Now there's an interesting job," Dad said in a conversational tone to the Mollers. "Laying brick. It looks easy to me. Dead easy. I don't see why these workmen claim that laying brick is skilled labor. I'll bet anyone could do it."

"Right this way, Mr. Gilbreth," said Mother's father. "We're having tea on the porch."

Dad wouldn't be hurried. "It seems to me," he continued in his flat New England twang, "that all you do is pick up a brick, put some mortar on it, and put it in the fireplace."

The bricklayer turned around to survey the plump but dapper dude from the East.

"Nothing personal meant," said Dad, with his most patronizing smile, "my good man."

"Sure, that's all right," said the workman, but he was furious. "Dead easy, eh? Like to try it, Mister?"

Dad, who had set his sights on just such an invitation, said he guessed not. Mother tugged at his sleeve and fidgeted.

"The porch is right this way," her father repeated.

"Here," the bricklayer said, handing Dad the trowel. "Try it."

Dad grinned and took the trowel. He grabbed a brick, flipped it into position in his hand, slapped on the mortar with a rotary motion of the trowel, placed the brick, scraped off the excess mortar, reached for a second brick, flipped it, and was about to slap on more mortar when the workman reached out and took back his trowel.

"That's enough, you old hod-carrier," he shouted, cuffing Dad affectionately on the back. "Dude from the East you might be. But it's many a thousand brick you've laid in your life, and don't try to tell me different."

Dad dusted off his hands gingerly with a spotless handkerchief. "Dead easy," he said, "my good man."

Dad behaved himself pretty well during the tea, but on later visits he'd sometimes interrupt Mother's parents in the middle of sentences and go over and pick up Mother from her chair.

"Excuse me just a minute," he'd tell his future in-laws. "I think Miss Lillie would look more decorative up here."

He'd swing her up and place her on the top of a bookcase or china closet, and then go back and sit down. Mother was afraid to move for fear of upsetting her perch, and would remain up there primly, determined not to lose her dignity. Dad pretended he had forgotten all about her, as he resumed the conversation.

We knew, too, that the first time Dad had been invited to spend a weekend at the Mollers' he had thrown himself with a wheeze and a sigh onto his bed, which had collapsed and enveloped him in a heavy, be-tasseled canopy.

"The things your daddy shouted before Papa and your Uncle Fred could untangle him from the tassels!" Mother tittered. " I can tell you, it was an education for us girls and, I suspect, for the boys too. Thank goodness he's stopped talking like that."

"And what did your family really think of him?" we asked her. "Really."

"I never could understand it," Mother said, glancing over at Dad, who was at his smuggest, "but they thought he was simply wonderful. Mama said it was like a breath of fresh air when he walked into a room. And Papa said the business of laying bricks wasn't just showing off, but was your father's way of telling them that he had started out by making a living with his hands."

"Is that what you were trying to tell them, Daddy?" we asked.

"Trying to tell them nothing," Dad shouted. "Anybody who knows anything about New England knows the Bunkers and the Gilbreths, or Galbraiths, descend through Governor Bradford right to the *Mayflower*. I wasn't trying to tell them anything."

"What did you lay the brick for then?" we insisted.

"When some people walk into a parlor," Dad said, "they like to sit down at the piano and impress people by playing Bach. When I walk into a parlor, I like to lay brick, that's all."

There were seven children in the family when we set out with Mother for California. Fred was the baby, and was train sick all the way from Niagara Falls to the Golden Gate. Lill, the next to youngest, had broken a bone in her foot three weeks before, and had to stay in her berth. Mother was expecting another baby in three months, and didn't always feel too well herself.

The chance to return with her children to her parents' home meant more to Mother than any of us realized, and she was anxious to show us off in the best possible light and to have her family approve of us.

"I know you're going to be good and quiet, and do what your grandparents and your aunts and uncles tell you," Mother kept saying. "You want to remember that they're very affectionate, but they're not accustomed to having children around any more. They're going to love you, but they're not used to noise and people running around."

Mother had spent a good bit of money buying us new outfits so that we would make a good impression in California, and she thought she ought to economize on train accommodations. We were jammed, two in a berth, into a drawing room and two sections. She brought along a Sterno cooking outfit and two suitcases of food, mostly cereals and graham crackers. We ate almost all our meals in the drawing room, journeying to the dining car only on those infrequent occasions when Mother yielded to our complaints that scurvy was threatening to set in.

She spent most of her time trying to make Lill comfortable and trying to find some kind of milk that would stay on Fred's stomach. She had little opportunity to supervise the rest of us, and we wandered up and down the train sampling the contents of the various ice water tanks, peeking into berths and, in the case of Frank and Bill, turning somersaults and wrestling with each other in the aisles.

At each stop, Mother would leave Anne in charge of the broken foot and upset stomach department, while she rushed into the station to buy milk, food, and Sterno cans. The rest of us would get off the train to stretch our legs and see whether a new engine had been switched on. Once the train started up again, Mother would insist upon a roll call.

After four days on the train, with no baths except for the sponge variety, we were not very sanitary when we reached California. Mother wanted us to look our best when we got off the train, and she planned to give each of us a personal scrubbing and see that we had on clean clothes, an hour or so before we got to Oakland.

Her oldest brother, Uncle Fred, surprised her and us by boarding the train at Sacramento. He found us in the drawing room, in the middle of a meal. Suitcases were open on the floor, and there was a pile of diapers in a corner. The baby, still train sick, was crying in Mother's arms. Lill's foot was hurting, and she was crying on the couch. Bill was doing acrobatics on the bed. There were bowls of Cream of Wheat and graham crackers on a card table. The place smelled of Sterno and worse.

Uncle Fred used to joke about it when we were older—it reminded him of a zoo, he said. But at the time you never would have known he noticed anything unusual.

"Lillie, dear, it's good to see you," he said. "You look simply radiant. Not a day older."

"Oh, Fred, Fred." Mother put down the baby, wiped her eyes apologetically, and clung to her brother. "It's ridiculous to cry, isn't it? But it means so much having you here."

"Was it a hard trip, dear?"

Mother was already bustling around, straightening up the drawing room.

"I wouldn't want to do it every day," she admitted. "But it's almost over and you're here. You're my first taste of home."

Uncle Fred turned to us. "Welcome to California," he said. "Don't tell me now. I can name each of you. Let's see, the baby here making all the noise, he's my namesake, Fred. And here's little Lill, of course, with the broken foot, and Billy . . ."

"You're just like we imagined you," Martha told him, hanging onto his hand. "Are we like you imagined us?"

"Just exactly," he said gravely. "Right down to the last freckle."

"I hope you didn't imagine them like this," Mother said, but she was happy now. "Never mind. You'll never know them in a few minutes. You take the boys out into the car, and I'll start getting the girls cleaned up right now. Of course, none of them will be really clean until I can get them into a tub."

We were presentable and on our best behavior when we finally arrived in Oakland, where Mother's sisters and other brothers were waiting with the three limousines. It was a wonderful welcome, but we thought our aunts were the kissingest kin in the world.

"They must think we're sissies," whispered Bill, who was five and didn't like to be kissed by anyone except Mother, and only then in the privacy of his boudoir.

"Lillie, dear, it's good to see you, and the dear children," they kept repeating.

Each of us had a godparent among Mother's brothers and sisters, and now the godparents began sorting us out.

"Here, little Ernestine, you come with me, dear," said Aunt Ernestine.

"Come, Martha, dear," said Aunt Gertrude. "You're mine."

"Give me your hand, Frank, dear," said Aunt Elinor.

"Dear this and dear that," Billy whispered scornfully.

"Where's dear Billy?" asked Aunt Mabel.

"Right here, dear," said Bill.

But Bill, like the rest of us, felt happy and warm inside because of the welcome.

The aunts led us over to the automobiles, where Henriette, in black puttees and with a stiff-brimmed cap tucked under his arm, was standing at rigid attention. Uncle Frank and Uncle Bill got behind the wheels of the other two machines.

The glassed-in cars seemed formal and luxurious as we drove from the station to Twenty-Ninth Street, and Henriette managed to remain at attention even when sitting down. We wondered what Daddy would say about Henriette. Certainly rigid attention wasn't the most efficient way to drive an automobile. Anyone with half an eye could see the posture was fatiguing to the point of exhaustion. It was some class, though.

Frank and Bill started to crank down the windows so they could put out their hands when he turned the corners, but Anne and Ernestine shook their heads.

"And the first one who hollers 'road hog' is going to get a punch in the nose," Ernestine whispered.

Mother's father and mother—Papa and Grosie, we called them —were waiting for us on the steps of the house. We thought they were picture-book grandparents. Papa was tall, lean and courtly, with a gates-ajar collar, string tie, and soft, white moustache. Grosie was short and fragile, with a gray pompadour and smiling brown eyes. Grosie kissed us and called us "dears." Papa shook hands, and said that each day we stayed in his house he was going to take all of us down to a toy shop and let us pick out a toy apiece.

"Honestly," Anne bubbled, "it's like stepping into a fairy tale three-deep with godmothers and with wishes that come true."

"That's the way we want it to be for Lillie's dear children," Grosie said. "Now what's your very first wish. Tell me, and I'll see if I can make it come true."

That was easy. After four days of Mother's drawing room cookery, with only infrequent trips to the dining car, what we wanted most was something good to eat; a real home-cooked meal.

"I hate to say it after the way Mother's been slaving over a hot Sterno can," said Ernestine, "but we're starving."

"If my wish would come true," Mother hastened to change the

subject, "you'd all be sitting in bathtubs right this minute, washing soot out of your hair."

Grosie said we were going to have a big dinner in about an hour
and a half, and that she didn't want to spoil our appetites.

"How about just a little snack right now," she suggested, "and
then baths and dinner? How about some graham crackers with
milk? I know how much little children like graham crackers, and
we have a great big supply of them."

The mention of graham crackers took away our appetites, and
we said we guessed we'd skip the snack and get our baths.

"Such dear children," Grosie squeezed us. "They want their
dear Mother's wish to come true!"

# EDWARD STREETER

#### ✠ ✠

*Families are enlarged by birth—and also by marriage.*
*In "Getting Acquainted," from* Father of the Bride,
*two sets of parents, soon to be in-laws, meet for the*
*first time.*

BUCKLEY, Kay informed her parents with her best Old School
irony, *also* had a father and mother. It seemed to her that the
situation called for a minimum display of interest from the Banks
family unless, of course, they preferred to make it look like a shot-
gun wedding and introduce themselves at the altar.

Mr. Banks agreed moodily. The obvious fact that he must do
something about meeting Buckley's family had been weighing on
him for some time. Although he had never considered himself a
shy man, the idea gave him as much pleasure as a summons to
appear before a congressional committee. He had been postponing
action from day to day in the same way that he put off wearing a
pair of new shoes to the office.

"I suppose Kay's right," he admitted gloomily to Mrs. Banks. "We've got to face it."

"I don't understand why you get in such a lather about it," she said. "What's so awful about meeting Buckley's father and mother?"

"Who said I was in a lather?" he retorted sharply. "All I mean is you'd think Kay might have picked out somebody we knew instead of a family we never laid eyes on and that are probably God-awful. I just know the kind of people they are. It's going to be terrible."

"Stanley Banks, for a grown man you sometimes don't make any sense. In the first place I don't see why you assume the Dunstans are terrible and in the second you're not marrying Buckley's family."

"I might just as well be," groaned Mr. Banks. "I'll probably have to support them."

The Dunstans eventually took matters into their own hands and invited Mr. and Mrs. Banks to East Smithfield for Sunday dinner; just the four of them—without Kay and Buckley—so they could get acquainted.

"That's the pay-off," said Mr. Banks. "They're the cozy type."

He made no further comment, but during the intervening days he showed all the symptoms of a debutante about to be introduced at Buckingham Palace. On Sunday morning he dressed carefully in a sport coat and slacks, then went upstairs after breakfast and changed into a business suit. He insisted on starting half an hour earlier than was necessary—just to allow for a blowout or something. The result was that they arrived in East Smithfield shortly after twelve.

Mr. Banks said he'd be damned if he was going to sit and moon at the Dunstans' for an hour. He preferred to slum around the town and get a line on the natives.

"I'll bet they won't even have a drink before dinner," he said gloomily.

"How do you know they won't?"

"Because I know. That's the kind of people they are."

"Well, suppose they don't. You're not an alcoholic, are you?"

Mr. Banks sighed but didn't pursue the argument.

"I think it might be more intelligent to find out where the Dunstans live instead of driving around aimlessly," said Mrs. Banks. "At least we won't end up by being late."

"I'll bet it's a shack," said Mr. Banks.

When they finally located it, the Dunstan shack turned out to be a large whitewashed brick house about a mile out of town. It sat well back from the road surrounded by old elm trees. The discovery that it was at least twice the size of his own seemed to add fuel to Mr. Banks' agitation. He looked at his watch.

"I'm going back to that hotel we passed and wash up," he announced.

"Nonsense," said Mrs. Banks. "You can wash at the Dunstans'. They probably have running water."

"I prefer to wash at the hotel," said Mr. Banks with dignity. She sensed that this was not the time to cross him.

When they drew up in front of the hotel he did not suggest that she get out, but hurried through the revolving doors. On his return, ten minutes later, it was obvious that he was more composed. The interior of the sedan immediately took on the Saturday night odor of a bar-and-grill.

"Stanley Banks, you've been drinking."

Mr. Banks did not take his eyes off the road ahead. "Why is it," he asked, "that a person can't take a casual drink without being accused of 'drinking'? It does seem to me that a man over fifty—"

"I think it's perfectly outrageous for you to meet the Dunstans smelling like an old whiskey bottle. It's humiliating, that's what it is. What in the world's gotten into you? And Sunday morning, too."

"What's Sunday morning got to do with it?" asked Mr. Banks, hoping to divert the argument. But Mrs. Banks was still being difficult when they turned in at the Dunstans' entrance.

The first meeting of in-laws is comparable to the original hookup of the Lewis and Clark Expedition with the Rocky Mountain Indians.

In the latter instance it is recorded that for a brief moment after the encounter both sides glared at one another with mingled hostility and curiosity. At this point a false move would have been fatal. If anyone had so much as reached for his tobacco pouch the famous Journals would never have seen the light of day.

Then, each side finding the other apparently unarmed, the tension eased. The leaders stepped forward, embraced, rubbed noses and muttered "How." Skins were spread and refreshments laid on them by squaws. The party was in the bag.

The Banks-Dunstan meeting followed similar lines. For a split second the two families stared at one another in the Dunstan entrance hall. During that instant Mrs. Banks took inventory of Mrs. Dunstan from hair-do to shoes. Mrs. Dunstan did the same for Mrs. Banks. Then, finding everything mutually satisfactory, they approached one another with outstretched arms, embraced and said, "My dear."

The two males merely shook hands awkwardly and said in unison, "It certainly is nice to meet you."

Mrs. Dunstan started to lead the way into the living room. "Would you like to wash your hands?" asked Mr. Dunstan.

"I've washed them," said Mr. Banks, glancing at him suspiciously.

"I can't tell you how crazy we are about your Kay," said Mrs. Dunstan.

"Well, that's just the way we feel about Buckley," said Mrs. Banks.

"Yes indeed," said Mr. Banks. Obviously something was called for.

As far as he was concerned that seemed about all there was to be said. He would have been quite ready to second a motion to adjourn.

The situation was saved by the appearance of a maid with a shaker full of martinis and a tray of hot hors d'oeuvres. Mr. Banks looked at this arrangement with pleased incredulity.

He took a martini and found it excellent. "I think we should drink to the bride and groom," said Mr. Dunstan. Mr. Banks drank deeply and relaxed like a deflating balloon. Mr. Dunstan refilled the glasses.

Warmed by this unexpected hospitality and his previous wash-up at the hotel, Mr. Banks felt impelled to words. "This is an important occasion," he said. "My wife and I have been looking forward to it for a long time. Personally I thought your son was a great fellow the moment I set eyes on him. Now that I've met his father and mother I like him even better. From here in I foresee that the Dunstan-Banks families will beat as one."

"I am sure we're going to be most congenial," said Mrs. Dunstan apprehensively, "and do call us Doris and Herbert, not Mr. and Mrs. Dunstan."

"And Stanley and Ellie," said Mrs. Banks somewhat over-eagerly.

There was an embarrassed silence.

"Have you ever been in Fairview Manor, Herbert?" asked Mr. Banks.

"No, we haven't, Stanley. We've heard a lot about it, of course."

"I love your house, Doris," said Mrs. Banks, who had by this time sized up and appraised critically every article of furniture in the living room.

"Thank you, Ellie. We like it. I'm crazy to see yours. Buckley's always talking about it."

"Another, Stan?" asked Mr. Dunstan.

"Well, just to help you out, Herb," said Mr. Banks.

His wife moved over beside him. "You'd better watch your step," she muttered.

It was too late. The release from supertension was more than he could combat. He graciously helped his friend Herb finish up the shaker.

"I think dinner is ready," said Mrs. Dunstan, who had known it for a long time.

She led the way toward the dining room. "You've got a wonderful place here, Edith," said Mr. Banks, falling in beside her.

"Doris," she said. "Won't you sit there, Ellie. And now we want to hear all about our new daughter."

"I'm afraid there isn't much to tell," said Mrs. Banks.

"Nonsense," said Mr. Banks. "Would you like to hear the story about how Ellie left Kay in her baby carriage outside the A. & P. and then forgot about her and went home?"

He told them in hilarious detail. A flood of memories and anecdotes poured from him like a mountain brook. He took them through Kay's childhood and school days step by step. Then, as a kind of appendix, he gave them a detailed account of his own boyhood, early manhood and married life. Occasionally one of the Dunstans broke in with a comment. Toward the end of the meal they ceased to compete.

After dinner Mr. Banks picked out a comfortable-looking chair in the darkest corner of the living room. He felt suddenly drowsy. "Now," he said, "you must tell us all about Buckley." The desire to take just forty winks became overpowering. As Buckley entered his first year in high school Mr. Banks' eyes closed and he was instantly asleep.

They drove back to Fairview Manor late in the afternoon, Mrs. Banks at the controls. Mr. Banks felt relaxed and happy. It was hard for him to understand why he had dreaded this meeting so much. He sought in vain among his acquaintances for a finer family than the Dunstans. Certainly no one could have been easier to talk to. He hummed a contented little song. Mrs. Banks said nothing.

# H. E. BATES

*To the standard commotions attendant on any trip undertaken by a large family, more may be added when the travels are in foreign territory—as is evidenced in* A Breath of French Air.

WHEN POP DREW UP the Rolls outside the Hôtel Beau Rivage at half past six in the evening of the last day of August a gale was raging in from the Atlantic that made even the sturdy blue fishing boats in the most sheltered corners of the little port look like a battered wreckage of half-drowned matchsticks.

Dancing arches of white spray ran up and down the gray quay

walls like raging dinosaurs forty feet high. Rain and spray beat at the windows of the little hotel, crashing pebbles on the shutter boards. A wind as cold as winter ran ceaselessly round the harbor with unbroken shriekings and occasional whistles like those of Mr. Charlton's much-loved, long-distant little train.

"For crying out gently, Charley," Pop said. "Where's this? Where the pipe have we come to? Lapland?"

With a sudden feeling of low, cold dismay Mr. Charlton stared silently at the Beau Rivage. The hotel seemed altogether so much smaller, so much shabbier, so much more dilapidated and inexclusive than he remembered it being in the last summer before the war. It seemed to have shrunk somehow. He had fondly pictured it as large and gay. Now it looked dismal, dark and poky. Its style of creosoted Tudor looked incredibly flimsy and insecure and now and then the blistered brown shutters sprang violently on their hooks and seemed like the rest of the hotel, ready to collapse, disintegrate and wash away. On the little outside terrace rows of colored fairy lights, strung necklace fashion between half a dozen plane trees pollarded to the appearance of yellowish skinning skeletons, were swinging wildly about in the wind, one or two of them occasionally crashing onto the concrete below. There was very little Beau about it, Mr. Charlton thought, and not much Rivage.

"Well, I suppose we ought to go in," he said at last and suddenly led the way with an appearance of remarkably enthusiastic alacrity into the hotel, hastily followed by Ma carrying little Oscar, then Primrose and Montgomery submerged under one raincoat, the twins, Victoria and Mariette, under one umbrella, and finally Pop carrying two suitcases and a zip canvas bag.

Pop was wearing thin blue linen trousers, a yellow sleeveless shirt, yellow canvas shoes and his yachting cap in anticipation of a long spell of French hot weather. In the short passage from the car to the hotel he half-rowed, half-paddled through rising lakes of Atlantic rain and spray. Several times he was convinced he was going under. Once he slipped down and one of the suitcases was blown out of his hands and began to wash away along the quayside. He grabbed it, battled on and a few moments later found himself shipwrecked inside the vestibule of the hotel, where he was at once assailed by a powerful smell of linseed oil, drain pipes, French cigarettes and leaking gas. One single electric bulb burned above the reception desk in the gloom of early evening and this was flickering madly up and down.

When Pop was able to get to his feet again he was more than glad to observe that Charley was already in charge of things at the reception desk. Charley, even if he didn't feel it, looked calm, self-possessed, even authoritative. He was speaking in French. Pop liked it when Charley spoke in French. It seemed to ease and resolve the most anxious of situations.

"*Et les passeports, m'sieur?*"

Behind the reception desk a small, bald, paste-colored man in pince-nez, with gray, hungry cheeks and brown molelike eyes, spoke to Mr. Charlton in a voice of schoolmasterly irritation, as if hoping to catch him out. But in a split second Mr. Charlton had everything weighed up. Swiftly the passports were on the desk: Mr. and Mrs. Charlton's, Pop's with the six children included on it and Ma's in her maiden name of Flo Parker.

"*Et qu'est-ce que vous avez comme bagage?*"

With a commanding, irritated palm the man in pince-nez struck a large desk bell such a resonant blow that little Oscar, startled, began loudly weeping.

Ma, sitting reposely in one of several decrepit basket chairs, at once decided that the best way of meeting the situation was to give him a little refreshment.

A few moments later an astonished elderly concierge in gumboots, sou'wester and plastic mackintosh arrived from dark regions somewhere behind the reception desk in time to see little Oscar bury his face in the contented continent of Ma. The hungry-faced man in pince-nez looked astonished too.

Pop then remembered that there was a good deal of baggage in the car, Ma and Mariette having brought three suitcases each, mostly full of beachwear, swim wear and summer dresses, and he followed the concierge into the driving, howling August rain.

Coming back, both shoes full of water, he saw Charley in process of being lectured, as it seemed, by the man in pince-nez. He looked extremely annoyed and seemed to be accusing Charley of some act of irresponsibility.

"What's up?" Pop called.

"He says he wasn't aware that one of the children was so small."

"Tell him we've only just had him," Ma said and moved herself as if to expose her bosom to larger, fuller and more public gaze. "I'm trying to fatten him up as fast as I can."

Earnestly, in French, Mr. Charlton spent some moments explaining to the cold eyes behind the pince-nez the reasons for little Oscar's immaturity. The man in pince-nez seemed not only unimpressed by this but more irritated than ever and began to snatch various huge brass-lobed keys from their hooks.

"And tell him we want a cup o' tea," Ma said and moved with squeaks of wicker irritation in her chair. "I'm dying for one."

With mounting impatience the man in pince-nez crashed the keys back on their hooks.

"He says—"

"Don't he speak English?" Ma said. "I'll bet he does or else he wouldn't have understood what I said just now. You speak English, don't you?"

"*Oui, madame*. Yes."

"All right then, why don't you speak it? Instead of standing there talking a foreign language?"

"*Oui, madame*."

"We all want a nice cup of tea. Quick. And if you can't make it I soon will."

"But in twenty minutes you may have dinner, madame."

"I daresay I may, but that's not tea, is it?"

The man in pince-nez snatched at a telephone, as if about to pour rasping orders into it, and then stopped.

"*Combien de*—how many teas, madame?"

"Everybody," Ma said. "All ten of us."

With piercing but sightless frigidity the man in pince-nez stared at the sight of little Oscar busily engaged in taking refreshment.

"Even the baby, madame?"

"Oh! he'll have gin. He likes it better."

With cold and extravagant restraint the man in pince-nez put the telephone back in its place and walked out, at the same time calling to the concierge, "*Dix-sept, dix-neuf, vingt-quatre, vingt-huit*," as if these were orders for prisoners going to an execution.

Pop stood looking at his new canvas shoes. They were full of water. It was running out of them in a stream. Water was coursing down his backbone, through his trousers and out of his shirt and socks.

There was a sudden smell of fried fish in the air and Ma, catching it, said:

"Smells like fish and chips for dinner, Pop. Why don't we cancel the tea and have it later? Go down well with the fish."

An old, premarital nervousness seized Mr. Charlton.

"I doubt very much if we ought to countermand the order now—"

"Oh! no, don't let's," Mariette said. "I'm dying for a cup."

"Me too," Ma said. "All right."

"Like a nice glass of hot port," Pop said. "I know that. With cloves and cinnamon. Like I rigged up last Christmas."

"Or else a Guinness," Ma said.

A fusillade of pebbles, sharp as shrapnel, hit the half-closed shutters. A cold blast chiseled at the door cracks and the smell of fried fish grew stronger. The smell reminded Ma that she was hungry. She said so in a loud voice and Mr. Charlton thought it a good moment to draw her attention to various framed certificates, diplomas and illustrated addresses hanging about the walls, so much evidence of the excellent, even high-class *cuisine* of the Beau Rivage.

"*Diplôme d'Honneur* Strasbourg 1907. Lyon 1912 and 1924. Marseille 1910, '27 and '29. Paris, six times, Dijon, 1932. Chevalier de Taste-Vin—*Foire Gastronomique* 1929—"

"See, Ma?" Pop said. "Cooking prizes."

"Anything for this year?" Ma said.

Mr. Charlton was saved the necessity of finding an answer to this pertinent question by the arrival of the tea.

The tea was in a huge white metal coffeepot, with thick white coffee cups to drink it from, and the bill was on the tray.

While Mariette sugared and milked the cups Pop, moving like a deep-sea diver who has only just surfaced, dripping water from every thread, picked up the bill and gazed at it.

"How much is two thousand three hundred and fifty francs, Charley boy?"

At this moment Victoria started crying.

"You take her, Mariette," Ma said. "You know how she is."

Whispering consolatory noises, Mariette took Victoria out, and Mr. Charlton, trying in the circumstances to be both discreet and casual, said:

"Oh! about two pounds. Just over."

"*For tea?*" Ma yelled.

For one moment her bosom seemed to rise into the air like an outraged, affronted puffball.

"I thought you said it was cheap?" Pop said.

"Well, of course, you've got to remember—in France—"

"Here," Ma said. "Hold Oscar."

Mr. Charlton found himself suddenly holding Oscar. Oscar, like Pop, was wet. Ma hastily covered up her bosom and bore down on tea and tea-cups, stunned to impotent silence while Mr. Charlton said:

"After all, tea in France is probably a pound a pound. Perhaps twenty-five shillings. I was reading in the *Times* only the other day—"

"And hot milk!" Ma said. "Feel this! They brought hot milk."

No one had any time to comment on this outrage before Mariette and Victoria came back, Mariette tightly holding her sister's hand.

"Hot milk, Mariette!" Ma said. "Two pounds and over for a cuppa tea and they bring hot milk. Hullo, what's the matter with you?"

"Nothing."

Mariette looked white and shaken.

"Look as if you'd seen a ghost or something. Look as if you'd had the bill and not Pop."

Mariette's lip was trembling. She was taking long, hard breaths.

"Whatever's the matter?" Ma said.

"I'd rather not talk about it. Just something out there."

"You can't sit down!" Victoria said. "You have to stand up!"

"Good God," Ma said. "Think of me."

There was nothing for it but to give Mariette the strongest cup of tea she could pour out. This was several shades paler than straw and looked and tasted like discolored water flavored ever so faintly with boiled onions.

After that Ma swished the teapot powerfully round and round

in an effort to bring strength where it was most needed, saying at the same time: "It'll be mice next. I know. I smelt 'em when we came in."

As if in answer to an outrageous signal the man in pince-nez appeared out of a door marked "Bureau" with the habit of a hungry burrowing mole. He busied himself for some moments behind the desk, sniffing and rattling keys, and then asked Mr. Charlton if he had yet filled up the forms.

Mr. Charlton had not filled up the forms. There were ten of them. He now gave Oscar to Montgomery, took out his fountain pen and sat down in one of the many decrepit, disintegrating wicker chairs. His hands were damp from Oscar.

As he started on the forms Ma called:

"I bet they haven't got television. Ask him, Charley. Ask him if they got telly."

Mr. Charlton looked up and asked the man in pince-nez, in French, if they'd got television.

"Pas de télévision."

"No telly, Ma, I'm afraid."

Pop was stunned. For crying out gently.

"Terrible. You'd never believe it," he said. "Never believe it, Ma, would you?"

"Well, good thing Montgomery brought the radio," Ma said. "Turn it on somebody. Let's have a tune. Should have brought the new Hi-Fi."

Primrose switched on the portable radio at full blast and dance music roared forth, momentarily louder than the wind, now punctuated by occasional thunder, that ripped like a half hurricane across the port.

Involuntarily startled, the man in pince-nez rang the desk bell, setting Oscar crying again.

"Ask him if there's a bar," Pop said.

Mr. Charlton, who in the confusion was having difficulty in remembering the date of his own birthday, looked up to ask the man if there was a bar.

"Oui, m'sieur. Par ici."

With one thin finger he indicated that the bar lay somewhere in regions beyond the Bureau, in the direction where Mariette and Victoria had found life so inconvenient for their sex.

"Yes. It seems there's a bar."

"Good egg," Pop said. "That's something." With relief he abandoned the tepid, onioned tea. "I think I'll buzz round and have a snifter."

"Not on your nelly!" Ma said. "Take hold of Oscar. I expect he wants changing. That's why he's roaring again."

The concierge came back. Pop took over Oscar. It was now so dark that Mr. Charlton could hardly see to write the forms. A tremendous crash of thunder broke immediately above the hotel, setting the shutters rattling, the radio crackling and the single dim light beside the telephone quaking even more like a candle in a wind.

The man in pince-nez spoke suddenly in French, with a slight sense of outrage, as if still offended by Ma's charge about speaking in a foreign language. Mr. Charlton translated:

"He says you can go up to your rooms now if you want to."

"Well, what the merry Ellen does he think we're sitting here waiting for?" Ma said. "Christmas?"

Oscar had stopped crying. The concierge picked up the remainder of the baggage and the children their things. Mr. Charlton said he'd come up soon, since the forms would take him at least another twenty minutes to finish, not that he'd even finish them then, in view of remembering all the birthdays.

"My belly's rattling," Petunia said. Zinnia said hers was too and they couldn't stand it much longer.

"We won't bother to unpack," Ma said. She knew Pop was starved. She was getting pretty well starved herself. "I'll just change Oscar and wash and then we'll all come down."

Everybody was ready to go upstairs except Ma and Mr. Charlton when a fresh and more stupendous crash of thunder occurred. The light above the telephone went completely out, came on, went out, came on and repeated the process six more times before going out altogether.

In the comparative silence after the thunder a strange new sound crept into the air. It was that of one of the wicker chairs squeaking, like a horde of mice, in protest.

It was the chair containing Ma.

"Here, hold Oscar, somebody," Pop said. "Ma's stuck."

Mariette took Oscar. Pop went over to Ma, solicitous but

unsurprised; it had happened before. Ma had always had difficulty in getting her two-yard bulk into the confines of strange furniture and still more difficulty in getting it out again.

"Give us a hand, Charley," Pop said, "before she goes under for the third time."

Pop and Charley started to pull at Ma, who began to laugh with huge jellified ripples. The man in pince-nez looked on with frigid, withdrawn, offended eyes. Pop and Charley pulled at Ma harder than ever, but with no result except to set her laughing with louder shrieks, more fatly.

Presently Ma went strengthless. It became impossible to budge her. Above the telephone the light came on again, illuminating Ma as a collapsing balloon that would never rise.

"Ma, you're not helping," Pop said. He pleaded for some small co-operation. "If you don't help you'll have to go round with the damn thing stuck on your behind for the rest of your natural."

Ma laughed more than ever. The vast milky hillock of her bosom, deeply cleft, rose and fell in mighty breaths. Her whole body started to sink lower and lower and suddenly Pop realized that even if she survived, the chair never would.

He started to uge Charley to pull again. In a sudden wrench the two of them pulled Ma to her feet and she stood there for some seconds with the chair attached to her great buttocks like a sort of tender.

Suddenly, with shrieks, she sank back again. Another peal of thunder, more violent than any other, rent the air above the hotel. The man in pince-nez pleaded *"La chaise, madame—je vous prie—La chaise!"* and for the ninth or tenth time the light went out.

When it came on again Ma was on her feet. Behind her the chair was flatter than a doormat and by the telephone the man in pince-nez had his head in his hands.

*"Madame, madame, je vous—"* he was saying. In distress the necessary language for the occasion did not come to him for some moments. When it did so his English was sadly broken up. "Madame, please could—Oh! madame, I ask—I please—"

With incredible swiftness Pop came forward to defend Ma. Irately he strode over to the man in pince-nez and struck the desk a severe blow with his fist, speaking peremptorily and with voluble rapidity.

"*Qu'est-ce qu'il y a?*" he shouted, "and *comment ça va* and *comment allez-vous* and *avez-vous bien dormi* and *qu'est ce-que vous avez à manger* and *à bientôt san fairy ann* and all that lark!"

The little man in pince-nez looked as if he'd been hit with a poleax. His mouth fell open sharply, but except for a muted gurgle he had nothing to say. A moment later Pop and Ma started to go upstairs, followed by the children, Ma still laughing, Pop glad in his heart of the excellent tuition given by Charley in various French phrases likely to be of use in emergency.

At the foot of the stairs he paused to turn with pride and perkiness to look back.

"Accent all right, Charley boy?"

"Perfick," Mr. Charlton said. "Absolutely perfick."

Pop waved a mildly deprecating hand.

"*Très bon,* you mean, *très bon,*" he said. "Don't forget we're in France now, Charley boy. We don't take lessons for nothing, do we? *A bientôt!*"

# AUTHOR INDEX

⚜ ⚜

# TITLE INDEX